BREATHLESS

BREATHLESS

WHY AIR POLLUTION MATTERS AND HOW IT AFFECTS YOU

CHRIS WOODFORD

ICON

First published in the UK in 2021
by Icon Books Ltd, Omnibus Business Centre,
39–41 North Road, London N7 9DP
email: info@iconbooks.com
www.iconbooks.com

This edition published in the UK in 2022 by Icon Books Ltd

Sold in the UK, Europe and Asia
by Faber & Faber Ltd, Bloomsbury House,
74–77 Great Russell Street,
London WC1B 3DA or their agents

Distributed in the UK, Europe and Asia
by Grantham Book Services,
Trent Road, Grantham NG31 7XQ

Distributed in Australia and New Zealand
by Allen & Unwin Pty Ltd,
PO Box 8500, 83 Alexander Street,
Crows Nest, NSW 2065

Distributed in South Africa
by Jonathan Ball, Office B4, The District,
41 Sir Lowry Road, Woodstock 7925

Distributed in India by Penguin Books India,
7th Floor, Infinity Tower – C, DLF Cyber City,
Gurgaon 122002, Haryana

ISBN: 978-178578-845-1

Typeset in Gentium by Marie Doherty

Printed and bound in Great Britain
by Clays Ltd, Elcograf S.p.A.

Contents

ABOUT THE AUTHOR

Chris Woodford had his first national magazine article published at the age of 13 and has been writing about science and technology ever since. He graduated from Cambridge University in 1988, where he specialized in physics and neuroscience. After spending much of the 1990s working as an environmental campaigner, he moved into educational publishing and has since written, edited, or contributed to dozens of popular science books, including the worldwide best-selling *Cool Stuff* series for Dorling Kindersley. His most recent book, *Atoms Under the Floorboards*, won the American Institute of Physics Science Writing Award for Books, 2016. Chris also writes the popular science education website Explain that Stuff, which demystifies everyday science for over a million readers a month. Chris now lives in Dorset surrounded by sheep and the sea.

Introduction

You've probably seen those side-by-side photos on cigarette packets. On the left, the healthy pink lung of a non-smoker; on the right, the clapped-out, blackened lump from a hopeless tobacco addict. What you might not realise is that air pollution – the kind you might be breathing right now – can have horribly similar effects. In Delhi, one of the world's dirtiest places, chest surgeons estimate that the tiny, toxic specks in the smog (technically, they're known as 'PM2.5 particulates') are as bad for you as smoking 50 a day (just like smoking, they can lead to pneumonia, asthma and lung cancer). Even a few days in Paris, Milan, London or Rome is like puffing your way through two or three cigarettes (either way, you'll be exposed to a similar amount of PM2.5s). [1]

According to one recent study, there are fifteen cities in the world where the air is so toxic that active exercise will do you more harm than good. But you don't have to live in a filthy metropolis to feel the harsh effects of polluted air. Even if you live in a tiny town, you still might wince in damp December when that strange, metallic tang hits your tongue, as the fug seeping from stalled exhausts bubbles up from the cauldron of the streets into a low-level cloud of malignant mist. Maybe you've worried about cycling in the sooty slipstream of an old bus, or drummed your fingers in a jam for half an hour, sucking hard on the tailpipe of the car in front? Ever regretted breathing in just a bit too deeply as another filthy truck wheezed by? Have you coughed or sneezed into your handkerchief and made the mistake of peeping, with hair-rising horror, at the nasty, black, Jackson Pollock of a mass you've just hurled up? [2]

Maybe it feels like a commendable public service you're doing, cleaning the air one breath at a time? After all, the filth you inhale from those dirty diesels lodges in your lungs, so the air you exhale is far nicer. You might be a kind of human Hoover, but don't be fooled into thinking you're making the world any cleaner. Even if all the people in a megacity like Mumbai sponged up all the pollution they breathed in, they'd still be cleaning as little as 0.01 per cent of the air swirling around them.

And the other catch, of course, is that your lungs clean the air at your own expense. If you're reading these words somewhere in an average world-class city, air pollution is shortening *your* life by anything from a few months to a few years. Collectively, the air we prize – the breath of life that keeps us alive – is positively toxic. It's killing more people prematurely than almost anything else on the planet: the equivalent of 7–10 million each year, which is five times more than road accidents, three times more than tobacco smoke, fifteen times more than all wars and violence and more than malaria and Aids combined. That's 2,500 times as many people as died in the 9/11 terrorist attacks, *every single year*. The SARS-CoV-2 (COVID-19) coronavirus that swept the world in 2020 was initially predicted to kill about 20 million – but in the noise and the panic, we forget that air pollution kills five times that many every decade. Polluted air is now heavily implicated in six of the world's top ten causes of death; not just obvious lung and breathing problems, but heart disease, cancers, stroke and dementia. These bald statistics mask a vast human cost. Any of the world's millions of air pollution deaths could follow years of chronic suffering: if dirty air is going to kill you, medical research suggests it will make your life smoulder for a decade before it snuffs the wick out for good. [3]

You can see the effects of air pollution wherever you look, however you measure. In Delhi, test-match cricketers gratefully gasp from oxygen cylinders while they wait in the safety of the pavilion. In parts of China, filthy air will kill you five years too soon. In Hong Kong, the smog is sometimes so grim that tourists stand in front of giant, sunny photographs of the city to take their selfies instead. In Mongolia, winter air pollution is strongly linked to high rates of miscarriage. In Europe, national governments are allowed a certain number of excessive pollution episodes each year; in London, the British burn through their entire annual quota during the first week of January. According to the World Health Organization, 92 per cent of the world's people live in places where its air quality guidelines aren't met. You're probably among them. [4]

Sometimes the effects of pollution are easy to spot: think soot-blackened city streets or praying cathedral angels blurred to gargoyles by acid in the air. From the Colosseum to the Taj Mahal, powerfully toxic air is cracking and staining the world's oldest buildings, turning priceless heritage – our collective civilised memory – to dust. Just as often, it's a case of out-of-sight, out-of-mind: although the pollution we make here and now might not bother us immediately, it can cause problems half a world away and half a century in the future. In the last few years, for example, agricultural researchers have found that ground-level ozone pollution from North America is responsible for the loss of 1.2 million tonnes of wheat each year in *Europe*. Others have found intriguing links between decades-old lead pollution (from paint

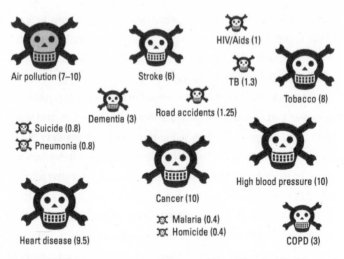

Figure 1. Air pollution is one of the world's biggest killers. When we fully understand the health problems it contributes to, it may even turn out to be the biggest killer of them all. Figures in brackets show millions of deaths per year. Source: World Health Organization.[1]

and poisonous vehicle fuel) and patterns of crime and antisocial behaviour in no fewer than seven separate countries. [5]

Compelling though these arguments sound, not everyone is persuaded by them. Isn't nature one of our biggest polluters? What about hay fever? Doesn't it affect more children (roughly 40 per cent) than traffic? What about Icelandic volcanoes that spew out

---

[1] Comparing how different public health problems like air pollution harm large populations is PhD-level complex and not something I'm going to go into in detail. I use the term 'early deaths' throughout this book for simplicity, but it's only part of the picture: not everyone harmed by pollution will die. There are numerous ways of quantifying the overall health impact, from a simple tally of deaths or years of life lost (so the death of a child counts for more) to disability-adjusted life years (which count suffering before death) and age-standardised death rates (which allow for some countries having older populations than others). For more detail, see the State of Global Air project's website and annual reports (www.stateofglobalair.org).

sudden smoke, like the one in 2010 that grounded 100,000 European flights with little or no warning? How about bushfires? Farm pollution? Dust from the desert? Now this is all true, but if you crunch the numbers, you'll still find the number of deaths from human-caused pollution exceeds natural-pollution deaths by a factor of ten. [6]

Perhaps you think pollution is nothing new and therefore nothing to worry about – an irritating throwback to the Industrial Revolution? You'd be half right, at least. Air pollution is as old as human history, dating back around a million years to the first use of fire; but 300 years after the invention of the steam engine – arguably the dirtiest machine ever developed – it remains the biggest environmental threat to public health. Though parts of the world are indisputably cleaner today than they were during Victorian times, the problem of pollution has never really gone away. The unavoidable reality of us being so many, on such a small planet, is that we're constantly recycling the same air – and inventing ever more ways to make it dirty.

The history of air pollution includes plenty of denial that it was ever really a problem. Back in the 1880s, Chicago coal magnate Colonel W.P. Rend proudly boasted: 'Smoke is the incense burning on the altars of industry. It is beautiful to me ... You can't stop it.' A century later, US President Ronald Reagan mounted a robust defence of the right to pollute in the name of economic progress: 'Approximately 80 per cent of our air pollution stems from hydro-carbons released by vegetation, so let's not go overboard in setting and enforcing tough emission standards from man-made sources.' At best, that's a non-sequitur: Reagan was right that trees pollute, but wrong to conclude it grants us a licence to pollute as well. Trees can't help themselves; we can. If money is your measure and you think pollution a price worth paying for progress, which is what Reagan was really arguing, you need to consider the World Bank's finding that dirty air costs the planet $5 trillion a year, including $225 billion in lost work days alone. That's about a third of the *total* cost of the financial crash of 2008 *each year*. In the UK, pollution costs £6–50 billion annually; in the US, estimates range from $45–120 billion. Globally, pollution chops 6 per cent off GDP – to put that in context, the world spends 2.2 per cent of GDP on defence and 4.8 per cent on education. [7]

Reagan died from dementia – a progressive condition increasingly correlated with pollution (one substantial recent study of 250,000 Canadians aged 55–85 found a clear association between the incidence of dementia and levels of air pollution). If Reagan had known that, would he have still defended the toxic clouds coughed out by cars and power plants? Supposing, just supposing, his dementia had anything to do with pollution, had it dulled his brain to an argument that might have helped save him? Are we all in the same leaky boat now? Our blunted brains slowing to mush, fingers drumming the traffic-jam dashboard, bothered neither by the past nor the future, the car in front nor the car behind, simultaneously lost and going nowhere in a breathless present that never ends? How frightening, if air pollution is making us stupid to the very problems it's causing. [8]

If all this sounds bleak, it needn't be; there are lots of solutions. Though technology caused the problems we experience today, it also offers plenty of fixes. We have lead-free fuel and catalytic converters; HEPA-filtering vacuum cleaners for asthma sufferers that trap more dust than ever before; 'rocket' and solar cookers that free people in developing countries from squandering their lives collecting wood fuel and choking to death (literally) over its fumes; bridges with absorbent concrete that soak up traffic fumes or construction dust; there are even buses with built-in

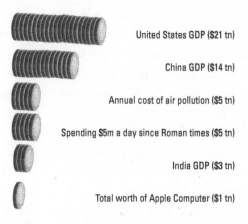

United States GDP ($21 tn)

China GDP ($14 tn)

Annual cost of air pollution ($5 tn)

Spending $5m a day since Roman times ($5 tn)

India GDP ($3 tn)

Total worth of Apple Computer ($1 tn)

Figure 2. Air pollution costs the world $5 trillion ($5,000,000,000,000) a year – more than the GDP of most countries and equivalent to spending $5 million a day since Roman times.

air filters on their roofs that suck smog straight from the sky. We've got the laws, too – from general worldwide curbs on passive smoking that will save millions of lives to specific national fixes like the US Clean Air Act, which has paid for itself in health and other benefits 30 times over. [9]

People power is also making a difference. A few years ago, 800,000 inspiring Indians from Uttar Pradesh (where dirty air cuts 8.6 years off people's lives) did their bit for climate change and pollution when they collectively planted 50 million tree seedlings in a mere 24 hours – and earned a worthy Guinness World Record in the process. When the British branch of the environmental group Friends of the Earth offered its members a chance to measure the pollution in their local streets, some 4,000 individuals and groups jumped at the chance. In the United States, over a million parents are members of an energetic pollution-busting group called Moms Clean Air Force, while 100,000 people take part in California's Clean Air Day each year. In China, an investigative film about the country's toxic air pollution was viewed 200 million times (before being banned by the government). Even in cyberspace, where you might think real-world problems are blissfully academic, over 3 million Facebook users have 'Liked' air pollution (listed it as an interest). [10]

Numbers like this confirm that air pollution is a matter of huge public concern. So why is it still a problem? One reason is that air pollution is complex and multi-faceted: it's a thorny thicket of an issue that mixes physics with medicine, chemistry with epidemiology and public health, geography with many different flavours of international law, and politics with economics. As we've already seen, the causes and effects can be separated by continents and decades (asbestos exposure, for example, can take as long as 50 years to translate into cancer), which makes the issue far harder for people to care about. As usual, there's the false and lazy trade-off between environmental issues and economic priorities: the idea that environmentalism is middle-class, naive dilettantism, rather than a sincere concern for the 3 billion of the world's poorest who have to burn solid fuel to stay alive and the 4 million of them who die from indoor smoke pollution each year. Another reason – and it sounds fatuous, but it's perfectly true – is that there's far more air wrapped around the world than you might think; and once it's dirty, it tends to stay that way. [11]

Ultimately, there's a lot to understand about air pollution, the sheer scale of which can leave you feeling powerless. That's where this book – a whistle-stop attempt to make sense of our polluted world – comes in. Starting with an overview of air pollution and its history, we'll explore the causes, effects and solutions in easy-to-understand, accessible terms. You won't need to be a scientist, a doctor, an economist or a politician to get something out of these pages – just a concerned citizen with a keen interest in clean air. Perhaps a parent who walks their children to school or a cab driver who sits in traffic, worrying about what's blowing in through the air intake.

So sit back, relax and read on.

It's time to get your breath back.

CHAPTER 1

What's your poison?

A closer look at the air you're breathing

The world's most poisonous substance, botulinum toxin, is so deadly that a mere ten-millionth of a gram would be enough to kill you. Is it hyperbole, then, to call air pollution a poison? It certainly sounds mischievous, even misleading, to talk about dirty air the way we'd refer to cloudy brown bottles, branded with a red skull and crossbones, locked in the back room of a Dickensian apothecary's store. But it isn't misleading at all. Poison is a substance that kills or harms you when enough of it enters your body; air pollution has the same effect, albeit more slowly, more cruelly and less obviously. Poisoned by pollution, your death won't take seconds or minutes, but years or even decades; chances are, you won't even notice you're being poisoned. But millions of people will die early this way, this year and every year for the foreseeable future thanks to the long-term effects of breathing poisoned, polluted air. [1]

Seven to ten million early deaths might not sound many in a world of nearly eight billion. It's about one person in a thousand, which sounds even less impressive. But poison doesn't simply kill. For every person who eventually dies from the chronic effects of dirty air, many more suffer pained and stunted lives. Living or dead, many are victims of seemingly unconnected medical problems like heart disease, stroke, dementia, diabetes and mental

illnesses that are, in fact, increasingly correlated with pollution.
According to the World Health Organization, air pollution causes
a quarter of all deaths from heart disease, a quarter of those from
stroke, over 40 per cent of those from chronic obstructive pulmonary disease (COPD[1]) and almost a third of those from lung cancer.
Some 90 per cent of us – 6.9 billion people – breathe polluted air,
indoors or out, and will have anything from a few months to a few
years shaved off our lives as a result. If you're 23 at the moment,
whether you're going to live to the age of 85 or 87 might seem
remote and academic; if you've reached 75 already, and the damage of living in a choking city is already done, it might give you
more pause for thought. Back in 1752 in Britain, so the famous
story goes, people rioted over the eleven notional days of life they
thought they were going to lose when the calendar switched from
Julian to Gregorian. A quarter of a millennium later, no one's pro-
testing that much about the months and years of life that pollution
really does steal away. [2]

Even knowing all of this, it can be hard to accept dirty air as
a poison. The case against air pollution feels tenuous and circum-
stantial: it's almost impossible to point to certain victims – or, as
scientists enjoy noting, no one's death certificate quotes 'air pollution' as the cause. Perhaps that's because 'air pollution' itself
feels like an oxymoron; instinctively, we harbour the notion that,
in a more ideal world, we might all be breathing naturally clean
air. As we'll see in later chapters, that idea is wrong-headed in
three quite different ways. First, even 'natural' air can fall foul of
a simple definition of pollution. From billowing volcanic plumes
to aromatic pine trees and wild (bush) fires sparked by lightning

---

[1] An umbrella term for various 'breathless' conditions like emphysema, bronchitis and asthma, common in cigarette smokers.

strikes, there are plenty of examples of natural air pollution that have nothing to do with humans. Second, it's hard to conceive of a world with completely unpolluted air and there's little prospect of achieving it any time soon. Virtually every step forward in human civilisation to date, from the use of fire to (as we'll see later) the silent sweep of electric cars, has involved making copious amounts of pollution. Humans are *essentially* – not accidentally – polluters, and perhaps they always will be. Third, we often pollute in well-meaning ways: whether you like it or not, you'll make air pollution building a school, driving an ambulance, putting out a fire or baking birthday cakes for your daughter. It's hard to see innocuous things like this as 'poisoning people'.

According to one authoritative definition, 'poisons can be swallowed, absorbed through the skin, injected, inhaled or splashed into the eyes'; just like a poison, air pollution can be absorbed through the skin and harm your eyes, as well as being breathed in.[2] In other respects, pollution has a different *modus operandi* from poison. Poisons startle us because they're so dramatic and rare; air pollution, by contrast, seems humdrum and ubiquitous. While it's tempting to focus on its worst victims (those multi-million deaths a year), it's important to remember that they're just the tip of the iceberg. Out of sight are $225 billion worth of lost work days, endless gasps from the asthma inhaler, countless trips to hospital or visits to the doctor and many more subtle problems that medics refer to as 'subclinical effects' (irritating health niggles not worth bothering the doctor about). But while the effects of air pollution are spread through all humanity, they affect some much more than others. Poor people, ethnic minorities, the elderly, children

---

[2] In developing countries, choking smoke from cooking stoves is a major cause of cataracts and blindness. [3]

in schools near busy roads, people living in developing countries, those with chronic medical conditions, even the unborn – all these are among the hardest hit. (We'll explore the medical aspects of air pollution in detail in Chapter 8.) [4]

Why does air even matter?

If you live a busy modern urban life, stressed by the school run or the hurtling charge of the commute, you might have explored things like meditation and mindfulness as a calming form of escape. One of the fascinatingly counter-intuitive things about meditation is the way it forces you to focus on something you normally ignore: your breathing. In one common technique, you visualise the air flowing in and out of your nose until your mind slips its chains and you float away on a magic carpet of altered consciousness. Air, in that moment of transition, in the short-haul flight from stress to calm, is all that matters. But why, in the bigger scheme of things, *does* air matter? Why is there even air on our planet at all?

Everything on Earth is pulled in by its gravity – even the blanket of gas we call the atmosphere – and it's hard for us to visualise and understand the implications of this. Earth's entire atmosphere is about 600 kilometres or 370 miles thick (about 1,500 times taller than the Empire State Building). But the bit that really interests us – the troposphere – is the 18 kilometres (11 miles) or so closest to the ground (50 times the height of that skyscraper). This is the home of weather, what we generally regard as 'air', and therefore air pollution. If you swim, snorkel or scuba dive, even if you merely duck down in your local pool, you'll be well aware of water pressure: the deeper you go, the more water there is above you and the harder it pushes down on you. Exactly the same logic applies to the gas that surrounds Earth. But, although we're tacitly familiar with the abstract idea of air pressure from weather forecasts, the practical reality of living in a compressed molecular soup, under 600 kilometres of air – like fish in the ocean, but forced to clump around on the seabed – somehow eludes us.

Air is something we can neither see nor feel (unless it whips past us quickly), but the gases it contains drive almost all life, all the same. Plants powered by sunlight photosynthesise, mopping up carbon dioxide and 'breathing' out oxygen; animals, nibbling on those plants and on one another, do (broadly) the reverse in a process biologists call respiration. If you're any kind of scientist, or merely curious, this prompts some fascinating questions. If, as we learn at school, air is about 80 per cent nitrogen and 20 per cent oxygen, why is it the *oxygen* our bodies use and not the nitrogen? Are there credible creatures that exist, anywhere on Earth, that don't breathe oxygen? And if pollution is such a problem, and has existed for at least a million years, why haven't our bodies evolved to dodge around it?

The answers are fascinating, too. Oxygen is the most useful chemical in the atmosphere – more generally reactive than nitrogen and better for liberating energy – and evolution has tapped into this. Our bodies can easily make energy from food with chemical reactions involving oxygen, whereas using nitrogen (or another gas, like hydrogen) is trickier and sometimes even energy-intensive. (Think of plants, which depend on lightning strikes to convert tightly bonded nitrogen in the air into a 'food' they can take up from the soil.) Even so, a few creatures do rely on oxygen less than we do, including snakelike giant tube worms, some 2.4 metres (almost 8 feet) long, that thrive in the bubbling jacuzzi of hydrothermal vents in the ocean floor, breathing hydrogen sulphide (the chemical smell we know as rotten eggs). And there are microscopic blobs called loriciferans that live at the bottom of the Mediterranean Sea, which can survive without any oxygen at all. It's no coincidence that creatures like this dwell on the seabed; landlubbers, given the choice, will pick oxygen every time. As to why we haven't adapted to survive pollution, we simply haven't had time. Human evolutionary changes take millions of years, while the real problem caused by fire – dangerously concentrated *urban* pollution – dates back only a couple of thousand years. As we'll see during this book, pollution itself is also constantly evolving: the often-invisible, 21st-century kind is very different from the in-your-face filth that people breathed in centuries gone by. [5]

Perfect air in a perfect world

If we could subtract humans from the picture altogether, what would theoretically perfect, unpolluted air actually look like?

Just as we learn at school, dry air is almost entirely made of two gases, nitrogen (78 per cent) and oxygen (21 per cent). Most of the rest is argon (one of those mysterious 'noble' gases that doesn't do much at all) and there's a dash of carbon dioxide. There are also tiny (trace) amounts of gases such as helium in Earth's atmosphere (60 times less than carbon dioxide) and flammable hydrogen (10 times less again).

Suppose you took a volume of air the size of a modest bedroom (about 25 cubic metres or 33 cubic yards). Nitrogen would fill all but a layer 50 centimetres (20 inches) or so thick, which would be the oxygen. Argon would line roughly the bottom 2.5 centimetres (1 inch), and the carbon dioxide would fit in five milk bottles in the corner. Now this is a slightly misleading picture, since 70 per cent of our planet is covered by water and the air isn't, in fact, dry at all. But even adding in water vapour doesn't change things that much. The other gases politely shift up to make room: adding about 3 per cent water vapour to the air (a typical amount) dials down the nitrogen content (to about 75 per cent), the oxygen content somewhat less (to 20 per cent) and the other gases less still. [6]

One way to appreciate the idea of a 'perfect' Earth atmosphere is to contemplate the atmospheres of other planets. All the speculation about aliens nipping down to Earth in flying saucers overlooks a fundamental problem with interplanetary tourism: curious creatures from outer space would struggle to survive in a climate as radically different as the one they'd find on Earth. On Mars, for example, the atmospheric tables are completely turned: the 'air' is almost entirely (95 per cent) carbon dioxide, while the gases common on Earth (nitrogen, oxygen and argon) are present there in only tiny amounts. Water, which may once have been abundant, is now very hard to find. Jupiter, on the other hand, is dominated by swirling clouds of hydrogen (about 90 per cent) and helium (almost 10 per cent), with trace amounts of things like ammonia, methane and water vapour. [7]

Imperfect air in an imperfect world

Back on our own imperfect Earth, depending on where you are, what you're doing and what's around you, the breath you're sucking in right now will contain many different air pollution gases and dirt particles. At the dawn of the 21st century, pollution scientists at the World Health Organization were tracking roughly three dozen significant chemicals known to present a risk to people and planet; of these, half a dozen or so are of most concern: [8]

Sulphur dioxide

Despite the growing importance of powering our planet with clean, green solar panels and wind, around 85 per cent of the energy the world uses (and two thirds of our electricity) still comes from fossil fuels; mainly coal, natural gas and oil. Coal might look like pure black chunks of carbon, but it also contains a few per cent of sulphur. When coal burns, the sulphur blends with oxygen in the air to make sulphur dioxide (SO_2), a pollutant that causes breathing problems and contributes to heart disease. SO_2 is the stinking gas belched out by the steam engines and coal-fired electricity plants that powered our industrialisation – the whiff of nostalgia you can smell if you ride the steam train on a heritage railway (as I will do, in the name of science, later in this book). When it meets water in the air, SO_2 turns to sulphuric acid and falls back to Earth as acid rain.

Interestingly, the very same sulphur dioxide is involved in a more minor but no less irritating example of air pollution: the way onion slicing brings tears to your eyes. When sulphur dioxide from factories and power plants returns to Earth as acid rain, it adds sulphur to the soil. Onions absorb that sulphur and use it to make a complex, tear-gas-like chemical (known as syn-Propanethial-S-oxide), which is released when you chop them up in your kitchen – and makes you cry. [9]

Ozone

The kind of oxygen our noses haul in contains two married molecules, O_2, but a mutant form of the same stuff has an extra one, O_3; a kind of chemical ménage à trois, it's the rapacious, predatory gas known as ozone. Ozone gets a mixed press. Historically, people confused it with the fresh, bracing air you couldn't get enough of when you stood by the sea shore. High in the atmosphere, in the infamous ozone layer, it's an effective sunblock protecting us from skin cancer brought on by the sun's UV rays; at ground-level, it's an aggressive and poisonous pollutant that plays a key part in smog, worsens breathing problems and destroys crops and trees. Ozone is not normally a problem indoors; O_3 quickly transforms itself into harmless O_2 when it bashes into something like a window or a wall.

Ozone is toxic and in very high concentrations (over 50 parts per million) can cause death within minutes. Despite this, alternative medicine practitioners have long touted something called 'ozone therapy', which involves pumping the stuff into a patient's body, supposedly to cure a wide variety of medical conditions, from Aids and arthritis to heart disease and cancer. The US government's Food and Drug Administration notes that there is 'no known useful medical application' of ozone and effectively banned all such uses in 2016. [10]

Nitrogen oxides

Flames look wantonly destructive, but the burning that powers them is a methodical chemical reaction (chemists call it combustion) in which carbon-based fuels react with oxygen in the air to give off (ideally) carbon dioxide, water and a rushing blush of heat. The trouble is, both fuel and air contain some nitrogen. That means that combustion – in things like wildfires, power plants and car engines – also produces nitrogen oxides (nitrogen oxide and nitrogen dioxide, often written NO_x for short) as a by-product. As we've already seen, nitrogen gas is normally unreactive, but in the dizzy heat of a roaring flame, some of the oxygen that ought to be burning up fuel reacts with nitrogen to make NO_x pollution instead.

Nitrogen oxide, nitrogen dioxide (which exacerbates health problems such as breathing difficulties) and ozone react together in various ways, under various conditions, to produce such things as acid rain and smog. But smog's not always the greatest danger. As we'll see later, using a gas stove can produce nitrogen dioxide levels in your kitchen that are many times greater than you'll breathe in a smoggy city street. [11]

Carbon monoxide

Thanks to better public health education, more of us know about the risk of carbon monoxide (CO) poisoning, which happens when fuels burn with too little oxygen to make generally harmless carbon dioxide (CO_2). While people in developed countries are used to having handy, electronic CO alarms next to their gas fires and boilers, those in developing nations are still at great risk from indoor CO pollution. Outdoors, there's not much most of us can do about carbon monoxide snaking from car tailpipes, steel-making furnaces, petroleum refineries, garden bonfires or forest fires. Bizarrely, back in the 1790s, carbon monoxide was tested as a treatment for various ailments by one Thomas Beddoes of the curiously named Pneumatic Institution for Inhalation Gas Therapy in the British city of Bristol: he believed it gave people rosy cheeks and an outward appearance, at least, of better health. [12]

VOCs

Every time you prise open a can of gloss paint, squirt out some glue, daub metal polish on a photo frame or even shine your shoes, you're releasing chemicals that make your head spin. You might not think of these things as poisons, but volatile organic compounds (VOCs), as they're known, are a significant source of air pollution ('volatile' simply means they evaporate at everyday temperatures – so they pollute almost by definition). In some parts of the world, such as the European Union, household products like paints must now clearly label their volatile chemical content, so you can actively avoid VOCs, to a degree. Outdoors, most VOCs come from chemical leakages (remember the smell of fuel on the filling station forecourt?) and vehicle exhausts. But they also come from natural sources. That pine tree aroma you love so much? It comes from VOCs called terpenes, also used to make smelly household chemicals like turpentine. [13]

Particulates

It's a mistake to think air pollution is just a mix of evil, dirty gases; it also contains microscopic solids and pinpoint drops of liquid. Look closely and you'll see heavy metal deposits, industrial waste, soot from wildfires and wood burners, drifting rubbed-off flakes from car brakes and tyres, fly ash from municipal incinerators, construction and demolition dust and chemicals that magically form when other pollutants bump together. Exactly what your local air contains depends on where you are: in Egypt, for example, you'll breathe in plenty of sand and organic, soil-like stuff blown in from the desert.

Swept along in the crowd of polluted air, these specks of dirt and tiny liquid droplets are called particulate matter (PM) or just particulates, and they come in varying shapes and sizes, commonly referred to with the suffix numbers 0.1, 1, 2.5 and 10. The coarse PM10s (less than 10 millionths of a metre in diameter – roughly ten times thinner than a thick human hair) and fine PM2.5s (less than 2.5 millionths of a metre – 40 times thinner than a hair) are mostly what we'll meet in this book. Smaller particulates do more damage to our health because they can penetrate deeper into our lungs (bigger ones are less harmful because they're heavier and fall to Earth faster, and also because they're more likely to be trapped in our noses or throats).

Fine PM2.5 particulates are the most dangerous kind of air pollution and pose a greater health risk for the world as a whole than
alcohol, lack of exercise and over-salty diets. They're currently
responsible for around 4 million deaths a year from heart disease,
stroke, lung cancer, lung disease and respiratory infections, and
while it's easy for many of us to improve our diets or take more
exercise, air pollution is usually beyond our control. [14]

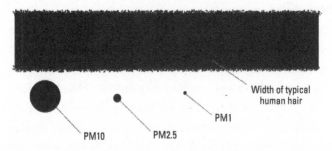

Figure 3. Particulates are specks of soot, dust and other things many times thinner
than a human hair. PM10s are about 10 times thinner than a hair, PM2.5s are
40 times thinner and PM1s are 100 times thinner. PM0.1s, which we don't meet
much in this book, are 10 times smaller again. You could fit about 750 PM10s,
3,000 PM2.5s, 7,500 PM1s or 75,000 PM0.1s on the head of a pin.

And that's just the start. To this little catalogue, we could add
all sorts of bit-part extras found in vehicle exhausts, industrial
gases from hundreds of different factory processes, household
chemicals and sprays and many more. Some of these we overlook
at great cost. Tobacco smoke alone contains over 7,000 chemicals,
70 of which cause cancer. Toxic lead, used in everything from
ancient wine production to modern paint, is largely now under
control, though its latent legacy will continue to poison us for
decades. Ammonia produced by agriculture and farming is a particularly neglected pollutant that, through complex atmospheric

chemistry, makes a major contribution to fine PM2.5 pollution. (One recent study estimated that a 50 per cent cut in ammonia emissions could save over 200,000 deaths a year in the 59 countries the researchers considered.) From acetaldehyde to xylenes, the US Environmental Protection Agency's catalogue of hazardous air pollution lists no fewer than 182 different chemicals in our air that 'present tangible hazard ... to humans and other mammals'. [15]

Living in the lab

The main reason air pollution is such a complex and intractable issue is that it's really multiple problems rolled into one. Each of its many components – every pollutant gas and particulate swirling around in the air – finds its way into your breath by a subtly different mix of chemistry and physics. It can be glib and misleading to refer to 'pollution' in general, when what we're really talking about is hundreds or thousands of different chemicals all swooshing around together. Different types of pollution may have little in common, other than the one thing that matters most: the fact that they do some sort of harm to people or our world.

Having said that, the vast majority of the pollution we should worry about is produced by human activity. Outdoors, the main culprits are road traffic and other kinds of transportation (ships and planes), agriculture, fuel-burning power plants, industry and construction. Indoors, in developing countries, burning solid fuel for cooking and heating is by far the biggest issue – a growing problem in developed countries once again, thanks to the cosy fashion for huddling around wood burners in winter. Also in developed countries, because we obsess over clean and tidy homes, we have to worry about VOCs from things like paints, household cleaners, lubricants, polishes, air fresheners and more.

One of the most interesting things about pollution is that it's not static and unchanging: it has a mind of its own. Some years ago, I went to an eye-opening talk by a chemistry professor who specialised in studying the water pollution produced near highways. After name-checking all the toxic things that 'run off' roads into the hedges, verges, forests and rivers alongside, he revealed the astonishing fact that vehicle pollution also produces weed killers (herbicides). How could that be? There are no weed killers in cars. It turns out that the various chemicals flung out from car exhausts, tyres, brakes and fuel leaks, along with those scraped off the road surface, mix and react together spontaneously to produce a kind of second-generation pollution – in the form of herbicides – that is arguably even worse.

Similar things happen in the air. Pollution begets pollution – it's born in the atmosphere as well as emitted directly. The classic example is smog; the thick, hazy fog that smothers cities choked with traffic. Cars don't vent that smog from their tailpipes, but they do exhaust nitrogen oxides and VOCs (including evaporated petrol). Chemically activated by sunlight, these things produce reactive chemicals called radicals that create ground-level ozone and tiny organic particles, giving smog its hazy appearance. They also produce a lung and eye irritant called PAN (peroxyacyl nitrate), which helps to ferry smog over long distances. Interestingly, though we think of smog as something quintessentially human-made, it can also be formed spontaneously in the natural world. VOCs emitted by trees (terpenes) can react with nitrogen oxides and ozone to produce a natural, blue-coloured smog. This is how places like the Blue Ridge Mountains of Appalachia and the Blue Mountains of Australia get their names. [16]

So we're not merely living and breathing in a world full of passive chemicals, but in an active, highly dynamic laboratory, where the things we fling into the atmosphere react together in dangerous and surprising ways.

Drawing the line

It's not just the 'quality' of air pollution (what it contains) that should worry us, but also the quantity. If we're going to call pollution a poison, the volume of gas or harmful particulates is crucially important. Does one molecule of ozone count as pollution, or one speck of soot from a diesel exhaust? What about a billion molecules or a trillion specks of soot? Is it the amount of pollution belching from cars that should worry us, or the toxic 'dose' our children receive? Where and how do we draw the lines? If your neighbour burns trash in her garden and fills your home with smoke once a year, is that punishable pollution? What if she does it once a month, or once a week? Does it matter how much trash she burns, or for how long?

One often overlooked point is the crucial difference between how much pollution things make ('emissions') and how much we breathe in over a period of time ('exposure'). There's an awful lot of focus on emissions in the news, but from a public health perspective *exposure* is what really counts. Praising ourselves for reducing emissions is certainly encouraging, but very far from the whole story; it's like congratulating yourself on losing weight and ignoring the fact that you're still morbidly obese. And reduced emissions don't necessarily mean lower exposure, as US Environmental Protection Agency (EPA) scientist Lance Wallace tellingly pointed out in the 1980s. Back then, Wallace noted, petrol-fuelled car exhausts were producing about 82 per cent of the *emissions* of benzene (a toxic, carcinogenic VOC) in the environment around us, compared to just 0.1 per cent from cigarettes. A case for cleaning up cars? Not so fast! Because we spend so much time indoors, and sucking on a cigarette is a particularly effective way of delivering chemicals into the body, Wallace found that cigarettes caused 45 per cent of our *exposure* to benzene, while automobiles accounted for just 18 per cent. That's one reason why the recent global crackdown on public smoking is such good news for people's health. [17]

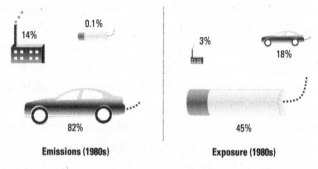

Emissions (1980s)   **Exposure (1980s)**

Figure 4. We assume most of the pollution we breathe in comes from chemicals expelled into the atmosphere by smokestacks and cars (emissions). When it comes to our health, however, what counts is the amount we inhale (exposure). Back in the 1980s, in the case of the toxic chemical benzene, much of people's exposure (about 45 per cent) came from cigarettes, even though they made a tiny amount of total emissions. Much less exposure came from cars and industry, which are more tightly regulated. Figures from Wallace (1995), US Environmental Protection Agency.

The definition of pollution is a little bit arbitrary and always has been. In her classic 1960s book *Purity and Danger*, anthropologist Mary Douglas famously defined dirt as 'matter out of place' – an endlessly fascinating idea (one that stresses the importance of context), but not one many of us will instantly relate to. In everyday life, 'pollution' is our name for the exasperation we feel when a particular environmental nuisance (a local incinerator, a traffic-clogged high street or whatever it might be) exceeds limits we can tolerate. It's complicated further by the fact that air pollution is highly dynamic, changing from day to day, year to year and season to season, and further still by our changing standards and social expectations. In the (relatively) eco-enlightened 21st century, none of us would be prepared put up with the kind of choking, smoky skies that were commonplace in the first part of the 20th century. But modern pollution is very different: the goalposts have moved, our standards have risen and we now know that pollution causes more harm, at lower 'doses', than previously believed. While there have been great gains in reducing some pollutant gases in some parts of the world (notably sulphur dioxide, thanks to the steady shift away from coal), others (notably nitrogen dioxide and ozone) are a cause for concern, and the health risks posed by low levels of particulates really only came to light in the 1990s. All of these factors help to explain one of the great contradictions that baffles many of us when it comes to understanding air pollution: even though the world seems cleaner now than in the past couple of hundred years, in some ways it's more polluted than ever before. [18]

Vague and woolly definitions of 'pollution' are no use for practical purposes, so it's obvious that we need formal, objectively scientific ways of measuring good or bad air quality. That's fair, for the purposes of laws and regulations, and it gives us a decent way of charting our progress at cleaning up the air over time (though our changing standards and expectations make it harder). Typically, we figure out air quality by measuring the concentration of each pollutant (the amount in a certain volume of air), expressed either as so many parts per million or billion (ppm/ppb) or as a certain weight of pollutant in a volume of air (usually so many micrograms, or millionths of a gram of pollution per cubic metre of air, which we write in the form $\mu g/m^3$). Parts per million is a revealing choice of measurement. In ordinary unpolluted air, we'd expect to find about 780,000 ppm of nitrogen (78 per cent) and about 209,000 ppm of oxygen (21 per cent), while carbon dioxide comes in at just 410 ppm, helium notches up 5 ppm and hydrogen just 0.5 ppm.

So where would you expect pollution to register on that scale? 10 per cent of the air? 5 per cent? 1 per cent? Typical amounts of nitrogen dioxide (one of our prime pollutants) in cities range between 0.01 to 0.05 ppm, while near very busy roads they're about 10 times higher, reaching 0.5 ppm – roughly the same amount as natural levels of hydrogen. How do we visualise that? Barack Obama's 2009 inauguration attracted a crowd of something like 2 million people. In theory, if the volume of that crowd represents the air, just one of those people represents a potentially harmful amount of nitrogen dioxide. In practice, it's more complicated because (as we saw above) *exposure* is what really matters – so we have to factor in the time we're breathing in pollution as well as the quantity. The same is true of particulates. The WHO's target guideline for the amount of fine particulates (PM2.5) that people in cities breathe is an annual average of 10 millionths of a gram per cubic metre (technically written 10 $\mu g/m^3$) – which is roughly the weight of a mosquito in a volume of air as big as a large armchair.[3] One startling fact, often repeated in the scientific literature but generally missing from popular news reports, is that there are no

---

[3] World Health Organization (WHO) experts have come up with guideline values for all the major pollutants. It's important to note that these are not legally binding limits; nor are they 'safe' thresholds (below which we can say people are at no risk). Why have them, then? Three reasons: they provide concrete targets to help governments improve the air; they offer a way of comparing anywhere in the world to an objective standard; and they help us identify places where people are at most risk. Throughout this book, I'll refer to these values as 'WHO guidelines'. [19]

safe lower limits below which PM2.5 particulate air pollution has no effect on our health (although the risk does decline). What all this tells us is very counterintuitive: our mental image of pollution might be thick black smoke, but *invisibly minuscule* concentrations of toxic gases and particulates – sometimes too small to see or smell – can do us actual harm. [20]

MEASURE FOR MEASURE

Back in the days when dirty clouds routinely drifted from smoke-stacks, the easiest way of measuring air quality was to hold up a series of cards, shaded from white to black, until you found the clos-est match. Invented by French professor Maximilien Ringelmann in 1888, this simple trick is still sometimes used today, though there are better ways to detect pollution now.

What about measuring the modern-style pollution you can't even see? That's the sort of challenge science geeks love to wrestle with. One simple method is to stick upside-down plastic tubes, filled with absorbent chemicals, on things like lampposts and road signs and leave them there soaking up the smog. Known as diffusion tubes, they sponge up gases, such as nitrogen dioxide, that seep ('diffuse') inside from the atmosphere; after a quick bit of lab analysis, they tell you the local concentration of the pollutant you're interested in.

There are also natural ways of monitoring pollution; lichens have been used for this purpose since at least the 18th century. One French team has studied dirty air in Paris by sampling mosses in graveyards. An inspired 'citizen science' project called StrawbAIRies, run by Professor Roeland Samson at the University of Antwerp, recently gave out thousands of strawberry plants to people in six different countries. The eager volunteers measured traffic pollution by moni-toring the size, shape and number of berries and pods the plants

continued

formed (presumably having controlled for variations in the local climate and growing conditions).

Although moss will react to pollution within ten seconds of exposure, diffusion tubes take a week to a month and strawberry plants take two months or longer, so methods like this don't give a minute-by-minute reading of the pollution in your street. For that, you need decent scientific instruments – and that's essentially why we don't have good, real-time, air quality measurements for the entire world.

Having said that, with the notable exception of Africa and parts of the Western Pacific, air pollution is now monitored in one way or another in most urban areas. The WHO maintains the planet's most comprehensive database of air quality, keeping rough tabs on the key pollutants in 4,300 cities in 108 countries. There are static air monitors in at least 5,000 urban and 800 rural sites in Europe alone.

What can you do if you want to probe the pollution where you live? People have been thinking of solutions for decades. Back in 1970, *Popular Science* magazine ran an article titled 'Build your own air pollution tester', with simple instructions for making a pollution monitor using a plastic bottle strapped to an old vacuum cleaner. Thankfully, science has moved on a bit since then; today, DIY air testing is easier than ever.

Throughout this book, I'll be running some informal tests of the air I come across with a pocket-sized gadget called Plume Flow. It looks a little bit like an old-fashioned radio microphone, but it's packed with laser-beam air sensors and sends real-time readings, via Bluetooth, to a smartphone app. Gadgets like this are great fun to use and give an interesting insight into everyday air pollution, although they obviously don't take lab-quality measurements and you do have to treat their data with caution.

At the opposite end of the scientific scale, you can get all kinds of astonishing machines that use cutting-edge chemistry and physics to give instant readings of the different air pollutants in a particular

continued

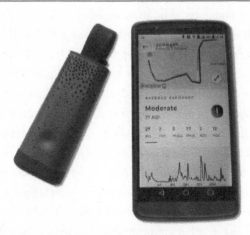

Figure 5. The battery-powered Plume Flow air monitor (left) takes real-time measurements of PM1, PM2.5 and PM10 particulates, plus VOCs and NO_2, and sends them to a phone app (right), which draws little maps of the pollution you encounter as you wander around.

place. There are drones with built-in, miniature air-sampling labs for sniffing air quality, in real time, high over a smoggy metropolis. One British lab even operates a wonderful electric truck called a Smogmobile, packed with air sensors – a kind of nose-on-wheels that can be driven through choking city traffic to give instant air readings. The most sensitive particle detectors use tiny optical fibres to detect PM0.1 particulates as small as 100 nanometres – half the size of a typical bacteria and about 1,000 times smaller than a human hair. [21]

Pollution at large

We've already seen that air pollution is active and dynamic; it can be useful to think of it having a finite lifetime (something that's born, lives and dies) and a trajectory (something that starts in one place, travels through the air and ends up somewhere else – perhaps in many different places). Pollution begins life at a source of some kind, which could be anything from a chemical plant or a truck exhaust (in the case of human-caused pollution) to a forest fire or a volcano (in the natural world); it could come from a 'point source' (a single smokestack) or something much more diffuse (an entire forest or ocean). Once released, it might accumulate in the atmosphere or react in various ways to produce second- ary pollution like smog, which lives its own polluted existence of birth, life and death. Or it could be slowly removed from the air by what are known in the trade as scavenging mechanisms. One example is the way sulphur dioxide from power plants reacts with oxygen in the air to make sulphur trioxide, which, in turn, reacts with rain, fog or other airborne water to produce the sulphuric acid that falls as acid rain. Dust and soot particles can disappear from the air when they smash and glue together, making heavier clumps that tumble to Earth, or crash into buildings and stick to the stone, blackening their faces. Different polluting gases and particulates have atmospheric lifetimes ranging from as a little as an hour (some VOCs), through 100 years or more (for some of the chlorofluorocarbons, CFCs, that damaged the ozone layer) up to 3,000 years (in the case of sulphur hexafluoride, a widely used industrial gas). [22]

Factories and power plants have smokestacks (very tall chim- neys) designed to make dirty air drift and disperse – at least, in theory. In practice, because prevailing winds tend to blow their 'plumes' in the same direction, they often make pollution some- one else's problem. When it was first commissioned in 1972, one of the world's tallest chimneys – the 380-metre (1,200-foot) high Superstack mounted on a copper-nickel metal smelting plant in Great Sudbury, Ontario – dramatically reduced toxic emissions in the immediate locality. Instead, it spread them over an area some 240 kilometres (150 miles) beyond. By the late 1990s, it was blowing out 52 tonnes of arsenic, 7 tonnes of cadmium, 147 tonnes of lead, 190 tonnes of nickel, 1,981 tonnes of particulates and 235,000 tonnes of sulphur dioxide each year, representing 20 per cent of the arsenic, 13 per cent of the lead and 30 per cent of the nickel emitted in the whole of North America. All that from just *one* chimney! [23]

Even if there's no wind to speed up the process, a small amount of one gas (like sulphur dioxide) released into the air will gradually spread apart through diffusion. Some pollutants stay in the air almost indefinitely, but most return to Earth as land or water pollution when something – maybe a human body, another kind of animal, a food crop, a tree, a building, a lake, an ocean – absorbs them.

Different kinds of pollution are born, live and die in very different ways, travel different distances by different means and meet their ends in different places, but Earth has only one atmosphere. Even if we sample and study the air we find in a single place – in the honking streets of Nairobi, perhaps, or the baked souks of Marrakesh – we'll be looking at a mixture of pollution that, if we traced its trajectory from source to sink, we could variously describe as local, urban, regional, national or even global. As you'll know very well if your neighbours are keen on garden bonfires, pollution is usually worst at the place where it's made (the source), but local pollution, from a single, easily identified source, can also be easiest to tackle. At the opposite end of the spectrum, none of us can point to parts of the ozone hole we helped to destroy by spraying aerosol cans (and the harmful propellants inside them) in decades gone by. And the global damage we're causing through climate change is so successfully diffused through the whole of humanity, past and present, that too few of us feel moved enough to make a difference.

If the atmosphere is effectively one big blanket of gas wrapped tightly around the planet, you might wonder why air quality varies from country to country. If gases all diffuse eventually, why doesn't all of Earth's pollution simply average out over time, making the problem pretty much the same everywhere? The answer – perhaps surprisingly – is that air quality around the world doesn't vary as much as you might think. Most countries suffer the modern mix of traffic, industry, agriculture and so on, so their pollution is often surprisingly similar. Even so, everywhere has its own subtle variations on the same basic theme: smoke from agriculture plays a big part in Delhi's winter pollution, for example, while Beijing suffers wind-blown desert dust in the spring. Local climate, weather and geography also play an important part. Some of the world's worst air pollution disasters, including the 1948 Donora incident in Pennsylvania and the Great London Smog of 1952 (which we'll explore in Chapter 3), were greatly exacerbated by a weather-related phenomenon called temperature inversion, where smog smothers a city like a pillow pressed on a face.[4]

As we'll see in the next chapter, air pollution is a truly global problem. We all make it; we all suffer from it – and it's everyone's problem to solve.

---

[4] Temperature inversion is when a layer of warm air above a cold city acts as a lid on top of a toxic soup of pollution, holding it in place until the weather changes but sometimes, horrifically, killing people in the meantime. Inversions are a notable cause of the persistent smog in low-lying, coastal Los Angeles, which is surrounded by mountains that slow down air movements.

TESTING TESTING

Air freshener

Air fresheners might seem like your best friend when you sneak from the bathroom with a guilty look on your face, but the long list of chemicals printed on the can is a bit of a worry. The list of warnings is scary, too: the can in my bathroom includes 'Use in a well-ventilated room'. What happens when you spray? According to my quick test with the Plume Flow air monitor, you'll instantly bump volatile organic compounds (VOCs) up to eleven times their background level – and they'll stay that way for a half hour or more. Why does that matter? A recent study by scientists at Seoul National University, Korea, argued air fresheners could have 'potentially harmful health impacts, including sensory irritation, respiratory symptoms and dysfunction of the lungs', but noted that 'effects do not manifest for many years'. [24]

I think I'll just open the window next time.

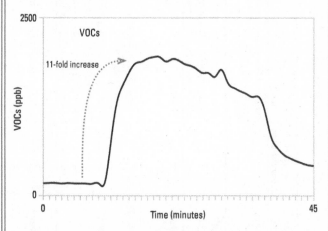

Figure 6. Chart shows: Y axis: Concentration of VOCs in parts per billion (ppb). X axis: time in minutes.

Table: A quick summary of six key types of air pollution. You might find it useful to bookmark this page and refer back to it in later chapters.

Pollutant	Formula/ abbreviation	Causes	Indoors/ Outdoors	Health effects	Other effects
Sulphur dioxide	SO_2	Power plants, ships, home fires, wildfires, volcanoes	Indoors/ outdoors	Breathing difficulties (including asthma), cardiovascular disease	Acid rain, crop damage, building erosion
Ozone (ground-level)	O_3	Secondary pollutant made indirectly by traffic, power plant emissions, refineries	Mostly outdoors	Lung disease and other respiratory illnesses	Smog, crop damage
Nitrogen dioxide	NO_2	Traffic, fuel combustion, wildfires	Outdoors/ indoors	Breathing problems, including asthma	Crop damage, acid rain, smog, ozone formation
Carbon monoxide	CO	Traffic, fuel combustion, smouldering fires	Outdoors/ indoors	Breathing problems	Crop damage
Volatile organic compounds	VOCs (many separate chemical formulae)	Vehicles, evaporating fuels, household chemicals, paints, tobacco smoke, wildfires and natural emissions from forests	Outdoors/ indoors	Many (from dizziness to cancers)	Ozone formation
Particulates (including heavy metals)	PM1, PM2.5, PM10 etc.	Engines, factories, trash burning, agriculture, wind-blown dust	Outdoors/ indoors	Many (heart disease, stroke, cancers, respiratory illnesses, birth problems)	Building erosion, crop damage

CHAPTER 2

Around the world

A world atlas of air pollution

Have you ever sat watching colours swirl around a soap bubble? Red here, orange there; yellow on one side, blue on the other; every imaginable colour refracted into your eye. Air pollution is a monochrome – indeed, sometimes barely visible – version of that soap film, trapped in the Earth's atmosphere, swirling around the surface of our world. The wind blows it from here to there, shifting its thickness, bouncing and bending it into our lungs and causing a whole spectrum of impacts on humans and the planet. Just as the colours change from one part of a soap bubble to another, so Earth's air pollution varies from one country and continent to another, from day to day, sometimes even from one minute to the next.

In this chapter, we'll set off on a whistle-stop tour, charting the shifting patterns of air pollution around the globe. From Singapore to Delhi and from Paris to Beijing, we'll explore how dirty air affects a dozen different places in a dozen different ways. We'll also see how it inflicts a hefty economic cost, chopping back the very wealth that might help poorer nations escape the problems that it causes.

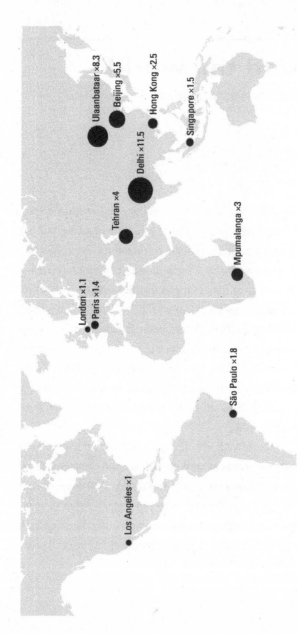

Figure 7. Some of the places featured in this chapter. The black circles give you an idea of how polluted each one is compared to Los Angeles (far from a model of cleanliness, but the least polluted place on this list). Based on PM10 particulate data from the World Health Organization's Ambient Air Pollution Database, drawn using Google Sheets.

A quick world tour

No one and nowhere is safe from pollution; you can find horrible examples anywhere you look.

There's no shortage of superlatives for **Ulaanbaatar**, Mongolia's bone-chilling first city: it's the coldest capital in the world, photographers say it sits among the planet's most spectacular scenery and travellers prize it as one of Asia's most neglected cultural destinations. But *TIME* magazine has termed it, simply, 'the most polluted capital in the world', with winter air quality far more harmful than dirty-air hotspots like Delhi and Beijing. At their worst, levels of fine PM2.5 particulates have sometimes exceeded 130 times the WHO guideline. It's easy to see why: the shivering city has a fatal addiction to coal, while its mountainous valley terrain and cold climate encourage temperature inversions that clamp the pollution firmly in place.

Some 1.5 million of the poorest people still live in traditional gers (felt-blanketed nomadic tents, also known as yurts) and use coal-fired stoves, often burning trash to keep warm. Unlike many African dwellings, gers have chimneys, so the air inside can be relatively clean. But once the smoke escapes it simply hangs outdoors, creating a smoggy atmosphere that causes 10 per cent of the city's deaths, including 40 per cent of those from lung cancer. One way or another, Mongolian women are at horrible risk of losing their babies to pollution. A recent medical study found 'alarmingly strong' links between air pollution levels and miscarriages; others have linked high lead levels in the air to neurological diseases in children that will mar their whole lives. [1]

Coal reigns supreme in **South Africa** as the source of most of its electric power: despite being one of the world's top three countries for harvesting solar energy, 80 per cent of its electricity still comes from this dirty old fuel. Drifting smoke from power-plant

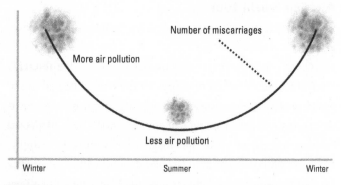

Figure 8. Mongolian women in Ulaanbaatar are at much more risk of miscarriage in winter, when levels of air pollution from home coal burning are highest. Simplified from the research of Enkhmaa et al (2014).

chimneys means that even *background* levels of sulphur dioxide now approach or exceed WHO guidelines. Alarmingly, the world's 24th biggest country is already the world's seventh biggest SO_2 polluter; incredibly, its emissions are now 70 per cent higher than the USA's.

Mpumalanga, where the country's biggest coal reserves are found, has the highest levels of nitrogen dioxide anywhere in the world. That's down to poorly regulated power plants, which are permitted to blow out ten times as much pollution as their Chinese counterparts. It's no coincidence that 550 people die from air pollution in the region each year and over 117,000 are hospitalised. Elsewhere in South Africa, in intensive mining areas such as gold-rich Witwatersrand, air and water pollution remain a major menace. Around the fringes of Johannesburg, the most polluted city in all of Africa, ash-grey slag heaps of waste from 600 mines blow toxic dust, filled with lead, arsenic, cyanide and even radioactive uranium, across the poorest parts of the city where more black people live. Elsewhere in South

Africa, raging veld (grassland) fires are a major source of sooty, fine particulates. All by itself, this type of pollution knocks 6 per cent off the country's GDP (as much as South Africa invests in education). [2]

In **Tehran**, 80 per cent of air pollution is caused by traffic. When smog hit three times permitted levels a few years ago, the government stopped issuing traffic permits and banned school sports. Shortly afterwards, with pollution at almost ten times the WHO's suggested level, and the nearby mountains blocked from view by the smog, the government closed all primary schools and ordered working mums to stay at home. Pollution causes 4,500 deaths a year in Tehran, and 20,000 in Iran as a whole. When scientists studied patterns among 40,000 deaths from respiratory illnesses, they found they matched up well with levels of the major pollutants. [3]

Hong Kong's pollution is three times worse than in New York City and twice as bad as in London. Although there's a higher density of traffic here than anywhere else in the world, the island 'imports' quite a bit of its pollution from the Chinese mainland. Made in China or homegrown, Hong Kong's pollution is responsible for 300,000 visits to the doctor and anywhere between 1,600 and 3,000 early deaths a year. [4]

There are 2,000 schools in the **United Kingdom** where levels of air pollution are illegal. Some 60 per cent of parents (and almost two thirds of teachers) would like traffic exclusion zones around schools, but not many are voting with their feet: the number of young children walking to school has plunged to its lowest-ever level (from 70 per cent in the 1970s to just 48 per cent today). Fear of traffic accidents is one of the main reasons and, perversely, spawns more car journeys that make matters worse. London is one of the world's most affluent cities, but its pollution is world-class too. European laws (that the UK was subject to during its 40-year EU membership) allow monitoring sites to exceed their pollution limits no more than 18 times a year – Putney High Street, one of the most polluted places in the capital, where I used to live, exceeded the limit over 1,200 times a year. Thanks to a determined effort to clean up its traffic, London's air has improved dramatically since 2016. Even so, 99 per cent of Londoners still breathe air dirtier than the WHO recommends. [5]

According to Greenpeace, India is home to eighteen of the world's twenty most polluted cities, which is why it has the highest rate of respiratory disease on the planet. You'd hope the pollution couldn't get any worse in **Delhi**, but every winter, when farmers in neighbouring states torch the stubble to make way for new crops, it always does; it's now at its highest level in two decades. Delhi's the place where test-match cricketers have struggled to play in pollution fifteen times worse than WHO guidelines. Cars pile up on expressways because drivers can't see through the smog (it's created partly by diesel engines burning fuel with up to 200 times more sulphur than in cleaner parts of the world). Firefighters are ordered to turn on high-powered hoses in a pathetic attempt to wash the air clean.

Almost every year, the city's smog grows thick enough for the government to declare a state of emergency. In 2016, the government closed thousands of schools as pollution levels briefly hit 40 times WHO guidelines. Three years later, when the smog returned, schools were closed once again, 1.2 million cars were banned from the roads and 5 million gas masks were given out to students. Chief Minister Arvind Kejriwal has started referring to the city as a 'gas chamber'. [6]

In **Beijing**, as in many other big cities, pollution and congestion go hand in hand. Cars creep along at a pathetic 12 km/h

(7 mph), less than half what they manage in either New York or London. Not so long ago, Beijing had a famously bike-happy population. In 2000, 38 per cent of its commuters cycled to work; by 2015, that figure had fallen to just 12 per cent. Pollution is doubtless a reason why so many have taken to the country's rapidly growing fleet of over 200 million cars. Between 1980 and 2015, levels of the main pollutants from road transport in China increased by six times (particulates), ten times (nitrogen oxides), and fifteen times (VOCs and carbon monoxide). A few years ago, with visibility sometimes as poor as 200 metres (650 feet), one Chinese entrepreneur, billionaire Chen Guangbiao, opted for a radical solution: selling cans of fresh air to the locals at $2 a time. Utterly convinced that traffic is to blame, his other stunts have included smashing up a Mercedes and giving away 5,000 bicycles.

Much more positively, years of adverse publicity have prompted the Chinese to clean up their act; as we'll see in Chapter 6, Beijing is nothing like the global 'poster child' of air pollution it once was. According to WHO figures, it was the world's 40th most polluted city in 2013; by 2018, it had dropped right down to 187th. Even so, though cities like Shijiazhuang and Baoding are often much dirtier, Beijing remains heavily polluted. [7]

California has been struggling to attack the major causes of its dirty air for decades. Ten of the 25 most polluted cities in the USA are in the state, with Los Angeles having held the dubious distinction of most ozone-polluted place in America for about twenty years, according to the American Lung Association (ALA). The San Joaquin Valley has some of the worst air quality in the whole country and locals insist that cars, windblown dust and factory pollution are to blame. In fact, over a third of the area's pollution comes from farms and agriculture – twice as much as from cars and four times as much as from factories. [8]

Back in the 1880s, Vincent van Gogh noted that 'the French air clears up the brain and does good – a world of good'; he might well change his tune today. There are winter days in 21st-century **Paris** when even the ubiquitous Eiffel Tower vanishes in the smog. In 2016, the French capital briefly became the world's most polluted city, with air worse even than Delhi or Beijing. In sensible desperation, the authorities have made it free to travel on public transport on the most polluted days. [9]

In **São Paulo**, as in the rest of Brazil, most cars run on flex fuel (typically a blend of 25 per cent ethanol, from sugar beet, and 75 per cent petrol). This relatively eco-friendly fuel theoretically burns more cleanly, avoids the need for unpleasant fuel additives and makes less carbon monoxide, nitrogen dioxide and other pollution. Unfortunately, ethanol-burning engines lead to more ozone, and other chemicals buzzing from flex-fuel tailpipes include acetaldehyde (a carcinogen that damages DNA), formaldehyde (which causes coughing, sneezing and makes your eyes water – and may also be a carcinogen) and acetone (the smelly solvent used in nail polish remover and paint thinner). São Paulo's cars may be a bit greener, but there are 7 million of them, and they exhale pollution at twice acceptable levels. According to online eco magazine Treehugger, they kill 'more [Brazilians] than car accidents, breast cancer and Aids combined'. [10]

Singapore's rapid economic growth and high GDP make it well-placed to dodge the polluted industrial path of countries such as Britain and the United States. But no country can avoid 'transboundary' air pollution from its neighbours. In 1994 and 1997, Singapore was one of the biggest casualties when 'slash-and-burn' land clearance in Indonesia – over 500 kilometres (300 miles) away

– threw a sooty, particulate haze over much of Southeast Asia. The 1997 episode led to a 30 per cent increase in hospital outpatient visits and a 19 per cent rise in asthma. In 2013, dry-season wildfires in Malaysia set a new record for air pollution in Singapore, where the average amount of PM2.5 particulates in the air is still nearly twice the WHO's guideline. [11]

Way down south, in **Antarctica**, if you're expecting to find little or no air pollution, you'll be disappointed. As geologist Joe McConnell pithily puts it: 'Lead pollution beat Amundsen and Scott to the South Pole by 20 years', due to 19th-century smelting and mining emissions drifting over from Australia. The infamous ozone hole initially appeared over the world's least populated continent in the late 1970s, thanks to those chlorine-based chemicals (CFCs) we were all blasting into the atmosphere as we freshened up our armpits.[1]

According to one popular theory, some of Antarctica's toxic pollution arrives by way of an intriguing scientific process nicknamed the Grasshopper Effect (also known as global distillation). Long-lasting chemicals called persistent organic pollutants (POPs), such as pesticides, evaporate in warm countries to form air pollution, fly into the sky, then cool, condense and fall back to Earth in different places. After repeated 'hops', they eventually arrive in the Arctic and Antarctica, where they systematically poison the food chain from the bottom up. That's one theory of how DDT, the most notorious pest-killer ever invented, came to find its way into Antarctic penguins and continues to poison their bodies

---

[1] Though chlorofluorocarbon chemicals (CFCs) rightly get the blame, they don't do the damage by themselves. When they get into the upper atmosphere, UV rays from the sun split them into voraciously hungry chlorine ions, and it's those that attack the ozone layer.

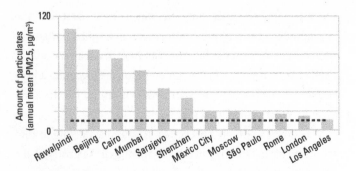

Figure 9. Cities at risk. This chart compares levels of dangerous fine particulates (PM2.5) in twelve cities; all exceed WHO guidelines (dotted line). Chart drawn using data from 'Ambient (outdoor) air pollution in cities' database, courtesy of WHO.

decades after being banned across much of the world. Not everyone buys this idea, however; other theories are that pollution is carried to the poles by fish and seabirds, or transported through the atmosphere and ocean currents. [12]

Continents adrift? A global view

We've got a better understanding of air pollution now than at any time in history. But what we have to remember – and it's evident from the little vignettes above – is that pollution isn't one problem, but many and varied. It's not just that we have 'pollutions' rather than pollution, but that the half-dozen or so key pollutants that choke or kill people in different parts of the world accumulate in the atmosphere for very different reasons.

Take sulphur dioxide. As we'll see in the next chapter, this sour-stinking gas, released by burning dirty oil and coal, was the prime suspect in 20th-century pollution disasters that killed thousands of people. Today, it's much less of a problem in places like Europe and the United States thanks to a wholesale switch to natural gas power stations, better air pollution scrubbers on the old coal plants that remain and more discerning oil refineries that give us cleaner fuel for our cars. But sulphur dioxide continues to billow from smokestacks in developing countries, such as South Africa, and the Asian powerhouses of China and India, with their heavy long-term dependence on coal.

Pollution solutions that help one place can cause new problems elsewhere. The towering smokestacks built to disperse SO_2 from power stations don't simply make it vanish into thin air: as we've touched upon already, they can cause acid rain in other countries entirely, and make (relatively) small urban areas cleaner by making relatively large rural areas dirtier. In parts of Europe, background levels of sulphur dioxide are now five times higher than they used to be thanks to the slow, steady drift from tall chimneys. It's a myth that you can disperse wholesale air pollution on the wind for year after year, decade after decade; the laws of physics tell us that waste chemicals all have to go *somewhere*. [13]

As we've just seen, pollution exists in most countries for many reasons, but people's different lifestyles also greatly influence how pollution affects them. Roughly half of the world's people rely on burning their own fuel for cooking and heating (either wood, dung, peat and so on – collectively known as 'biomass' – or coal), so *indoor* air pollution is by far their biggest concern. For people in developed countries, *outdoor* (ambient) air pollution is usually a much bigger issue. In terms of global deaths from air pollution, the split is very roughly 50-50: 4.2 million early deaths are caused by outdoor pollution; 3.8 million by dirty air indoors. [14]

All of these things make it difficult to generalise about air pollution; it might be a global problem, but it doesn't necessarily have global solutions. With all these quibbles and qualifications, it's a wonder we can make any general statements about air quality at all. But let's zoom out a bit, spin the globe once more, and make some broader assessments of how pollution varies in different regions of the world.

Africa

It's hard to quantify exactly how bad the pollution is in Africa – at the last count, only eight out of 47 countries in the continent (less than a fifth) were supplying data to the WHO's air quality database. We do know that (along with Latin America and Asia) the poorest parts of Africa now have some of the highest levels of sulphur dioxide and coarse PM10 particulates in the world. Africa's outdoor pollution is largely due to coal-powered heavy industry (along with things like cement factories and oil refineries), growing reliance on car transport, wildfires and the wanton burning of household trash. Indoors, the heavy dependence on biomass for home cooking and heating remains the major problem (though this kind of pollution eventually pollutes the outdoors as well).

Some African nations already seem fatally committed to following the polluted path of the industrial West; South Africa is the world's 33rd biggest economy, but the fifteenth biggest producer of fossil fuel emissions. Despite being one of the best places in the world to harvest solar energy, Morocco was, until recently, burning a million tonnes of (mostly imported) fossil fuels a year. Some African cities are growing at a rate of more than 10 per cent annually; the pressure to develop and escape poverty is a pressure to industrialise and urbanise – and a licence to pollute. Shockingly, air pollution now causes more early deaths in Africa than dirty water or childhood malnutrition. [15]

Figure 10. Dirty world: the black areas of this map are places where 75–100 per cent of people are breathing dangerous (fine PM2.5) particulates at levels higher than WHO guidelines. In most parts of Africa and Asia, almost 100 per cent of the population is at risk. Drawn with Google Sheets using data from World Bank/ Brauer, M. et al. 2017, for the Global Burden of Disease Study 2017, published under a Creative Commons (CC BY 4.0) Licence. [16]

Europe

The Danish have more wind power per person than any other country; the French make 87 per cent of their electricity from nuclear and hydro (and just 8 per cent from gas and coal); the Germans pioneered 'Passivhaus' insulation that reduces the need for home heating; and the cycle-friendly Dutch have been putting cars in their place for decades. Attitudes like these, you might suppose, would make Europe the cleanest continent on the planet, but it still has plenty of problems with air quality. As we saw above, Paris is occasionally named the world's most polluted city and many other chic European places, from Prague and Milan to Florence, Vienna and Rome, easily exceed WHO levels for particulates. Nearly two thirds of Europeans live in places that don't meet the 'limits' for PM10, while a staggering 92 per cent live in areas that exceed the 'limits' for PM2.5. Fine particulate pollution chops almost nine months off an average European life; modestly reducing particulates to recommended levels would increase average life expectancy in Europe by almost two years. [17]

Asia

Overall, the low- and middle-income countries of Asia have the world's highest levels of pollution; the people of Southeast Asia *routinely* experience air quality five times worse than WHO guidelines. There's certainly been some improvement in tackling pollutants like sulphur dioxide in recent decades, but particulates remain the major issue.

What matters in Asia is not merely high levels of pollution, but high urban densities that put more people at risk. The air isn't always worse; it's just that there are far more people – and increasingly older and more vulnerable ones – trapped in its path. Asia's urban population will exceed its rural population by 2030, so urbanisation is going to become an even bigger part of the overall picture. But just because more people are packing into Asian megacities, it doesn't mean more must suffer air pollution as a result. Through sensible urban planning and transportation, there are real opportunities to save and improve millions of Asian lives. Cleaning India's air to WHO-recommended levels would boost average life expectancy by around five to ten years in the country's most grossly polluted areas, such as Uttar Pradesh and Delhi. [18]

Australia and New Zealand

As you might expect, these isolated Pacific nations have some of the world's cleanest air: according to the Our World in Data project, the dirty-air death rate here is the lowest in the world and about 50 times less than that in Afghanistan (the highest in the world). That helps to explain why, in a recent Ipsos survey, a mere 15 per cent of Australians rated air pollution a top-three environmental problem in their country (less than any other place surveyed except South Africa).

Particulates are generally less of a problem in this region than almost anywhere else on the planet. In Australia's bigger cities, however, Sydney and Melbourne, particulate levels are roughly the same as in Europe and North America; for Australia as a whole, PM2.5s cause around 2,800 early deaths a year. Wood burners are a major menace: according to the New South Wales Environmental Protection Agency, they produce 75 per cent of PM2.5 particulates in Sydney and pose a bigger risk than either cars or cigarettes. Wildfires exacerbated by climate change are another big concern. During the summer of 2019/2020, as raging fires ripped through New South Wales and Victoria, nearby Canberra was demoted from the world's third cleanest capital to the most polluted place on the planet.

Levels of sulphur dioxide and nitrogen dioxide are lower in Australia than the global average, although a continuing dependence on coal-fired power plants (and lax regulation of them) doesn't help. According to Environmental Justice Australia, a legal campaign group, some power stations in New South Wales are allowed to emit 33 times as much toxic mercury into the atmosphere as Chinese plants and 666 times as much as American ones. Even if Australia embraces renewable energy, that won't spell the end of its major contribution to the world's coal-pollution problem. Vast reserves of coal in Queensland are now scheduled to be mined by India's giant Adani company, shipped back to India and used to fire coal plants there, some of which will make electricity for Bangladesh.

Meanwhile, over in New Zealand, Christchurch was heavily polluted by home coal and wood fires until relatively recently. In 2020, the government announced it would gradually be phasing out coal fires and old wood burners in an effort to save a total of $820 million in health care costs over the coming decade. [19]

America

The good news here is that, thanks to measures like the relatively tough Clean Air Act, emissions of the key pollutants have fallen by a whopping 22–88 per cent over the last three decades. Investing in clean air seems to have paid off handsomely; according to the US Environmental Protection Agency (EPA): 'From 1970 to 2017, aggregate national emissions of the six common pollutants alone dropped an average of 73 per cent while gross domestic product grew by 324 per cent.' [20]

The bad news is that lower emissions don't mean no exposure. People are still at risk from harmful air pollution, as *The New York Times* accurately summed up in a 2019 headline: 'America's Skies Have Gotten Clearer, but Millions Still Breathe Unhealthy Air'.

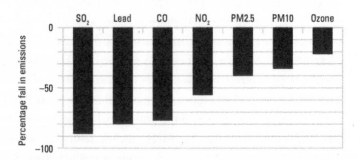

Figure 11. Cleaner skies over America? There have been impressive improvements in cleaning up the major pollutants over the last three decades – though millions are still exposed to dirty air. Figures: US EPA.

Even in today's statistically cleaner United States, more die from
air pollution than from gun shootings and car accidents combined.
A recent relaxation of tough controls on air pollution is making
matters worse: the number of days when US air is unhealthy, very
unhealthy or hazardous increased significantly following the election of President Donald Trump. The broad-brush numbers and
trends also gloss over a more complex picture in which poorer
people and minorities suffer most. Affluent white Americans buy
and use more things and produce more pollution, while other ethnic groups consume less and make less pollution but breathe in
more of it. Latinos live in places with the dirtiest air (almost 50 per
cent live in the top 25 most ozone-polluted cities), while black
Americans breathe significantly higher levels of dangerous PM2.5
particulates than whites. In the South Bronx of New York City,
where 40 per cent of people live in poverty (many of them black
or Latino), particulates from traffic and industry bump asthma
rates to four times the national average. [21]

Some of the world's worst pollution is found in Latin America,
in places such as Mexico City, Santiago de Chile and São Paulo.
PM10s, nitrogen dioxide, sulphur dioxide and ozone can be as
bad here as anywhere in the world. Back in 1968, Mexico City's
thin, high-altitude air helped athletes set world records at the
Olympics; in the 1990s, it was the pollution setting world records
instead. Today, wildfires and traffic can still whack levels of PM2.5
particulates up to six times the WHO guidelines. Just like in Asia,
levels of air pollution in this region conspire with urban density
to produce high levels of early death and illness (Latin America
is home to four of the world's twelve 'megacities'). A particular problem for this region is that the (partly) tropical climate
encourages ozone production, especially during hot summer
afternoons. [22]

What does it all cost?

When we read headlines like 'Air Pollution Costs Global Economy Trillions Annually, World Bank Says', what we're seeing is a complex financial valuation of life and death. Mostly it's the latter, calculated according to how many premature deaths occur in different parts of the world, and carefully weighted so that a child's death counts for more than an adult's (because more years of life are lost). The World Bank/IHME 2016 report trailed by that headline found that air pollution 'cost the global economy about $225 billion in lost labour income, or about $5.11 trillion in welfare losses worldwide. That is about the size of the gross domestic product of India, Canada and Mexico combined – and a sobering wake-up call.' Now some people struggle with arguments like this. How can you really put a price on lives or suffering? But if you don't, how can you justify the massive investments needed to clean up polluted places when there are so many competing priorities for public spending? [23]

What about individual countries? In the UK, air pollution has variously been costed at £6–50 billion a year, with government estimates suggesting particulates alone may be doing harm equivalent to £16 billion. A large, brand-new, single-site, city hospital in the UK costs about £550 million, so air pollution effectively robs the country of up to 100 big hospitals a year. In the United States, estimates range from $45–120 billion, and it's been calculated that even tiny increases in pollution can have a 'substantial economic effect'. [24]

However you measure it, there's no question that pollution has a huge price tag: it slashes 6 per cent from global GDP, which might not sound like much until you recall that the world as a whole spends under 5 per cent of GDP on education and about 2 per cent on the military. (The exact figure for pollution varies wildly around the world, from 0.7 per cent in Finland and 13 per cent in Poland all the way up to a whopping 34 per cent in Serbia.) Put the argument this way, as a drag on the economies of the world, and you miss a bigger, crueller point. Economists are fond of arguing that wealth creation through industrial development is crucial for poorer countries to escape poverty. So, on that basis, the crushing irony of air pollution is that it simultaneously pushes poorer countries towards rapid development that makes the problem worse, and reduces the wealth they could otherwise generate that might help them solve their problems altogether. [25]

Cost $37–44 billion

Benefit $157–777 billion

Figure 12. Paying for clean air makes better sense than paying for dirty air. A decade of air improvements between 2004 and 2014 cost the United States an estimated $40 billion (black circle), but earned back between four and twenty times as much in economic benefits (white circle), mostly in the form of avoided early deaths. Figures from US Office of Management and Budget (OMB). [26]

However we look at pollution, as a blurred blot on the globe or a crisp graph on the page, as a simple economic debit or a complex human tragedy, it's clear that how it affects any given individual is very much a geographic lottery. In fact, that's always been true – and it was the case long before the Industrial Revolution, as we'll explore in the next chapter.

TESTING TESTING

Burnt toast

In the worst industrial parts of China, average annual PM10 levels can be hundreds of micrograms per cubic metre (ten times higher than in polluted cities elsewhere). What's that like in practice? Burn some toast and you'll find out. In the name of science, I set up my air monitor, put two slices of bread under my grill and waited till they began to smoke and char. The kitchen wasn't full of fumes, but was unpleasantly smoky. Here's what my air monitor recorded. At the worst point, levels of coarse PM10s reached 300 µg/m³, which is roughly the annual level in Shijiazhuang, one of China's most polluted cities.

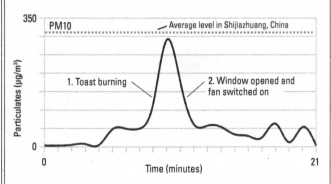

Figure 13. Chart shows: Y axis: Concentration of PM10 particulates in µg/m³; X axis: time in minutes.

CHAPTER 3

Caesar's dying breath

Air pollution: the story so far

How likely is it that you just breathed in a molecule of Julius Caesar's dying breath? The answer to this infamous, school-science brain-teaser is 'almost certainly'. Do the maths and you'll discover there's at least one of Caesar's molecules lurking in every lungful of air you could possibly inhale, wherever on Earth, whenever in time you happen to be breathing. The surprising consequence of this is that we're breathing not just little bits of expiring emperors, but nitrogen that danced in the flames of the very first human fire, oxygen atoms that roared through Thomas Newcomen's original 18th-century steam engine, laughing gas that numbed the pain of late-19th-century dentistry and even some of the air that rocketed Neil Armstrong to the moon in 1969. Loosely speaking, every breath we take is a chemical cross-section through time – and, since it samples much of the combustion that's ever happened, anywhere on the planet – a miniature history of air pollution.[1] [1]

---

[1] In practice, our breaths don't sample everything that has ever happened: different chemicals stay in the atmosphere for very different amounts of time. Nitrogen and oxygen have very long lifetimes (nitrogen perhaps a million years, oxygen thousands of years), laughing gas (nitrous oxide) lasts perhaps 120–150 years and nitric oxide (NO) can disappear in a matter of seconds. So while we're potentially recycling old oxygen and nitrogen, other things don't stay in the air as long. If you're wondering whether we

When it comes to reflecting on that history, most of us make two quite contrary mistakes. The first is to believe that dirty air is essentially just an irritating *old* throwback to Thomas Newcomen and other oil-painted characters from the Industrial Revolution who trailed in his wake – a problem we've almost (but somehow never quite) cracked. Three hundred years after the invention of the steam engine, however, air pollution remains the biggest environmental threat to public health. The second mistake is to think that, because industrialisation and urbanisation are relatively recent innovations in the broad sweep of human history, air pollution is essentially a fairly *new* problem as well. This is very wrong, too: as we'll see in a moment, even Julius Caesar breathed tainted air and his dying breath would have contained, among other things, lead, copper, sooty particulates of varying sizes and many more things we're still breathing to this day.

Early days

Air pollution needs air, but where did air begin? If you could hurtle back through history to the very birth of the Universe – the Big Bang, roughly 14 billion years ago – you'd find yourself breathless in the wings of an explosive early drama. In the real beginning, there was no air and no atoms, just a crazy whipcrack of pure energy, unbelievably dense and hot, creating everything we now know – the gaping, star-spangled chasm of space – from a pinprick of pure energy smaller than an atom. This frantic burst of

---

might still be breathing stray specks of dust from the eruption of Krakatoa in 1883, for example, the answer is no: it doesn't remain in the atmosphere long enough. [2]

energy forged simple subatomic particles, and those clumped into heavier particles like protons and neutrons (the essential building blocks of atoms). But it took hundreds of thousands more years for these, in turn, to form the two most basic elements – hydrogen and helium – in clouds of spinning gas, which eventually condensed to make the very first stars. Millions more years passed before heavier elements like oxygen and nitrogen (the key ingredients of what we now call air) arrived on the scene and percolated through the Universe. In the billions of years that followed, things haven't changed quite as much as you'd think. At the dawn of time, the Universe consisted entirely of hydrogen (about three quarters) and helium (the rest). Today, 98 per cent of the matter in the Universe is still made of just these two elements (although there's relatively little in our own planet's atmosphere because they're so light and easily escape its gravity). Oxygen, carbon and nitrogen – the building blocks of most air pollution, as well as air – make up a further 1.5 per cent; all the other elements comprise a mere 0.5 per cent. [3]

Now in theory, air pollution was around long before humans (think dust clouds from volcanic eruptions, choking smoke billowing from forest fires and other forms of natural pollution – we'll explore those in the next chapter). Although if we define pollution as something harmful to human health and life, it really started with people – not merely as the producers of pollution but also, crucially, as its consumers. The systematic use of fire (or, more correctly, someone choking on the smoke as the flames leaped to life), which began roughly a million years ago, marks the dark dawn of human air pollution. [4]

Is it a stretch to argue that toxic air was an issue in prehistoric times? Not really. As we've already discovered, roughly half of those who die early from dirty air today are living what we'd call 'primitive' lives in developing countries, burning fuel indoors for domestic cooking, heating and light. That practice dates back to the late Stone Age. Logically, it seems reasonable to suppose that even the earliest human settlers, crowding around the camp fire for buffalo stew, choked on its smoke just like many people in developing countries do today. There's plenty to support that idea. Peering closely at mummified remains, archaeologists have found ample evidence of anthracosis (blackened lung tissue), which is closely linked to breathing in soot. Modern air pollution might be a toxic cocktail, but it's perfectly apparent that smoky fumes from poorly ventilated home fires would have had our ancestors coughing and spluttering just as much. [5]

As civilisation developed, it wasn't only the simple soot (carbon deposits) in smoke that bothered people. The Bronze Age ushered in not just metalworking but also dirty industrial practices like mining (which kicks up clouds of particulates) and smelting (separating the ores you've mined by heating them, which coughs heavy metals like lead high into the air), beginning around 7,000 years ago. In Europe, the Romans were famous for their fatal love of lead (in water pipes, on roofs, in coins and, most egregiously, in *defrutum* and *sapa*, concentrated wine preservatives they boiled up in lead pans), but the practice of mining and exploiting metals began much earlier, in the Balkans. Modern archaeological evidence from peat bog samples tells us that lead pollution in this area dates back to the early Bronze Age (3600 BCE), a good three and a half millennia before Caesar sucked in his dying, dirty breath. Samples taken from Greenland ice confirm that heavy-metal pollution has been a problem ever since: drilling out ice 'cores' more than a kilometre (0.6 miles) deep, scientists have found evidence of lead pollution (up to four times natural, background amounts) dating to 500 BCE. [6]

Heavy skies

From the ice-core traces of early metalworkers to the blackened lungs of Egyptian mummies, from the Aleutians to the Peruvians and the Babylonians to the Assyrians, there's evidence that air pollution was an issue in almost every ancient society.[2] But were people actually aware of the problem and what, if anything, did they do about it? The Greeks, who pioneered modern medicine, certainly knew about lung diseases and the importance of clean air – and connected the two. Hippocrates, best known as the author of the doctor's oath, wrote a treatise called *Airs, Waters and Places*, in which he made a link between poor air quality and human illness, stressed the importance of checking the cleanliness of the air whenever you went somewhere new and wrote of cities where people's 'voices are rough and hoarse owing to the state of the air, which in such a situation is generally impure and unwholesome, for they have not the northern winds to purify it'. Thoughts like these were absorbed into the concept of 'miasma', the idea that foul air carried disease, which clung on as a pseudo-medical explanation until germ theory gained firm scientific support in the late 19th century. [7]

For the Romans, things seem to have been an order of magnitude worse. Although they had no single pejorative word meaning 'pollution', as we understand it today, they were certainly familiar with the concept. They grumbled about *gravioris caeli* ('heavy skies') and *infamis aer* ('vile air') and, as legal scholars have noted,

---

[2] Excellent accounts of the early history of air pollution have been provided by Peter Brimblecombe, Stephen Mosley and other scholars, whose work I've gratefully drawn on in this chapter. Peter Brimblecombe's *The Big Smoke: A History of Air Pollution in London Since Medieval Times* (Methuen, 1987; Routledge, 2012) remains one of the best introductions to this subject.

fought court battles over contaminated air and water. Famously, they warmed chilly buildings with ingenious underfloor central-heating systems called hypocausts, which included flues for hot waste gases running up through the walls. Those were the stubby ancestors of modern chimneys and smokestacks and, it might be argued, mark the invention of long-range human air pollution. [8]

Dust and smoke there was – and plenty of it. Grottarossa, one of only two mummies ever recovered from ancient Rome, shows tell-tale signs of anthracosis, despite being only about twelve or thirteen years old when she died. The superabundance of dirt inspired Emperor Justinian to declare clean air and drinking water a fundamental human right: 'The following things are by natural law common to all – the air, running water [and] the sea.' That's something we've somehow lost since then, a crucial protection that eludes the majority of Earth's people over two millennia later. The poet Horace noted the sad, blackened faces of Rome's proud buildings. Seneca, the Roman stoic known for his unflappable indifference to pleasure or pain, was far from indifferent to filthy air, commenting on 'the oppressive atmosphere of the city and that reek of smoking cookers which pour out, along with clouds of ashes, all the poisonous fumes they've accumulated in their interiors'. [9]

These early advocates of clean air were fighting something of a losing battle, however, given the huge increase in industry that was going on in Greek and Roman times. Up in Greenland, according to geologist Joe McConnell of the Desert Research Institute, Nevada, and colleagues, the ice cores tell their own story. There, lead emissions 'recorded' in the ice between 1100 BCE and 800 CE show a fascinating correlation with events happening over in Rome; rising with wars and imperial expansions, falling with

plagues and the Empire's collapse.[3] Similar shifts in lead production can also be picked up in samples from peat bogs, which
faithfully record the rise and fall of the Roman Empire (plus the
more recent dawn of the Industrial Revolution, and even the
fluctuating fortunes of leaded petrol in the 20th century). And it
wasn't just lead the Romans had to suffer. Fascinating studies of
the rib bones of impeccably preserved skeletons buried under the
eruption of Mount Vesuvius in 79 CE show clear signs of pleurisy
(inflammation of the tissue wrapped around the lungs) that doctors have linked to sooty, indoor air pollution from burning wood,
dung and other dirty fuels. [10]

The ancients, in short, understood the value of clean air and
our entitlement to it; they had forms of air pollution legislation
and weren't afraid to use them; they witnessed the effects of dirty
air on their cities and on their health; and they died (perhaps
months or years early) with its dark deposits deep in their lungs.
All these things remain just as true today.

Middle-aged spread

Contrary to what most of us believe, air pollution was firmly
entrenched as a problem hundreds of years before industry
took hold. Ice-core analysis, once again, shows that between
ancient times and the Middle Ages, mining and smelting
increased lead exposure by a factor of ten. In England, where
the world's Industrial Revolution would later begin, the growing population, early industry (from lead smelting and herring

---

[3] Other researchers have used similar techniques to match rising-falling lead
levels in ice cores from the Swiss Alps to social changes and political events
in 12th-century Britain, including the assassination of the Archbishop of
Canterbury, Thomas Becket. [11]

smoking to blacksmiths' forges, leather tanning and wholesale lime production in open kilns) and the pressing urbanisation of places like London started to put a strain on natural resources. Even so, William Fitzstephen, administrator to Thomas Becket, Archbishop of Canterbury, noted around 1180 that London was a fine place 'known for its healthy air and honest, Christian burghers'. [12]

Yet polluted air was becoming increasingly common: London itself was almost entirely deforested for building materials and fuel by the early 13th century, prompting a switch to so-called 'sea coal' (imported from distant Newcastle by sea), which was rich in noxious, smelly sulphur. And then the problems really began. Even today, homes with reasonably tall chimneys and well-designed flues for wood burners can collectively waft out enough sooty PM2.5 particulates to create dangerous local levels of pollutants. But back in the Middle Ages, chimneys were measly, minimal things and often didn't clear the roofs of either their own or the neighbouring buildings, so smoke struggled to disperse. There are plenty of anecdotal reports that coal burning was a well-established nuisance in England during the 13th century; in 1273, King Edward I went so far as to prohibit the use of sea coal in furnaces. But a full three centuries later, towards the end of the Middle Ages, Queen Elizabeth I was still wrestling with the issue. In 1578, she found the air quality in London so poor (she was 'greatly grieved and annoyed with the taste and smoke') that she refused to enter the city, and a dozen years later, in 1590, she tried to bar coal use in London altogether. As these centuries-long failures to bring the problem under control clearly demonstrate, coal burning – and the air pollution that went with it – were intractable issues long before the steam engine chuffed into action. [13]

GETTING A GRIP ON THE AIR

Confusing early science didn't do people any favours when it came to understanding why the air they were breathing was so poor. Aristotle, for example, saw air as one of the four basic elements (with earth, fire and water) and believed we breathed it to cool the fire in our hearts. Quite how he would have explained modern air pollution, it's hard to say.

These wrong-headed ideas persisted until the 17th century, when English 'sceptical chemist' Robert Boyle (1627–91) pointed out how scientifically useless they were: you couldn't really combine Aristotle's four elements to make familiar everyday substances or extract them, in any meaningful way, from real-world materials. Sweeping ancient abstractions aside, Boyle set science straight with a clear idea of the difference between elements (substances you couldn't break down with chemistry alone), compounds (elements fused to make new things) and mixtures (everything else). Boyle, though not an air pollution scientist, was therefore a key figure in the history of air pollution science. Only with the help of his acute 17th-century insight is it possible to understand air pollution as we do today, as a shifting mixture of gases (molecules made of elements or compounds), aerosols (solids or liquids, usually dispersed in gases), and particulates (tiny bits of elements or compounds taking the form of solids or liquid droplets). [14]

If Boyle's ideas were crucial in helping us see air as a mixture, the job of understanding exactly what that mixture contained fell to a group of 18th-century European scientists. Initially, it was thought air came in several, quite different flavours. Scotsman Joseph Black (1728–99) discovered 'fixed air' (what we now call carbon dioxide) by heating limestone (calcium carbonate) to free a gas trapped inside, while his student Daniel Rutherford (1749–1819) isolated what he called 'noxious air' (nitrogen). When Henry Cavendish (1731–1810) discovered hydrogen, he called it 'inflammable air' and found he

continued

Figure 14. Robert Boyle equipped us with scientific ideas to make sense of air pollution. Credit: Wellcome Collection. Published under a Creative Commons (CC BY) Licence.

could burn it to make water. Joseph Priestley (1733–1804) penned a full six volumes of *Experiments and Observations on Different Kinds of Air*, and in the process, famously discovered something he called 'dephlogisticated air' that we now know as oxygen. It's much less well known that he also discovered and studied 'nitrous air' (nitric oxide, NO), 'dephlogisticated nitrous air' (nitrous oxide, NO_2), 'vitriolic acid air' (sulphur dioxide, SO_2) and carbon monoxide (CO) – four of the key ingredients in air pollution.

Priestley's work was revolutionary and influential; it spurred Frenchman Antoine-Laurent de Lavoisier (1743–94), father of modern chemistry, to disprove a very wrong-headed but popular notion of how things burn in air, known as the phlogiston theory. The basic idea was that some things burn well because they contain a magic

continued

substance called phlogiston, released when they go up in flames;
Lavoisier proved that oxygen in the air was the real reason those
things burned (or didn't). Like Boyle's insight and Priestley's research,
Lavoisier's discovery was a milestone in the science of air pollution,
most of which is caused by combustion of one kind or another.

Old problems in the New World

Once we abandon the notion that toxic air began to billow out
across the world during the Industrial Revolution, we can challenge the idea that it necessarily began in the countries where that
revolution first took hold: Britain and the United States. In fact,
there's compelling evidence that some of the earliest, large-scale
pollution started in South America. Smelting began there around
1400 BCE, and metal production greatly accelerated following the
16th-century Spanish conquest, which was partly motivated by a
desire to plunder the continent's vast mineral wealth. The Spanish
introduced new kinds of mining and refining that released toxic
metals such as lead, mercury and bismuth, either mixed in with
the ore or used in the refining process. The huge expansion of
silver mining, in countries such as Bolivia and Peru, blew clouds
of this dust high into the air, which was then swept far across the
continent.

How do we know all this? Several years ago, Earth scientist Paolo Gabrielli and his colleagues ventured 5.5 kilometres
(3.4 miles) up into the Peruvian Andes to take ice core samples
from the pristine Quelccaya Ice Cap, where alternating wet
and dry seasons lay down chronological layers of atmospheric
dust that can be read like pages in a history book. According to
Gabrielli's colleague Professor Lonnie Thompson, cores like this
are a 'Rosetta Stone' of the historic climate. The team found traces

of metals (and other elements related to metal production), such as copper, lead, antimony, arsenic and silver dating back to before Columbus – and a good 200 years before the Industrial Revolution. And what's interesting is not just that large-scale pollution was released and transformed the environment, but that it travelled so far. One of the largest silver mines in operation at that time was located at Potosí in modern-day Bolivia, some 800 kilometres (500 miles) from the ice-core evidence discovered at Quelccaya. So this isn't just some of the world's earliest industrial-scale pollution, it's also some of the earliest transboundary (international) pollution. According to Gabrielli: 'This evidence supports the idea that human impact on the environment was widespread even before the Industrial Revolution.' [15]

FUMIFUGIUM

Cities like London were suffering from dirty air long before Abraham Darby fired up the world's first coal-powered blast furnace in 1709, ushering in the smoky urban age built on iron and steel. In 1661, English gardener, scientist and sometime diarist John Evelyn (a founder of the Royal Society) decided to offer his friend, King Charles II, some original solutions. The pithy pamphlet he produced, *Fumifugium; or The Inconveniencie of the Aer and Smoak of London Dissipated*, paints a woeful picture of a charming city fatally compromised by filthy air. The world's first book on air pollution, it makes fascinating reading to this day.

In tip-toeing prose that sounds a touch perambulating to modern ears, Evelyn begins by pointing out to the King how he first noticed 'a presumptuous Smoake issuing ... to such a degree, as Men could hardly discern one another for the Clowd', and how 'Your Majesties only Sister ... did in my hearing, complain of the Effects of this Smoake

continued

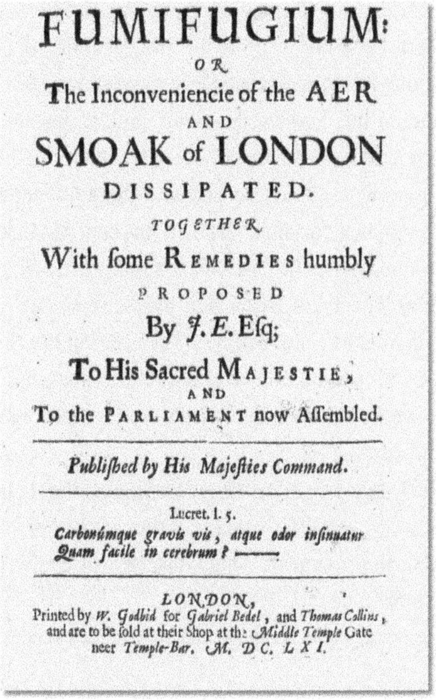

FUMIFUGIUM:

O R

The Inconveniencie of the A E R

AND

SMOAK of LONDON

DISSIPATED.

TOGETHER

With fome REMEDIES humbly

PROPOSED

By *J. E.* Efq;

To His Sacred MAJESTIE,

AND

To the PARLIAMENT now Affembled.

_____

Publifhed by His Majefties Command.

_____

Lucret. l. 5.

Carbonúmque gravis vis , atque odor infinuatur
Quam facile in cerebrum ? ——

LONDON,
Printed by *W. Godbid* for *Gabriel Bedel* , and *Thomas Collins* ,
and are to be fold at their Shop at the *Middle Temple* Gate
neer *Temple-Bar. M. DC. LXI.*

Figure 15. *Fumifugium* – the first ever book about the problem of air pollution.

both in her Breast and Lungs, whilst She was in Your Majesties Palace'. 'Aer that is corrupt,' Evelyn noted, 'insinuates itself into the vital parts immediately', and comes from things like 'the immoderate use of and indulgence to Sea-coale [which] … exposes [London] to one of the lowest Inconveniences and reproaches that can possibly befall so noble, and otherwise incomparable City'.

Such was Evelyn's starting point for a series of original reflections and practical suggestions: 'by which the Aer may not only be freed from the present Inconveniency; but (that remov'd) to render not only Your Majesties Palace, but the whole City likewise, one of the sweetest, and most delicious Habitations in the World'. First, he'd ban

continued

polluting industries from the capital, including 'Brewers, Diers, Soap and Salt-boylers, Lime-burners and the like'. Second, he'd encourage gardeners to construct sweet-smelling plantations using 'the most fragrant and odiferous flowers [lavender, juniper, jasmine and rosemary], and are aptest to tinge the Aer upon every gentle emission at a great distance ... should so perfume the adjacent places with their breath; as if, by a certain charm, or innocent Magick, they were transferred to that part of Arabia which is therefore styl'd the Happy, because it is amongst the Gums and precious spices'. The inspiration? Evelyn's amused recollection of how, during the Great Plague, a ship 'freight with peeled onions should pass along the Thames by the City ... to attract the pollution of the aer and sail away with the infection to the sea'.

It was nearly two centuries after *Fumifugium* that London gained its first public park, and the Greater London area now enjoys something like 1,000 green spaces. Sadly, the rest of Evelyn's ambitious plans never came to pass. [16]

The age of smoke

These days, it's hard for us to imagine just how dirty the sky became in an age when steam engines produced not just power but pollution in industrial quantities, perhaps because the creative accounts we have of life back then romanticise the smoggy-foggy atmosphere of the period.

Consider the paintings of J.M.W. Turner, whose chrome-yellow sunsets apparently reflect the high levels of (natural, volcanic) pollution in the world at that time. One of his most famous pictures, *Rain, Steam and Speed* (1844), captures the hasty progress of the 19th century in a snatched, dirty blur. Or how about (a few decades later) French impressionists such as Claude Monet and Camille Pissarro, who steamed to London to paint the choking charms of a city smeared through smoke in the late 19th century?

'In London,' Monet famously commented, 'what I love above all is the fog.' Charles Dickens might well have agreed. His *Bleak House* (1852) opens with a positively cosy account of city pollution: 'Smoke lowering down from chimney-pots, making a soft black drizzle, with flames of soot in it as big as full-grown snowflakes – gone into mourning, one might imagine, for the death of the sun ... Fog everywhere ... rolls deified among the tiers of shipping and the waterside pollutions of a great (and dirty) city ... fog in the eyes and throats of ancient Greenwich pensioners, wheezing by the firesides of their wards.' Meanwhile, in the United States, writer and naturalist Henry David Thoreau was twiddling his thumbs by Walden Pond in Concord, Massachusetts, musing on the coming of the railway: 'with its steam cloud like a banner streaming behind in golden and silver wreaths ... [making] the hills echo with his snort like thunder, shaking the earth with his feet, and breathing fire and smoke from his nostrils'. [17]

The steep climb in 19th-century coal mining tells the same story more prosaically. In 1800, London burned about a tonne of coal per resident; a century later, that had risen to two tonnes per resident of the now much bigger city. Over in Germany in 1850, there were roughly 300 coal mines operating in the country's mighty industrial Ruhr area (around Dortmund) in a region that had only begun to industrialise in 1815. Coal production there increased six-fold between 1815 and 1850 and over 150-fold between 1815 and 1900. By 1860, the Ruhr had the highest density of coal mines and blast furnaces anywhere in the world. There were similar increases in production in France, Belgium and Britain. Over in the United States, mining was growing even faster, by a factor of about 30 between 1850 and 1900, by which time the country had overtaken Britain as the world's biggest coal producer. [18]

While smoke and sulphur dioxide from coal burning were starting to become a serious nuisance for 19th-century cities, the sudden growth of those cities was also a major problem. As Stephen Mosley of Leeds Beckett University points out, there were only six cities in the world with half a million inhabitants or more in 1800; by 1900, the number had risen to over 40; today, there are hundreds. In 1800, about 30 per cent of the population of England and Wales was classed as urban; a century on, that figure stood at 80 per cent. So then, as now, the problem wasn't simply pollution but rapidly rising population in increasingly polluted areas. (Current public health problems in developing-country megacities stem as much from dense urbanisation as from pollution.) [19]

And the effects were much as we might expect – notably a huge increase in death and illness from breathing in smoke and other forms of filth. During the worst of the Industrial Revolution, in the second half of the 19th century, the death rate rose by about twelve times. For those who weren't coughing themselves to death, there were other horrors to contend with: endless smog thick enough to stop trains and 'foggy' days for over half the year in some parts of London during 1885, with a sharp rise in crime closely correlated with them. There was even an apparent stunting of people's growth (for reasons that aren't very clear, people in the most polluted areas were up to eight centimetres shorter than those living in places with cleaner air). [20]

Remember how John Evelyn had complained about 'presumptuous Smoake' making London 'pernicious and insupportable' as far back as 1661? Now imagine how much worse things had become in 1861, in the middle of the Industrial Revolution, and you can probably understand the public clamour to put things right. Britain's parliamentarians, spurred on by wealthy landlords worried by the damage to their property and mostly fought by industrialists worried by the damage to their profits, chewed the matter over in 1819, 1843 and 1845; spawning a rash of national, anti-pollution laws during the late-19th and early-20th centuries. Meanwhile, over in the United States, there were no comparable (federal or state) anti-pollution laws, though local (municipal) laws and regulations did begin to appear towards the end of the 19th century. Other changes were also making a difference. In overflowing cities such as London, more people were migrating to the suburbs where the air was cleaner. And there was a steady shift to other power sources, notably natural gas (less polluting than coal) and then to electricity, which outsources pollution from the home to the power station – putting it, at least in theory, out of sight and out of mind. [21]

Technology historian Daniel French calls this the moment 'when they hid the fire'; what they didn't do, unfortunately, was hide the smoke. As French points out in a compelling book on the history of electricity in the United States, smoke became a universal nuisance in 19th-century America. The downtrodden masses, with their soot-stained walls, aligned themselves with strident social reformers like Harriet Beecher Stowe (author of *Uncle Tom's Cabin*), who clearly understood the importance of clean air. With her sister Catharine Esther Beecher, Stowe described indoor air pollution from badly ventilated stoves as 'murder of the most hideous character', in their book *The American Woman's Home*: 'The great majority of the American people, owing to sheer ignorance, are, for want of pure air, being poisoned and starved; the result being weakened constitutions, frequent disease and short-ened life.' All this sounds surprisingly modern to me. So, too, do French's tales of dogged air-pollution denial by the coal industry – the idea that soot particles were a disinfectant – typified by one magnate, Colonel W.P. Rend of Pittsburgh, who went so far as to declare coal 'a benefit to public health'. (That was, in fact, a widely held view well into the 19th century, and its origins can be traced back to the ancient Greek miasma theory.) [22]

No one ever realised just how grossly polluting power stations would become; that much is clear from Thomas Edison's decision to build the world's first proper one at Pearl Street, in downtown New York City, in 1882. Limited by how far it could transmit electricity,[4] it had to be sited near to customers (and investors on Wall Street), but the smoke that spilled into the air from the moment its 27-tonne electricity generators leaped to life prompted immediate complaints from the neighbours. Pearl Street was a modest prototype; the huge electric power plants that soon followed, built by pioneers such as Edison and his great rival George Westinghouse, were at least ten times more powerful and required huge investments and a certain payback. So one often-overlooked objective of the new age of electric convenience (instant electric lighting, washing machines and factory machines powered by electric motors instead of coal-powered steam engines) was to create demand for an apparently clean and tidy new power source fuelled by an apparently limitless supply of coal – prompting demand for even more power stations. At that time, no one cared much about the runaway environmental implications, and no one noticed the human cost (more miners contracting crippling diseases such as pneumoconiosis or 'black lung' and more people dying from outdoor air pollution). [23]

---

[4] That was because Edison championed low-voltage, short-range, direct current (DC) electricity in a famous technological battle with Nikola Tesla and George Westinghouse known as the War of the Currents. The easy-to-transmit, high-voltage, long-range alternating current (AC) we rely on today allows power plants to be located far from our towns and cities.

But more demand brought more problems. During the 18th century, steam engines, originally a static source of power for mines and factories, were miniaturised to the point where they could power railroad trains and road cars, taking pollution with them wherever they went. (We'll explore this in greater detail in Chapter 5.) In the 19th century, the steam engine evolved into the petrol-powered car and created a whole new kind of pollution. In the 20th century, growing demand for affordable, mass-produced products, such as Henry Ford's Model T car, led to vast factories like Ford's own River Rouge plant at Dearborn, Michigan, which burned six tonnes of coal for every car it made. Factories like these pushed out pollution not just from their chimneys but from the tailpipes of all the cars they produced (about 4,000 a year in 1900, rising to 4 million a year by 1940 and twice that number by 1950). So it wasn't simply production (industrialisation and urbanisation) that powered pollution at the dawn of the 20th century, but also consumption (mass-produced goods, affluence and the easy convenience of mechanised lifestyles) – the very things that continue to power pollution to this day. [24]

Darkness falls

In 1880, an English meteorologist called Rollo Russell wrote an influential little pamphlet about the growing problem of smoggy fogs, noting how: '... smoke in London has continued probably for many years to shorten the lives of thousands, but only lately has the sudden, palpable rise of the death-rate in an unusually dense and prolonged fog attracted much attention to the depredations of this quiet and despised destroyer'. Even so, it wasn't till the middle of the 20th century that the world woke up to the reality that smoggy air pollution could kill in very large numbers, following a series of major international disasters. [25]

One of the first happened in mid-Belgium, between Liège and Engis, in early December 1930. A temperature inversion (as we've already seen, that's a layer of warm air over cold, trapping pollutants like a lid) conspired with the geography of hills and vales to hold a suffocating blanket of air pollutants (notably smoke and sulphur dioxide) from two dozen factories and household coal fires above an 18-kilometre (12-mile) stretch of the Meuse valley. Over five days, hundreds reported being short of breath and 63 died. Although the tragedy was reported around the world, and the risk of a repetition was abundantly clear, the lessons were largely ignored. Jean Firket, a local medical professor who investigated the episode, warned that 'London ... might be faced with the responsibility of 3,200 sudden deaths if such a phenomenon occurred there'; his words were prophetic. [26]

Another warning sounded on 28 November 1939. The American city of St Louis, Missouri suffered 'Black Tuesday – the day that didn't shine' when it, too, was smothered by a temperature inversion that trapped a lid of thick smoke from low-quality coal. (Just half a century earlier, according to Daniel French, the smoke in St Louis had been lauded as a major health benefit – a cure for the 'plagues and torments that afflict other cities'.) No one died on Black Tuesday, and though the city took its own steps to encourage cleaner coal, the broader lesson still wasn't learned in other places. A decade later, and almost 20 years after the Meuse disaster, on 27 October 1948, the skies suddenly turned dark and foggy over the town of Donora, about 30 kilometres (18 miles) from Pittsburgh, Pennsylvania, and stayed that way until a rainstorm cleared the air four days later. During that time, Donora's smog was so thick that emergency vehicles had to be guided by a person edging along in front with a flashlight and, later, as the fog steadily worsened, by slowly bumping their way along the kerbs. Just as in the Meuse Valley and St Louis, the cause was a temperature inversion. This one trapped a blanket of sulphur dioxide, carbon monoxide, hydrogen fluoride, sooty particulates and other toxic pollutants over the town, where it choked 5,900 people (almost half the population of 14,000) and killed 20 (another 50 died within a month). The final death toll isn't known, although recent research has shown that the episode led to higher than expected rates of heart disease and cancer for years afterwards. [27]

By the time of the Donora tragedy, the conditions that made it possible – factories and power plants concentrated in dense urban areas, where people also lived and kept warm by burning coal – were replicated in countless other places around the world. It was only a matter of time before the same thing happened again. In fact, it was a mere four years later when yet another inversion trapped deadly polluted fog over a densely populated area; this time, in December 1952, it was the turn of London, England. The infamous Great London Smog lasted less than a week but killed between 4,000 (the estimate at the time) and 12,000 (a newer estimate), and the legacy of misery it left behind has never been fully quantified. Recent research suggests the episode caused a 10 per cent increase in adult asthma among those exposed at the time and a 20 per cent increase in childhood asthma among those exposed during the first year of life. [28]

Lessons learned?

This series of deadly disasters, their outcome all too predictable, was the wake-up call the world needed. Bold and firm laws, such as the Clean Air Acts of 1956 (in the UK) and 1963 and 1970 (in the United States), suggested lessons had finally been learned. But

had they, and were they the right ones? In the aftermath of the
Great London Smog, Britain's 1956 Act contained measures to curb
domestic coal-burning, shift power plants out of urban centres
and heighten chimneys to spread the smoke they made – a very
specific set of solutions aimed at tackling the problems that had
led to the 1952 tragedy. But moving power plants to other places
or sticking taller chimneys on them wasn't really stopping air pollution; it was simply moving it elsewhere. The Clean Air Act was a
bit of a misnomer; it was making the dirt less of an acute problem
by spreading it over a wider area. Even so, it was a milestone. As
atmospheric chemist Professor Peter Brimblecombe pointed out
in a review of the law written 50 years later: 'It remains a sem-
inal piece of legislation because it created a belief that a better
environment was possible and worthwhile despite the fact that
at times it would restrict our individual freedom.' In the United
States, the 1963 Act became the first major piece of federal law
aimed at controlling air pollution, but its focus was on science
and research; it didn't establish air quality standards, much less
enforce them. Two more temperature inversions in New York City,
which killed 405 people in 1963 and 168 in 1966, underlined the
need for tougher action. [29]

Meanwhile, as the 20th century rolled on, new threats were
jostling alongside growing environmental consciousness. In the
1950s, US nuclear testing at Bikini and Enewetak atolls in
the Marshall Islands hurled apocalyptic clouds of radiation high
into the stratosphere. Terrified scientific observers watched in
awe and horror in November 1952 as Ivy Mike, the first hydrogen bomb, 700 times more powerful than the weapon dropped on
Hiroshima, obliterated the island of Elugelab under a 160-kilometre
(100-mile) wide mushroom cloud sitting on a 50-kilometre
(30-mile) high stem. Today, over half a century later, some of the

areas affected by the 67 Marshall Islands tests still have radiation levels 1,000 times greater than the sites of the Fukushima and Chernobyl nuclear power plant disasters. [30]

Persistent pollution was also the theme of Rachel Carson's groundbreaking 1962 bestseller *Silent Spring*, which woke the world to the horrors of toxic chemicals in the environment with eloquent arguments years ahead of their time. She noted, for example, that spraying garden pesticides could result in 'finely divided particles of whatever insecticide the probably unsuspecting suburbanite has chosen to distribute, raising the level of air pollution above his own grounds to something few cities could equal'. Later that decade, evidence of another surprising kind of pollution emerged from Swedish research into airborne chemicals that swept between countries and were affecting things like crops, lakes and rivers. Soil scientist Svante Odén is credited with raising international public awareness of the issue in a highly provocative newspaper article titled 'An Insidious Chemical Warfare Among the Nations of Europe'. A few years later, US ecologists discovered the first compelling evidence of acid rain at Hubbard Brook Valley in New Hampshire – and several hundred poisoned American lakes. Acid rain became a major political issue worldwide in the 1980s and 1990s. [31]

Acid rain – air pollution pouring back to Earth as sulphuric or nitric acid – was slow and steady poisoning. The sudden toxic gas leak at the Union Carbide chemical plant in Bhopal, India in 1984 could not have been more different: it's now estimated to have killed somewhere between 10,000 and 20,000 people, and injured half a million more. Though barely mentioned today, it remains the world's worst industrial disaster. The year after Bhopal, three scientists from the British Antarctic Survey in Cambridge discovered the hole in the ozone layer. In 1986, an explosion at the

Chernobyl nuclear plant in Ukraine hurled a high cloud of radio-active fallout over much of western Europe, spurring fears of a slow-motion Hiroshima. [32]

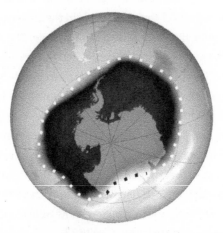

Figure 16. The biggest ever hole in the ozone layer, recorded over Antarctica in September 2006, measured a vast 29.5 million square kilometres (11.4 million square miles) – about 20 per cent bigger than the total surface area of North America. By 2019, it had shrunk to less than half this size (16.4 million square kilometres or 6.3 million square miles). Photo courtesy of NASA. [33]

The new pollution

Epic disasters like these gave the 1980s quite an apocalyptic feel at times, leading to a surge in environmental consciousness towards the end of the 20th century. There were Earth days, Earth hours, the World Commission on Environment and Development ('Brundtland') Report in 1987 and the UN Rio Conference on Sustainable Development in 1992, to name but a few. Steady progress was also being made in clearing up air pollution – or what had generally passed for air pollution up to that point. The United

States and Britain, two industrialised nations that had pioneered pollution, saw notable curbs in sulphur dioxide, the prime suspect in the mid-20th-century disasters at Donora and London. (In the United States, SO_2 levels have fallen by 91 per cent since 1980, while in the UK, they've been slashed by 97 per cent since 1970.) Meanwhile, acid rain, having leaped to the top of the political agenda as very visible evidence of air pollution, was being brought under control thanks to efforts like the 1990 Clean Air Act in the United States, ushered in by President George H.W. Bush with bipartisan support. The arrival of catalytic converters, in the mid-1970s, was also paying dividends, slashing emissions of at least some traffic pollutants – hydrocarbons, nitrogen oxides and carbon monoxide. But much more still needed to be done. In the United States, the American Lung Association doggedly filed lawsuits against the US Environmental Protection Agency (EPA) during the early 1990s to force even tighter regulation of sulphur dioxide, ozone – and particulates. [34]

Particulates, though long considered harmful, emerged as the supreme urban menace in the second half of the 1990s. That was thanks, in large part, to a couple of groundbreaking public health studies by American epidemiologists Douglas Dockery and Arden Pope (known as the Harvard Six Cities and American Cancer Society or ACS studies), which provided firm scientific evidence that fine particulates, even in very low doses, were killing people in worrying numbers. Dockery and Pope's work proved hugely controversial, prompting a furious backlash from industry and years of legal battles that went right up to the US Supreme Court before the EPA really began cracking down on particulates in 2001, although the controversy rumbles on to this day. As we'll see in Chapter 8, the dangers of fine particulates have been a central focus for air pollution research ever since. [35]

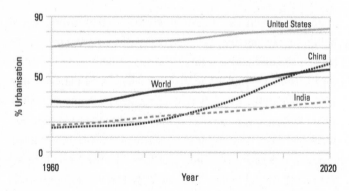

Figure 17. Urbanisation drives pollution. In fact, urban pollution increases at a faster rate than urban density, so doubling the population of a city more than doubles its pollution. The trend toward bigger and more polluted cities puts more vulnerable people in harm's way. This chart shows how the percentage of people living in urban places continues to rise throughout the world. Based on data from United Nations Population Division. World Urbanisation Prospects: 2018 Revision/World Bank. [36]

To be continued

And so the story continues, with a (relatively) new shift in emphasis to a very different kind of air pollution, in the shape of the greenhouse gas emissions (mostly carbon dioxide and methane) that are driving climate change. Back in the world of old-style pollution, there have been some spectacular successes: the removal of lead from petrol, the banning of the chlorofluorocarbon (CFC) chemicals that tore holes in the ozone layer and the steady war on tobacco smoking (which still kills 8 million a year). And some equally spectacular failures: the fatally misguided shift to diesel cars and the growing popularity of cosy (but highly toxic) wood burners, to name but two. How all the gains and losses weigh up against one another is debatable, but one thing seems clear: the fact that dirty air remains the world's biggest environmental public health issue, and one of the world's most flagrant, reckless serial killers – still hasn't hit home. In the words of World Health

Organization Director-General, Dr Tedros Adhanom Ghebreyesus, it's a 'silent public health emergency. Despite this epidemic of needless, preventable deaths and disability, a smog of complacency pervades the planet.' [37]

HOW DO WE KNOW?

Science attempts to explain the world with theories, then uses experiments to find evidence that builds those theories up or knocks them down: either way, the evidence is key. But when it comes to the question of how dirty air harms health, ordinary scientific experiments aren't much use. We can't clamp masks over people's faces, pump them full of diesel exhaust and see if they die – so what can we do instead? Two alternative sources of evidence are controversial animal experiments (where lab rats and other creatures are systematically dosed up with pollution to see what happens) and epidemiology.

Epidemiology[5] means gathering statistical data for a group of people who experience something like traffic pollution over a period of time, measuring how their health changes and carefully 'controlling for' (cancelling out) the effects of every other variable factor (cigarette smoking and so on) that might provide an alternative explanation. Most of what we know about the harmful effects of breathing dirty air comes from studies like this. The connection between tobacco smoking and lung cancer came from groundbreaking epidemiological work by Richard Doll and Austin Hill in Britain around 1950, for example.

More recently, epidemiological studies have helped to establish a powerful link between breathing fine particulates and suffering serious health problems – and the work of two American scientists, Douglas Dockery of Harvard and Arden Pope of Brigham Young

continued

---

[5] For a simple overview, try *Epidemiology for the Unitiated* by D. Coggon, G. Rose, and D. Barker, published online on the British Medical Journal website at tinyurl.com/tne5jw4

University, has been especially influential. In 1993, when Dockery and Pope compared air pollution measurements and death rates in six large US cities, controlling for the effects of cigarette smoking and other health risks, they found some of the first powerful evidence that fine particulates (or pollution mixtures containing them) increase the death rate. Lots of other studies have confirmed and extended their work.

Arden Pope had already made his name with another influential (but controversial) study – one of the first to put particulates on the map of real pollution concerns. Pope had heard about a boy who got sick when the local steel mill was operating, recovered when it closed down for a year-long strike, then got sick once more when the mill started up again. Carefully probing the connection, he found shifting patterns in hospital admissions for bronchitis and asthma when the mill was either operating normally or closed down, which led him to argue that its particulate pollution was, in fact, a significant cause of respiratory illness in the local community. Although that research made him powerful enemies – he was labelled a 'long-haired environmentalist' and accused of practising 'bad science' by supporters of the economically important mill – he was fully vindicated by follow-up research.

Though pollution can sometimes seem bleak and daunting, the opposite is actually true: every air pollution scientist is on a personal crusade to make the world a cleaner and better place. The determined focus on dangerous particulates in today's research stems directly from Pope and Dockery's work – and growing efforts to clear the air, ultimately inspired by their groundbreaking research, will save many millions of lives. [38]

CHAPTER 4

Natural born polluters?

Why worry about pollution if it's a perfectly natural thing?

Nature good, humans bad – so runs the traditional (but somewhat threadbare) environmental refrain. And it would be easy to interpret air pollution in that light – those naughty old humans, wrecking Eden again – were it not for the simple fact that quite a lot of the pollution our lungs sponge up comes from trees, oceans, deserts, volcanoes and other natural sources. If we could magic away our traffic and industry, farming, power generation and other energy-intensive activities, might Earth still qualify as a polluted place? Just how serious is all this natural pollution, compared to the more obvious filth that drifts from things like smokestacks and car tailpipes? Does it actually kill people? And does natural pollution, as US President Ronald Reagan was fond of pointing out, put 'real' pollution in a different context: if pollution is such a natural and unavoidable thing, do we really need to worry about it at all?

Most types of the pollution we've already explored can also be generated by natural sources. Sulphur dioxide, for example, wafts out from volcanoes, along with the nitrogen oxides that can leap to life through lightning bolts. Carbon monoxide and particulates billow from wildfires (often caused by lightning, but arguable forms of 'natural' pollution, since they can also be sparked by careless cigarettes and are now exacerbated by human-caused climate change). Different kinds of particulate dust whip in from the deserts and beaches and oceans on the wind. Volatile organic compounds (VOCs), similar to the ones in traditional paints and polishes, also leak out from aromatic trees. Methane and ammonia burp from both ends of farm animals. If you could turn the natural world over and read its list of chemical ingredients, it might not seem so natural after all.

So much for the 'quality' of natural pollution, but what about the quantity? You might think the contribution nature makes to our polluted world is trivial compared to the filth from, say, a billion car exhausts, but that's far from the case. Back in the 1980s, when dirty coal power plants were still the norm, the United Nations Environment Programme (UNEP) estimated that natural sources were releasing up to four times as much sulphur dioxide and nitrogen oxides into the air compared to human activities. Today, with SO_2 emissions from coal-burning substantially reined in (across the Western world, at least), that comparison would be even starker. Natural pollution really is something to take seriously, but where exactly does it all come from? [1]

A growing problem

Hurtling to work on the freeway, soaring through the sky in a jet-powered tube, sitting at home pawing at our smartphones or slouched in front of the TV, it's easy to forget that our entire, planetary existence depends on plants going about their business – being born, living, reproducing, dying – in parallel. Primitive plants (like ferns and mosses) lack flowers and reproduce in furtive ways, but colourful plants engage in an open-air orgy of flamboyant, flowery sex that all of us are party to. I'm talking, of course, about pollen. Pollen is the raw-stuff of plant repro- duction: male cells wrapped up in grains that travel, by breath of wind or hitching a helpful ride on a passing bee's leg, to the sticky female parts of other plants, where they bring about fertilisation.

Intricate and fascinating, dressed in creamy whites, oranges and yellows, pollen grains under the microscope look like abstract, tiny sea creatures or aliens from space, pimpled with stars and blobs, spikes and tentacles. But all's not what it seems. Pollen is pollution – and plenty of it. In some countries, up to 30 per cent of adults and 40 per cent of children now suffer from hay fever, technically known as allergic rhinitis (inflammation of your nasal passages that causes cold-like symptoms). In the United States, the economic cost of allergic rhinitis (from all sources) has been estimated at $24.8 billion. Each year, around 3 million Britons feel the need to take time off work to sniffle with hay fever, effec- tively stealing over £7.1 billion from the economy (enough to build about fourteen big hospitals). Worldwide, around 10–40 per cent of people are affected by hay fever – so, do the maths, and the economic impact of airborne plant sex is substantial. And it may be even greater than supposed, given that hay fever is widely undiagnosed (half of all sufferers mistakenly think they have a persistent summer cold). [2]

All these numbers make for quite an abstract account of a most miserable form of natural pollution (about 60 per cent of adults and nearly 90 per cent of children with hay fever have trouble sleeping, for example). So what's actually going on inside your nose? On summer days when the pollen forecast is very high, there will be about 450 pollen grains in a volume of air the size of a typical sofa (3 cubic metres or 3,000 litres), which might not sound like many. But at a normal rate of breathing (say, a litre of air fifteen times a minute), one grain will be itching its way up your nostrils every 20 seconds or so. Pollen grains from different plants cause trouble at different times of year, from spring through to autumn, and come in all shapes and sizes, but (using the same measurements we use for exhaust fumes and other dirt) generally qualify as larger particulates (typically PM10, but up to 10 times bigger). Each of these can, however, be shattered into hundreds of smaller and more irritating particulates (closer to the dangerous PM2.5 scale) by things like sudden storms – giving rise to the strange phenomenon known as 'thunderstorm asthma'. [3]

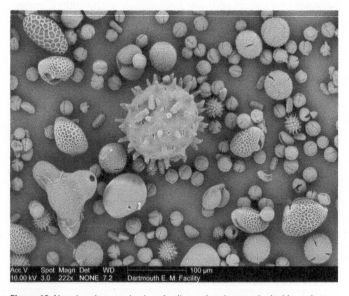

Figure 18. Nose invaders: a selection of pollen grains photographed with an electron microscope. The large one in the centre is about 100 millionths of a metre across, roughly the width of a human hair and ten times bigger than a PM10 particulate. Photo by Louisa Brown, Dartmouth College Electron Microscopy Facility.

It seems fairly obvious that pollen is a natural form of pollution – but things aren't quite so simple. One of the really intriguing things is that so many more people suffer from hay fever today than several decades ago, when the Western world was less urbanised although, in some ways, more (and differently) polluted. In 19th-century urban Britain and the United States, both caught up in the white heat of the Industrial Revolution, few people suffered from hay fever. One of the first to describe the illness, in 1819, was Englishman Dr John Bostock; the condition was later traced to pollen in the early 1870s by Harvard professor Dr Morrill Wyman and Dr Charles Blackley, a British physician and hay-fever sufferer. Their vague speculations were slow to gain traction at a time when germ theory (the idea that microorganisms, such as bacteria and viruses, cause or carry most diseases, promoted by such luminaries as Louis Pasteur and Robert Koch) was really taking root. Wyman termed his complaint 'Autumnal Catarrh', and pondered its similarities to 'Summer Cold', 'Rose Cold' and the English 'Hay Fever' (also called 'Summer Catarrh' or *Catarrhus Aestivus*), which he considered an 'objectionable' misnomer ('hay does not cause the disease'). Over in Britain, Blackley wasn't sure whether the apparent increase in cases was due to more attention from the medical profession or 'the greater prevalence of those conditions which act as predisposing and exciting causes'. Today, we'd plump firmly for the latter: Blackley noted that Dr John Bostock had recorded a mere eighteen cases of hay fever in his first decade studying the disease. Around 150 years after Bostock, in the 1980s, hay fever was hitting one person in eight and it's twice as common today. [4]

So why the dramatic increase? Although there are quite a few possible explanations, the complex (and still not completely understood) links between pollen, hay fever, asthma and insidious

modern forms of air pollution appear to be at least partly responsible. Forty per cent of hay fever sufferers have asthma (or are
at greater risk of developing it), while 80 per cent of asthmatics
suffer from rhinitis. Hay fever can make asthma worse (to the
point where it causes acute attacks that put people in hospital),
and air pollution makes both asthma and hay fever worse, even
when the pollen count is low – so all these things interact. Air
pollution exacerbates the effects of pollen in various ways. First,
as we saw in the last chapter, localised weather patterns (notably temperature inversions) can trap smog like a lid over densely
populated and highly polluted urban areas. But smog itself can
also act like a lid, holding pollen in place over the noses of thousands or millions of city dwellers, like a particularly itchy blanket.
That's why, perversely, hay fever can be more common in towns
and cities than in rural areas where the plants are more likely to
be located, because their pollen is also more likely to disperse. The
second effect is that pollution joins forces with pollen to make
both things more problematic. The pollution grazes your airways,
making them more susceptible to pollen penetration. It also sticks
to pollen grains, which give it a swift ride into your lungs. Among
the pollutants that most affect pollen are nitrogen dioxide and
ozone – both heavily correlated with traffic. So one theory is that
ever-increasing traffic levels and urbanisation are substantially to
blame for the modern epidemic of hay fever, which means pollen
is not nearly so natural a form of pollution as it seems. Today,
pollen and pollution go hand in hand. A few years ago, a leading
pharmacy chain tried to couple the phenomena by coining a horribly clumsy new word, 'pollenution', to describe what it called
the 'toxic storm' that pollen and pollution unleash on vulnerable
people (largely, it appears, in an attempt to sell more antihista-
mine tablets). [5]

Into the trees

Henry David Thoreau 'took a walk in the woods and came out taller than the trees', but President Ronald Reagan shrank firmly back from that romantic idea. Famously, in 1981, he claimed that 'trees cause more pollution than automobiles do', which sounds – and was treated as – just about the most fatuous claim an anti-environmentalist could ever make. Trees, to most of us, are gifts from god, especially if you live and choke your waking, working days in town. Urbanites are fond of describing them as 'green lungs' that purify the air, making city life possible, if not always pleasant. One study of 31,000 Canadians found that having just ten more trees in a neighbourhood produced as much improvement in local people's well-being as a pay rise of $10,000 or being seven years younger. No wonder Reagan's idea (that something as wonderful as a tree could be more malign than a car's exhaust pipe) seems so preposterous. And yet there was more than a grain of truth in what he said: trees really aren't as green as they seem. On the positive side, it's true that they cool the sweltering city and create favourable little microclimates all around them (for example, by acting as wind breaks, sun shades or improving the local humidity). And they certainly mop up dust that would otherwise burrow its way into our lungs. But on the minus side, they give off toxic chemicals that really do make air quality worse, and they can trap pollution clouds in avenues or under their canopies. [6]

If you're familiar with volatile organic compounds (VOCs) – and we briefly introduced them in Chapter 1 – most likely you've come across them in the context of household chemicals like paints and polishes. VOCs make the head-spinning stench when you paint your windows with gloss or prise the lid off a new can of shoe shine; they're particularly unnatural forms of pollution. Yet similar chemicals come in a much more natural flavour known as BVOCs (biological VOCs). It's hardly surprising to discover that aromatic trees such as pine and eucalyptus give off chemicals (it's no coincidence that so many air fresheners are pine-scented), but humdrum trees like oak, poplar, sycamore and willow release them, too. The chemicals involved include camphene (an ingredient of essential oils), isoprene (used to make synthetic rubber), limonene (from citrus, used as a scent and solvent in household cleaners and polishes), pinene (from pine resin) and terpene (the base ingredient of turpentine/white spirit). The amount of chemicals released depends on how much the tree is photosynthesising and how hot it is (so it varies with the time of day and the strength of the sun). Natural VOCs are also thrown into the air when it rains. That delightfully earthy, 'just-rained' smell, technically known as petrichor, comes from volatile chemicals released from plants and enhanced by rocks and soil bacteria. [7]

Why are BVOCs an issue? First, because they're VOCs – so some of them are pollution in their own right. Second, in cities, they can either exacerbate the production of ozone and carbon monoxide from other sources or, conversely, help to mop up ozone. Also, when trees are cut down, sanded and sawn, that releases BVOCs in a way that would count as human-caused pollution.

But aren't these tree emissions pretty minimal? And doesn't planting an avenue of trees alongside a busy road more than compensate, automatically making it cleaner and quieter for people living nearby? Well, no. The overall emissions are far from negligible: some studies suggest plants and trees emit about two thirds of total atmospheric VOCs (which is where Ronald Reagan's apparently outrageous claim comes from). And while trees can certainly soak up noise, their impact on pollution is more moot. A tree canopy can act like a roof across a road, trapping smog like a lid. If trees are working as a windbreak, they slow or stop sideways air movements that help pollution to disperse. Even the popular belief that trees mop up pollutants is open to challenge (urban planning commentator Jane Jacobs once rubbished it as 'science fiction nonsense'). According to a recent study, they do little or nothing to reduce gaseous pollutants, though they do have an impact on particulates. For an authoritative rebuttal of the idea that trees can do no wrong, look no further than the UK's National Institute for Health and Care Excellence (NICE): 'It is not always true that trees reduce air pollution. Their effect is dependent on factors including species, canopy density, time of year and wind direction.' [8]

The bottom line with urban trees is that everything depends on what species they are and where they're planted. If you stick tall, low-VOC-emitting trees all around a car park, for example, shading the vehicles from the sun, you'll keep those cars cooler and substantially reduce emissions of petroleum-based VOCs from their engines and (largely plastic) interiors. If you use evergreens in a city, they'll be soaking up dust and dirt all year round. But let's not overstate the importance of urban trees: as one team of Chinese researchers studying the area round Beijing recently reported, even dramatic changes in a city's tree population are less effective than a determined effort to control emissions. Then again, let's not forget that green areas in cities help us indirectly: if you plant trees in a park or avenue that encourages lunch-hour city workers to wander away from busy roads or other polluted places, you're helping them breathe cleaner air irrespective of what the trees themselves are doing. On balance, when it comes to pollution, trees are usually a force for good – except, that is, when they catch fire. [9]

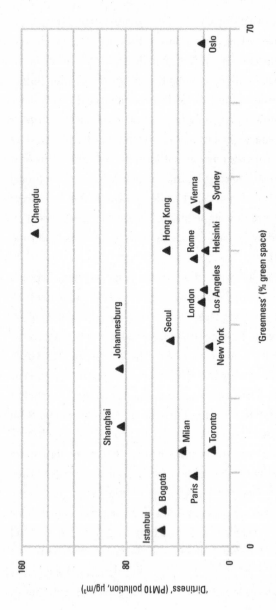

Figure 19. Are greener cities cleaner cities? Not always. I've picked some typical cities and plotted their dirtiness (level of PM10 pollution, measured in μg/m³) against their greenness (the percentage of the city devoted to green space). As you can see, there is no obvious connection. Istanbul/Shanghai (dirty and urban) and Sydney/Oslo (clean and green) support the theory, while Toronto (clean and urban) and Chengdu (green and dirty) go the other way. Drawn using data from World Health Organization/World Cities Culture Forum. [10]

Burning issues

There's a simple reason why we don't notice or do much about everyday pollution (from traffic, industry, agriculture and the other usual suspects): it's a chronic, mundane, predictable, invisible and therefore easily ignorable problem. Wildfires, made for Hollywood (and often blazing not so far away from it), turn all these things on their head. Raging flames rampaging around million-dollar homes, belching out ground-level clouds of thick black smoke, like something out of a disaster movie, are sudden, wildly unpredictable, utterly devastating and impossible to ignore. We've all seen the TV news footage of Californian hillsides exploding in flames – typically forcing tens of thousands of panicking people to flee from their homes, killing dozens and torching, in some years, areas the size of whole counties.

Wildfires include burning plants, grasses, heathland and trees, so they're generally classed as a natural form of air pollution; but, like everything to do with pollution and trees, it's a bit more complicated than that. In Europe, roughly 90 per cent of all wild forest and grassland fires are either accidentally or deliberately caused by people (through discarded cigarettes, careless camping, insane pyromania, farm stubble burning and so on); in the United States, the figure is 84 per cent. Spontaneous, summertime tinder fires do happen, often triggered by lightning strikes, and though they're in the minority, they're a growing problem. In 2019, lightning and climate change were blamed for a huge spate of wildfires across several Arctic countries (in Russia alone, an area the size of Belgium went up in smoke). As towering flames tore through millions of hectares of southern Australia in the blistering summer of 2019/2020, many argued that the incendiary influence of (human-caused) climate change made it harder to classify bushfires as a natural phenomenon. However they happen, fires like this are more common than you might suppose. The EU Fire Database reveals that something like 95,000 fires occur in Europe, devastating an area of 600,000 hectares (roughly four to five times the area of Los Angeles or three times the size of Tokyo), each year. [11]

The old adage of there being no smoke without fire applies equally in reverse: there's no (wild)fire without smoke. Natural or human-caused, the end result is the same: wildfires are acute episodes of life-threatening pollution that smother entire communities with the whole range of toxic gases and particulates. In theory, if wood were made from nothing but hydrocarbons and burned completely, it would transform into nothing worse than water (steam) and carbon dioxide. In practice, it contains other things besides hydrogen and carbon and its combustion is always what chemists call 'incomplete', so we also get carbon monoxide, ammonia, formaldehyde and huge clouds of thick, black soot. Burning trees and plants throw out dangerous PM2.5 particulates, as well as those BVOCs we noted above (even the trees that don't burn, but are near the fire, will release significantly more BVOCs as their temperature rises), plus toxic chemicals like benzene, dioxins and furans and over 80 other gases (albeit often in minute, or 'trace', quantities). Just as in car engines, these heady natural bonfires produce nitrogen oxides and carbon monoxide, which encourage the formation of ozone downwind, especially when fires have been burning long enough to generate intense temperatures. And, with certain types of wildfires (notably those involving peat and soil), sulphur dioxide emissions can also be a problem. [12]

Put it all together and the amount of pollution wildfires throw out is staggering. In the 2017 season alone, Californian fires hurled out as much pollution in a mere two days as all the vehicles in the state – something like 10–20 million of them – produce in a year. But what begins in California doesn't end there. Whipped up on the wind, wildfire smoke can sweep particulates to other countries and even continents. During the 2004 wildfire season in Alaska, after 4.5 million hectares (11 million acres, an area the size of New Hampshire and Massachusetts combined) were torched, some of the pollution released was tracked all the way to Europe. According to Gabriele Pfister from the National Center for Atmospheric Research in Boulder, Colorado, the Alaskan fires released 30 million tonnes of carbon monoxide (as much as everyone in the United States produced by other means during the same timeframe). That, in turn, helped to ramp up ground-level ozone levels in the United States by as much as a quarter and by 10 per cent thousands of kilometres away in Europe. In the 2017 wildfire season, when the Northern Californian counties of Napa, Sonoma and Solano caught fire, more than 10,000 tonnes of highly dangerous PM2.5s crackled into the air. A wildfire can increase local particulate levels tenfold within a matter of hours, briefly producing levels of pollutants comparable to those people routinely endure in Asian megacities. [13]

Thanks to all its Hollywood-hillside, movie-star mansions, California is the TV-news poster child of wildfires, but it's far from the only place affected: huge forest fires can spring up almost anywhere on Earth. The infamous Southeast Asian forest fires of the mid- to late-1990s (caused by deliberate land clearance) produced extreme levels of particulates. In Indonesia, where the fires were mainly burning, PM10 levels hit 1,800 micrograms per cubic metre (90 times higher than WHO guidelines). For several months during the 1994 fires, PM10 particulate levels in Kuala Lumpur reached 409 micrograms per cubic metre; three years later, in Sarawak, Malaysia, they topped 930 micrograms per cubic metre (50 times the guidelines). In summer 2019, Mexico City became one of the world's most polluted places, thanks to choking wildfire smoke:

some 9 million people were told to stay indoors as levels of the finer PM2.5 pollutants hit 158 micrograms per cubic metre (sixteen times WHO guidelines). It's disappointing that Mexico City should suffer so much, given its determined recent efforts to improve its air quality – but that's the problem with wildfire pollution. Wild by name and wild by nature, it's both beyond our control and often dramatically worse than chronic pollution from local traffic and industry. [14]

Even countries with relatively pristine air (such as Australia and Tasmania) can't escape the acute effects of an unpredictable wildfire. Bushfires are, in fact, Australia's biggest source of air pollution; in the 2018/2019 fire season, particulate levels of 750 parts per million were recorded (150 times the normal background level). During the country's 'apocalyptic' wildfires in summer 2019/2020, Sydney's air quality plunged to levels routinely seen in the worst parts of India and China: PM2.5s set new records, reaching 50–90 times WHO guidelines, and paramedics treated over 5,600 people with breathing difficulties in one month alone. Such sudden releases of pollution often prompt incautious statements from politicians, keen to claim that the natural world dwarfs the pollution we make with all our cars and power plants. In 2013, Australia's Warren Truss seized on a bushfire episode to claim 'there'll be more CO_2 emissions from these fires than there will be from coal-fired power stations for decades'. In fact, it's exactly the reverse. Bushfires make insignificant carbon dioxide emissions when you compare them to power plants and much of the CO_2 they do emit will be reabsorbed when forests grow back. Coal plants, on the other hand, rapidly release carbon that has been safely 'locked away' for millions of years – and, until we perfect carbon capture technology, do nothing to repair the damage they cause. [15]

Wildfires torch people's health as well as forests and scrub. We've already seen that slow, steady, seeping pollution from indoor wood (and other biomass) smoke is the world's single worst pollution problem. Wildfires, in effect, replicate that on a much bigger scale, outdoors, for an entire community of hundreds, thousands or (in the case of Mexico City and Sydney) even millions of people. Typically, wildfires provoke a sudden increase in hospital admissions, especially among the elderly, in children, in females (for reasons that are not yet understood) and for people with existing heart and lung conditions. One study found a 30–40 per cent increase in reported respiratory illnesses during a wildfire episode; another study, of a Native American reservation, found a 52 per cent increase in medical visits following a large, nearby fire. The long-term health risks may be relatively low when people are exposed to wildfire pollution for only a few hours or days, and do their best to avoid it by staying indoors with the windows shut, but the long-term effects of sudden pollution episodes are very hard to quantify. (In the previous chapter, we noted how the Donora disaster may have increased heart disease

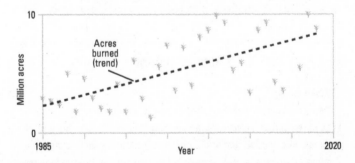

Figure 20. Wildfire damage in the United States has increased enormously over the last few decades. Though the number of fires has dropped slightly, the total area destroyed has increased dramatically – and climate change will make things much worse. Each burned tree shows the number of million acres lost in a given year; the dashed line shows the overall, upward trend. Drawn using statistics from the National Interagency Fire Center. [16]

and cancer rates for years afterwards, while the Great London Smog caused a significant increase in asthma.) Usually, and very fortunately, the immediate danger passes quite quickly. The residents of golden California manage to avoid the worst effects of air pollution because it doesn't last that long (emissions are high, but exposure is low); their exasperated counterparts in cities like Delhi aren't nearly so lucky (emissions are similar, but long-term exposure is much, much higher). [17]

Thanks to climate change, wildfires are going to be one of the great environmental challenges of the 21st century, but smart forest management can do a lot to help. Wildfires are a natural phenomenon and fundamentally important to the regeneration of some forest ecosystems; the trick is to allow certain areas of forest to burn and so prevent more dramatic, uncontrolled burning further down the line. According to green group WWF, giving local communities more responsibility for protecting their local forests is also a major step in the right direction. They cite the example of a Namibian project where sensitive management of forests by local people reduced wildfires by 30 per cent in just three years. [18]

TESTING TESTING

Wood smoke

When I was at school, we had to do a summer project on air pollution. I still remember learning the astonishing fact that wood smoke (from things like garden bonfires) contains cancer-causing chemicals, some of which are also present in tobacco smoke. In an age when the risks of smoking are very well known, I struggle to comprehend why people who'd never dream of smoking feel it's a great idea to

continued

light garden bonfires that blow palls of toxic filth into their own (and other people's) lungs for hours at a time.

I thought I'd run my own quick tests of a neighbour's garden smoke with the Plume Flow air monitor. I measured the air in my home for about ten minutes, braved the smoke for ten minutes (grey central band), then came back inside for a final ten minutes. As you can see here, levels of particulates (PM10, PM2.5 and PM1) and VOCs all increased dramatically. PM10 levels quickly shot far above the average in Delhi (grey dotted line), VOCs doubled and levels of dangerous fine PM2.5s and PM1s increased by about 30 times. Please don't burn your garden waste. Compost it or dispose of it at the municipal dump. [19]

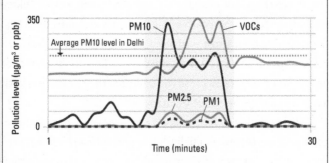

Figure 21. Chart shows: Y axis: concentration of various pollutants in bonfire smoke in μg/m³ or parts per billion (ppb); X axis: time in minutes.

Farming harm

Even if humans are the only animals who drive, fly, run factories and shovel coal into power plants, Ronald Reagan was right to note that we're not the only ones who poison the planet. Virtually all things in nature produce toxic waste through simple metabolic processes; swamps and marshes release methane, while oceans and coastal salt marshes give off methyl chloride and methyl bromide. But as with trees and forest fires, this kind of 'natural' pollution isn't always what it seems.

Take farm animals, for example. People who like to deny the importance of human-caused climate change often flag up the important but slightly misleading issue of farm animals producing methane, the second most harmful greenhouse gas. Methane is responsible for about a quarter of current global warming, and its levels have risen by about 150 per cent over the last 300 years (much more steeply over the last decade or so). The suggestion seems to be that animals are polluting the world all by themselves and would continue to do so even if we weren't around to encourage them. But methane is produced by many other things (including termites, paddy fields, natural gas and petroleum systems, melting permafrost, coal mining and landfill sites). And farm animals are, of course, *farmed* animals – working in the service of people and their stomachs, so the pollution they produce is both natural and anthropogenic (human-caused). [20]

What pollution do farm animals produce? Cows, horses, sheep, goats and pigs (in order of polluting importance, per animal) produce methane as part of their normal digestion; the waste they excrete produces methane, too, and gives off ammonia when it collects in slurry lagoons. This gas is directly toxic to nearby plants and other vegetation, such as lichens, but it also helps to form nitric acid in the atmosphere, which can wash back to Earth in the form of acid rain. Animal waste and agriculture are jointly responsible for about 90 per cent of the world's ammonia emissions. So what? Why does that matter? Emissions of ammonia indirectly lead to substantial quantities of air pollution from what are called secondary PM2.5 particulates (ones that aren't emitted directly but that form in the air from other things). This is one reason why countries like China continue to suffer from serious pollution hazes, despite having worked hard to reduce levels of other pollutants such as sulphur dioxide. [21]

Even if we all went vegan (farming no animals for our own use), we'd still need to grow food crops, and agriculture would still be polluting the planet. Fertilisers and manures – even organic ones – are based on nitrogen, which adds nitrogen oxides to the air. In 2017, about 80 per cent of all US nitrous oxide emissions came from agriculture, soil and manure management, compared to just 5 per cent from transportation. [22]

Dust to dust

What could snuff out life on Earth? An asteroid strike from space (like the one believed to have wiped out the dinosaurs), slow and steady climate change (of the kind scientists are constantly nagging us about), an angry nuclear fist-fight between stupid superpowers ... or perhaps the pent-up energy of a long-frustrated volcano?

Volcanoes in full flow are the ultimate demonstrations of truly natural air pollution: they can vent dust up to 50 kilometres (30 miles) into the atmosphere at up to 700 km/h (430 mph) – twice the top speed of a Formula 1 race car. In our own lifetimes, we've only glimpsed the tiniest possibilities of how Earth's seething, natural chimneys can blot out the sun and alter the climate. The last truly major global eruption was the one from Mount Pinatubo (in the Philippines) in 1991, which blew 20 million tonnes of sulphur dioxide into the sky, significantly affecting Earth's climate for two years afterwards. And there are plenty of examples in history of much more devastating volcanic power. Way back in 1883 in Krakatoa, Indonesia, the most famous eruption in history hurled 10 billion tonnes of magma into the sky, spreading dust as

far as New York City, and cooling the global climate by as much
as 0.5°C for a full five years. [23]

From a safe distance, volcanic eruptions look much like drifting smoke from scaled-up bonfires, but much of it is just steam
– although it does vary from one eruption to another. Some volcanoes produce more ash, others more lava and toxic gases such as
sulphur dioxide, and the end product can be a foggy haze that geologists nickname 'vog' (volcanic smog, commonly seen in Hawaii). On
closer inspection, what volcanoes hurl out are clouds (technically,
aerosols) containing relatively small amounts of all the major pollutants we've already explored – plus a few more on top: particulates

Other 3%

SO$_2$ 6%

CO$_2$ 12%

Steam 79%

Figure 22. Volcanic eruptions look spectacular, but make a much smaller contribution
to air pollution than you might think: most of what you see in the plume is steam; the
rest is mainly carbon dioxide and sulphur dioxide. Photo by R. Russell, US Fish and
Wildlife Service. [24]

(ash, soot, bits of pulverised rock), carbon monoxide and carbon dioxide, sulphur dioxide and hydrogen sulphide, hydrogen halides (chloride, fluoride, and bromide) and trace quantities of many other things, including toxic metals such as mercury. Pollution from volcanoes certainly poses a threat to humans and other living things, but it's important to keep it in proportion and not be misled by climate-change sceptics. For example, it's very wrong to suggest that volcanoes make a bigger contribution to climate change than people. According to the US Geological Survey, volcanoes produce about the same amount of CO_2 each year as 24 large (1 GW) coal-fired power stations (roughly 2 per cent of the world's total coal-fired power-plant capacity). That's around 100–150 times less than human emissions over the same time period. [25]

Volcanoes do produce significant amounts of sulphur dioxide, however, and that matters even more now that human emissions of the gas (from things like power plants) have plummeted in countries such as the United States and the UK. Even so, our old friend Ronald Reagan was being a little disingenuous when he made another of his famous pronouncements on natural pollution in 1980:

> 'I have flown twice over Mt. St. Helens out on our west coast. *I'm not a scientist and I don't know the figures, but I have a suspicion* that that one little mountain has probably released more sulphur dioxide into the atmosphere of the world than has been released in the last ten years of automobile driving or things of that kind that people are so concerned about'. [26, italic emphasis added]

Cars produce very little sulphur dioxide, so that may well have been true.

Really big volcanic eruptions that affect the whole Earth are
mercifully rare events, but even small eruptions can spread significant amounts of fine, powdery ash over the immediate local
area. Europe's volcanoes are mostly found in the Mediterranean
countries of Italy and Greece. Iceland, the world's most iconic
geothermal country, is famous for temperamental volcanoes, but
most of the world's active volcanoes are located on the opposite
side of the world. Indonesia is home to more active volcanoes
than any other country: about 140, roughly half of which are still
classed as active. One of them, Mount Tambora, holds the record
for the biggest volcanic eruption in recorded history. In 1815, two
months before Napoleon was defeated at the Battle of Waterloo,
an estimated 71,000 people died (directly and in the famines and
epidemics that followed) when Tambora blew its volcanic lid. Four
times as powerful as Krakatoa, the roar could be heard 3,000–
5,000 kilometres (2,000–3,000 miles) away – roughly the distance
from New York City to Los Angeles. Something like 100 cubic kilometres of pulverised rock (enough to fill 100 trillion litre bottles)
was hurled into the sky, reducing the size of the mountain by
50 per cent in the process. All that ash cooled the global climate
by about half a degree Celsius, causing food shortages across the
entire Northern Hemisphere in 1816, which, as a result, is now
popularly remembered as the 'Year Without a Summer'. Going
back further in history, some 39,000 years ago, the eruption of
Italy's Campi Flegrei was three times the size. It covered large
parts of Europe in ash up to 20 centimetres (8 inches) deep and
cooled Europe's climate by up to 4°C, helping to push the already
struggling Neanderthals into extinction. [27]

Geologists are fond of debating whether an event like this
could wipe out life on Earth, probably in the aftermath of the
climate catastrophe that would follow. But we don't have to wait

that long to feel the disruptive effects of more modest eruptions, which happen somewhere on Earth roughly once a week. One particularly notorious example dominated news headlines in 2010: over 100,000 European flights (and many transatlantic ones) were grounded when Eyjafjallajökull, an Icelandic volcano, fired a huge plume of dust into the atmosphere. No one died, though hundreds might have been killed if some of that volcanic pollution had jammed a plane's engine in mid-flight, and vulcanologists say they can't rule out the possibility of deaths in future indirectly related to the eruption, as well as long-term impacts on people's mental and physical health. [28]

Even in a small country like Iceland, remote from other centres of population, volcanic eruptions can have far-reaching consequences. In August 2014, another Icelandic volcano, Holuhraun, blew out 2 million tonnes of SO_2 (more per day than all of Europe's industry added together) in the biggest sulphur-polluting episode the country had seen since the Laki eruption of 1783. If the Laki eruption were repeated today, scientists have estimated it would cause something like 100,000 early deaths in Europe alone. Since it's fired so high into the air, pollution from volcanoes can affect the air quality whole continents away. Holuhraun's eruption was picked up by air monitoring stations up to 2,750 kilometres (1,700 miles) downwind; studies of other volcanoes have detected potentially harmful pollution at distances 1,400 kilometres (900 miles) away. [29]

The different polluting gases and particulates in volcanic smoke have a wide range of short- and long-term health impacts. The steam and water vapour – the vehicle that carries them – is harmless enough, but the carbon dioxide they give off can build up to toxic levels in the local area around a volcano. The sulphur dioxide is the same stuff that drifts from old-fashioned power plants and homes that burn dirty coal, and one of the major culprits of the Donora and Great London Smog disasters. The hydrogen-based gases (hydrogen sulphide, fluoride, chloride and bromide) are irritating to our breathing systems (at best) and highly toxic (at worst). Exactly what overall impact volcanoes have on our health isn't known, but everything they throw out, with the exception of the water vapour, has the potential to harm people, plants, animals and buildings. [30]

Volcanoes might be a worry if you live in one of those countries beginning with I (Indonesia, Italy or Iceland); elsewhere in the world, dangerously dusty natural pollution can occur for a raft of other reasons. Where I live, in northern Europe, it's not unusual for weather forecasters to flag up a sudden migration of dust from the Sahara, thousands of kilometres further south and east. Certain combinations of air pressure, wind flow and ocean–atmosphere interactions make long-haul flights of 'African Dust' (as it's sometimes known) particularly likely. Wind-blown dust means the world's highest average concentrations of PM2.5 particulates are typically in North Africa, West Africa and the Middle East. In Cairo, for example, drifting desert dust is the most significant source of particulates, which can blow to heights of several kilometres and remain in the atmosphere for months at a time. It might sound unlikely, trivial or both, but even in Europe, African Dust can reach dangerously high levels. In Cyprus, PM10 levels of 200 µg/m³ and even 1,000 µg/m³ have sometimes been recorded (10–50 times WHO guidelines). It's a significant enough source of pollution to push air-quality monitoring stations over the legal limits for particulates, making it much harder to assess the contributions from other sources of particulates such as diesel exhaust fumes. And Africa's far from the only victim: further east, winds whistling over the desert produce a widespread nuisance called

Asian Dust (or Kosa 'yellow sand' Dust) in China, South Korea and Japan each spring. [31]

You don't have to live near a desert to suffer this kind of attack. Soil erosion (green fields turning steadily to dusty desert) is one of the world's biggest, least reported and fastest-growing problems. Back in 2001, then UN Secretary-General Kofi Annan issued the first major international warning of how dire the situation could become, when he pointed out how 'drought and desertification threaten the livelihood of over 1 billion people in more than 110 countries around the world'. What he didn't mention was an important secondary effect: when the wind blows over dusty worked-out fields, we get a cloud of particulates high in chemicals like potassium and nitrogen, commonly found in rich layers of topsoil – so soil erosion and desertification can be an important source of air pollution. [32]

Other natural sources of air pollution

Randy plants, misplaced trees, raging wildfires, belching cows, pent-up volcanoes, drifting deserts – these are a few of the bigger sources of natural air pollution (most of them exacerbated by human activity), and there are plenty more. Earth might seem like a static, stable rock in space, but it's geologically dynamic. The rocks you're (indirectly) standing or sitting on right now contain chemical elements, some of which decay radioactively to produce others, including a toxic gas called radon. While it's not normally a problem for most of us, radon does leak naturally from the ground into buildings, sometimes rising to dangerous levels in basements. Around 10 per cent of all lung cancer deaths are due to radon; after smoking, it's the second biggest cause of lung cancer, and the biggest cause among non-smokers.

Fortunately, once the problem comes to light, it's very easily fixed. [33]

Lightning, as we saw above, is a minor cause of wildfires and the rolling black particulate clouds they spread around, but it can also make pollution in other ways. Most of us learn at school that flashes of lightning play a major part in the nitrogen cycle (the various processes through which nitrogen is recycled by the air, oceans and soil around us): it helps to 'fix' nitrogen gas from the air into solid forms that plants can absorb. As a by-product, lightning also produces significant amounts of nitrogen oxide and ozone, which can dramatically alter air quality locally, regionally and much further afield. The 77 million lightning strikes that annually batter the United States can affect air quality as far away as Europe. [34]

Exactly which forms of natural pollution are likely to affect you depends on where in the world you live. In my case, just a few kilometres from the sea, I find my windows regularly coated with sand and salt deposits blown inland by relentless easterly winds. No big surprise there, but what is surprising – even astonishing – is that sea-spray has been charted at distances up to 1,400 kilometres (900 miles) from the nearest ocean. The scientists who discovered this estimate that the salt in sea-spray effectively hurls 10 billion tonnes of chlorine into the air each year – and that matters because chlorine plays a part in the formation of smog, as well as harming plant growth and nibbling away at buildings. [35]

Most kinds of natural pollution are easy to avoid once you know about them, but some are surprisingly and dangerously unpredictable. Back in 1986, a mysterious cloud of carbon dioxide gas shot up from under the waters of Lake Nyos (formed over an inactive volcano in Cameroon) at a speed of 100 km/h (60 mph), drifted over the local town, and asphyxiated 1,800 people and

3,500 animals. It was an example of what's called a limnic eruption ('lake explosion'), where a huge bubble of gas dissolved deep
underwater suddenly burps to the surface in a volume and concentration dense enough to kill people. Episodes like this show that
nature – and natural pollution – will always be unpredictable. [36]

Death by natural causes?

We know that air pollution cuts about 10 million lives short every
year, but just how significant is *natural* pollution as part of that
bigger picture? To put it in perspective, let's see if we can figure
out a ballpark estimate for yearly deaths from all such 'natural
causes'.

In the United States, pollution from wildfires kills around
15,000 a year (a number projected to rise to 40,000 a year over
coming decades) and the current global total is credibly estimated
at 339,000 per year. We don't know how many people die because
of pollen and other plant and tree emissions, though asthma
(closely linked to hay fever) contributes to around 400,000 deaths
worldwide each year (pollen might cause a fraction of that total
– maybe a few tens of thousands). Radon kills 21,000 a year in
the United States alone and, if we work on the assumption that
it's behind a tenth of all lung cancer deaths (1.8 million), perhaps a worldwide toll of about 180,000? It's impossible to say how
many people die from volcanic ash and smoke each year, but it
seems several hundred are killed in explosions alone, so let's take
that as a (not very reliable) proxy figure instead. Those are the
main forms of natural pollution we've considered in this chapter.
Add the numbers and you might notch up somewhere between
half a million and a million deaths each year from natural air
pollution. [37]

Now that's a huge and worrying number – roughly as many people as the world loses to malaria – but it's still far short of the estimated 7–10 million death toll from all human-caused air pollution. Importantly, as we considered up above, some of the supposedly 'natural' air pollution (things like wildfires and pollen-provoked asthma attacks) are, arguably, human-caused as well. So the bottom line is that, however serious natural air pollution might be, it still pales in significance compared to pollution from things like traffic smog, indoor wood smoke and all the rest.

It's also worth bearing in mind that natural pollution is closely tied to our human activities in another important way. Climate change is predicted to worsen many of the things we've considered in this chapter. A warming world lengthens the pollen season, for example, so any health impacts that pollen pollution has at the moment will only worsen in future. (That's a major concern in Australia, which already has some of the highest rates of asthma and allergic rhinitis in the world, and in the UK, where the number of people suffering from hay fever is predicted to double by 2030.) If the world warms, trees warm too, which means they'll routinely give off higher levels of BVOCs. The number of wildfires and their duration and intensity is predicted to increase steeply as the average global temperature continues to creep up. According to a study by scientists at Harvard and Yale, the 82 million residents of the western United States will see a 44 per cent increase in multi-day impacts from wildfires by the late 2040s. Climate change will also exacerbate soil erosion and desertification, worsening dust and particulate pollution in some parts of the world. So tomorrow's pollution may be very different from today's. [38]

In the future, as renewable energy pushes aside fossil fuel, filthy diesels give way to (hopefully) cleaner electric cars, and more people in developing countries switch to less dangerous forms of cooking and heating such as better-ventilated or solar stoves, deaths from human-caused pollution should start to fall. But what if the gains we make through more sensible use of energy, transport and other technology are offset by steady increases in natural pollution in a dry and dusty, warming world? What if our fate is to be plagued by dangerous 'new' problems like rampaging wildfires, brought about by climate change, and caused not by our continued use of fossil fuels but by our *historic* dependence on them? What an irony if Ronald Reagan's apparently absurd assertion – that nature is our biggest polluter – starts to ring true, and really comes back to haunt us.

CHAPTER 5

Going places?

In many countries, road transport is the biggest single cause of air pollution

It sounds like some sort of pact with the devil. A billion of us gain the magic power to go anywhere, anytime; but in return, millions cough and die, crops shrink and wither, fish pickle in acidic lakes and our vibrant, verdant planet disappears under concrete. Back in 1990, in *Autogeddon*, a book-length prose poem that spits bile at our fatal addiction to vehicles, the radical English poet Heathcote Williams described streets as 'the open sewers of the car cult' – and it's easy to see his point three decades on. For what drifts above the highway today is a smoggy miasma: a toxic cocktail so powerfully appalling that it can turn back time, reverting the world's finest cities, those fibre-optically connected, steel-and-glass powerhouses of the 21st century, to the kind of 19th-century, smoke-choked workhouses of Dickensian times. In London or Madrid, New York or Paris, Milan or Tehran, on the street where you live, work and walk your dog, cars (and other road vehicles) are overwhelmingly to blame for fatally poisonous levels of filthy air. [1]

The rise and fall of the horse

One way we try to square this inconvenient little circle is by convincing ourselves we've been here before: that past transport pollution was worse than it is in the present. I think that explains why I keep stumbling on amusing anecdotes about late-19th-century cities disappearing under mountains of horse poop. Over the last few years, for example, the Internet has nurtured a fake news story called the Great Horse Manure Crisis of 1894. One typically gullible website tells us that the 'problem came to a head when in 1894, England's *The Times* newspaper predicted ... "In 50 years, every street in London will be buried under nine feet of manure"' – a dubious claim recycled right across the Net. Another website piles up copious (but unconvincing) evidence that horses turned New York City into something it called The Big Crapple. [2]

The only trouble is, there *was* no Great Horse Manure Crisis in 1894. *The Times* never said any such thing. You'll find no mention in any reputable history book or scholarly article. In fact, the 'Great Horse Manure Crisis of 1894' turns out to have been invented retrospectively, as recently as 2004. [3]

Manure was certainly deposited wholesale. With a typical urban beast dropping up to 22 kilograms (50 pounds) of faeces a day (the weight of two men each week), horses and their waste were definitely an issue. England's *Times*, in August 1827, certainly did mention 'the putrid mixture of gore and excrementitious matters proceeding from the animals' in Whitechapel; 50 years later, one of its writers estimated that London horses 'daily deposited in the street to the extent of at least a thousand tons'. Of course, the problem wasn't confined to London: in New York City, around 1900, the collective horse fleet produced 600 tonnes of manure per day. And yet, for all this steaming dung, one *Times* writer tellingly observed in 1909 that 'It would shock many beautifully dressed ladies who are fond of allowing their gowns to sweep the pavement to be told that what was clinging to the hem of their expensive garments ... was nothing less than dried horse manure.' [4]

Why would the 'beautifully dressed ladies' be remotely shocked, if they were used to wading through muck? Simply because then, as now, the world's major cities employed energetic street cleaners to keep the horse pollution in check. In 1896, *The New York Times* extolled the wonders of 'Berlin's Clean Streets; Example Of What Good Municipal Government Can Do', noting the 'Nine Million Square Yards of Pavement Kept in Perfect Order at a Cost of About $500,000 a Year' by 'A Department Conducted with Military Exactness'. The previous year, the same paper had described Scotland in similarly glowing terms. Such expensive public services were viable because a shortage of manure for agriculture boosted its value to the point where it was even traded internationally. And all of it was put to good use. In Baltimore, Maryland, scavenged horse poop yielded '15,000 heads of cabbage and 22,000 tomatoes', which were then sold back to the people of the city. But even though there was never apparently a Great Horse Manure *crisis*, as leading expert Professor Joel Tarr of Carnegie Mellon University has made clear, the sheer difficulty of maintaining and cleaning up after horses in big cities – Chicago alone had 83,330 of these thunderously defecating beasts at the start of the 20th century – held the door wide for another technology: the 'horseless carriage'. The horse's days, in other words, were done. [5]

Among the first to twig this was Henry Ford, the American industrialist who made cars affordable by pioneering assembly line mass-production. A succession of horse-related mishaps, culminating in serious injuries from (irony of ironies) an overturning manure wagon, had firmly imprinted 'four legs bad' in Ford's mind. In his 1922 autobiography, *My Life and Work*, he recalled how he'd arrived at an inescapable conclusion that 'horseless carriages' were the future: 'I felt perfectly certain that horses, considering all the bother of attending them and the expense of feeding, did not earn their keep. The obvious thing to do was to design and build a steam engine.' [6]

Steam dreams

This wasn't a particularly original thought. Steam machines had long since proved their worth for draining the rainwater that flooded mines and made them unworkable. Over in the English town of Dudley, Thomas Newcomen had bolted together the world's first practical steam pumping engine in 1712, about 150 years before Ford was born. 'Atmospheric engines' like his, which worked using steam and air pressure, were hugely ineffi-cient, wasting 993 of every 1,000 shovels of coal they gobbled up. But the black stuff was cheap and plentiful and they did the job well. Ultimately, around 3,000 atmospheric engines were built, mostly in rural mining areas like Cornwall and Devon, and since they burned anthracite (relatively clean coal), pollution wasn't immediately an issue. [7]

Atmospheric engines were fine for mines, but were too big, clumsy and inefficient for anything else; going places would mean coming up with something better. Around 1800, another Englishman, Richard Trevithick, figured out how to use steam at much higher pressure. This meant he'd be able to bolt a small, lightweight engine to a carriage to drive a road vehicle. The result was *Puffing Devil*, a chuffing steam boiler on wheels power-ful enough to carry passengers. The first successful example of steam-powered transportation, it was also – the clue is in the name – a smoky premonition of vehicle pollution. In the United States, meanwhile, the idea of using high-pressure steam occurred to Oliver Evans at exactly the same time. Evans built the first of many

Figure 23. The coming of smoke: a steam-powered fire engine pictured at the Columbian Exposition in Chicago in 1893. Photograph by Charles Dudley Arnold, courtesy of US Library of Congress.

cars to take to the roads in that country (an ambitious, amphibious 17-tonne vehicle that could chug down streets or dredge rivers, named the *Oruktor Amphibolos*). [8]

Today, it's obvious that the coming of steam meant the coming of smoke, but in those days no one realised how big a problem pollution would become. One steam engine back then, like one car today, wasn't really an issue; the trouble began when steam engines were built in their thousands and dirty cities grew up around them. The statistics speak for themselves. In 1800, Britain, for example, was burning its way through 15 million tonnes of coal. By 1850, that had risen nearly five-fold to 72 million tonnes. At the outbreak of World War I, in 1914, total mine production for factory machines, steam locomotives and all other forms of coal power had increased by almost 20 times from pre-industrial levels to 292 million tonnes, with 1.1 million men hammering away in over 3,000 mines. Unlike steam-powered factories, which filthied their immediate environment, steam trains, cars and buses puffed out pollution wherever they chuffed. By 1800, cutting-edge steam engines were doing four times more work than Newcomen's for each lump of coal they burned; even so, such a massive leap in steam power brought a corresponding surge in pollution. [9]

Exactly why this happened is interesting, because, at one point, it was written into English law (the Locomotive Act 1861) that steam-powered road engines should keep their pollution to themselves: 'Every Locomotive propelled by Steam or any other than Animal Power to be used on any Turnpike Road or public Highway shall be constructed on the Principle of consuming and so as to consume its own Smoke' or face a fine of five pounds a day (£300 or $500 today). In practice, 'consuming its own Smoke' often meant burning smokeless fuel (coke, in other words) – but the intention was still good.[1] [10]

This commendable idea of building non-polluting vehicles dates back even earlier, at least to 1826, when another English Act of Parliament insisted that every locomotive on the world's first completely steam-powered railway (Liverpool to Manchester) must 'consume its own Smoke'. But it seems to have been forgotten pretty quickly. When George Stephenson's pioneering *Rocket* locomotive took part in the Liverpool to Manchester trials, just three years later in 1829, *The Mechanics' Magazine* drew attention to

---

[1] There are various ways something can 'consume its own smoke'. The simplest is to burn relatively clean fuels such as anthracite and coke. There are also ways of slowly firing an engine (or indeed a stove) so the coal burns more cleanly. Another method is to design an engine so the smoke passes back through the burning coals to remove any unburned carbon by what's called secondary combustion. A similar technique (secondary burning of the smoke) is used in modern wood burners to improve efficiency and reduce pollution.

'its very partial fulfilment of the condition that it should effectually consume its own smoke'. The first proper steam locomotive set a precedent – and pollution from steam trains became the norm. [11]

Petroleum power

Filthy, lumbering and hopelessly inefficient, steam engines – on road, rails or at sea – were only ever going to last until a better way of powering vehicles came along. Engines that burned liquid fuels made from petroleum[2], born in the mid-19th century, were fundamentally more efficient for two reasons. First, petrol packs about 50 per cent more energy than the same weight of coal. Second, internal combustion (burning fuel and making power in the same cylinder, as a car engine does) is at least twice as efficient as external combustion (where a coal-fired boiler makes the steam, then blasts it down a pipe to a separate cylinder some way away, which is how a steam engine works). Put these two advantages together and you can go several times further without refuelling. Add in the convenience of liquid fuels (a breeze to pump and store, no need for irritating water stops or a dedicated fireman shovelling mountains of black slack by your side) and it's easy to see why petroleum has powered most of the world's vehicles since the early 20th century. [12]

But not everyone agreed that 'petroleum' should automatically mean petrol. Far more efficient than steam, petrol engines are still far *less* than the 100 per cent efficiency permitted by science. Thermodynamics, the theory behind heat engines (ones that

---

[2] In this book, I use 'petroleum' to mean the crude oil drilled from the ground and refined to produce a whole collection of oils, waxes and so on, ranging from light liquid fuels such as petrol (gasoline) to heavier diesel (used in trucks and cars) and bunker fuel (used in ships).

make power by burning fuels), was first figured out in 1824 by a brilliant, 27-year-old French military engineer named Nicolas Sadi Carnot, son of physicist and politician Lazare Carnot. Up till then, heat engines – like those of Newcomen and Trevithick – had been cobbled together by trial and error. Building on his father's ideas, Sadi Carnot figured out the maths of what makes engines good or bad that scientists still swear by today: his ideas explain why many of us are driving around in diesel cars, polluting the air, 200 years later. Because, even while petrol engines were stealing a march on steam, German engineer Rudolf Diesel realised he could build something better, directly inspired by Carnot's principles. [13]

What Diesel came up with was a 3-metre (10-foot) high, industrial-strength internal-combustion engine that squashed the air about twice as much as a petrol engine, thereby burning the fuel at a higher temperature and notching up greater efficiency. The first time Diesel tried his engine, in 1894, it spluttered for a mere minute before conking out. By 1896, it was chugging away for 50 hours at a time with an efficiency of 20 per cent (30 times better than Newcomen's engine and a slight improvement on petrol engines, which managed about 17 per cent). Diesel engines have been overtaking petrol ever since, notably since the 1970s, when that decade's oil crisis prompted the world's first collective push to energy efficiency. [14]

Though Rudolf Diesel relished the riches that came with a world-changing invention, he was really motivated by the technical challenge of making a better engine. To his mind, diesel engines enjoyed three crucial advantages over petrol ones. First, being more efficient, they used less of the world's limited fossil fuel supply (a forward-looking notion in the early 20th century). Second, they could feed on almost any energy-rich fuel. In 1900, at the World Exhibition in Paris, the French government showed off

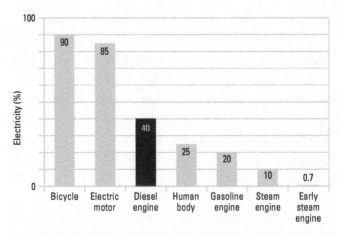

Figure 24. Why did the world shift to diesel? Efficiency (what we get out of machines compared to what we put in) explains why the world moved away from steam power to petrol and diesel – and why a shift to electric cars is also now inevitable. It's interesting to note that raw human power compares well with engines and machines.

a small diesel engine running on peanut oil. Today, engines commonly run on biodiesel, which can be made from eco-sounding stuff like algae and soybeans, or even recycled sewage and old cooking fat. Something of a socialist, Diesel imagined local communities or even empowered individuals running their own small engines on home-grown fuels, freed from the tyranny of the coal companies and centralised factory power. Third, he was one of the first people to call out the inevitable pollution of petrol engines, believing (incorrectly, as it turned out) that his well-behaved machine made less. [15]

Although these arguments resonate in modern eco-ears, none of them made much impact at the time. If petrol, to Rudolf Diesel, was a bad solution to the problems of steam, diesel engines were an equally poor solution to the problems of petrol – yet it was gas and diesel that would lead the world. In fact, they'd lead it astray, because there was already a better alternative than either. At the dawn of the 20th century, when the prolific American inventor Thomas Edison was switching the world to the clean convenience of electricity, battery-powered vehicles looked like the future. By 1900, an astonishing 38 per cent of cars were electric (today, even in California, which has the highest adoption rates in the United States, the figure is a measly 5 per cent or so). That year, long before his name became synonymous with sleek German sports cars, Dr Ferdinand Porsche caused a stir at the Paris World Exhibition (in the very same pavilion where a diesel engine was chugging away on liquified peanuts) when he unveiled the first petrol-electric hybrid, the Lohner-Porsche. A century ahead of his time, Edison prophetically commented: 'Electricity is the thing ... no dangerous and evil-smelling petrol and no noise.' In 1914, Henry Ford told *The New York Times* that 'Mr Edison and I have been working for some years on an electric automobile which would be cheap and practicable'. [16]

In fact, it was neither – certainly not for Ford, who wasted about $40 million (in today's money) before discovering that the most vital of components, Edison's batteries, weren't up to scratch. The high cost of electric cars (the Lohner-Porsche was twice as expensive as a petrol car, far heavier and more complex and costly to maintain) shifted them to the technological back burner, where they simmered through the 20th century until their recent spectacular return to the boil. Diesel filled the gap: on the railways, initially, and later on the streets. As Rudolf Diesel argued a century ago, his eponymous engine is certainly more efficient than its petrol equivalent. But the pollution that diesel engines belch out, as we'll discover in a moment, can be thick with sooty particulates and nitrogen oxides that are far more deadly in the choking city streets.

WHO WAS TO BLAME FOR 'DIESELGATE'?

Looking back, it wasn't the best start for the brand. When Adolf Hitler asked Germany's carmakers to come up with a 'suitable small car', what he got in return, in 1934, was the Volkswagen Beetle. By the time World War II was over, any lingering association with Hitler might have proved fatal – certainly outside Germany. But at the end of the 1950s, VW took the inspired step of buffing up its brand with rule-breaking 'anti-advertising' devised by Bill Bernbach, founder of the Doyle Dane Bernbach (DDB) agency, widely regarded as one of the most talented Madison Avenue admen of all time. Far from boasting about the brilliance of VW cars, Bernbach persuaded the punters with clever self-deprecating headlines like 'Ugly is only skin deep' and 'If you run out of gas, it's easy to push'. The VW Beetle, as Bernbach sold it, was straightforward, practical, value-for-money and – above all – honest. And customers loved it.

Volkswagen embodied these values for six decades, by which time it was selling roughly 10 million cars a year. But it was shaken to its core in September 2015 by the so-called Dieselgate scandal, in which its engineers were found to have rigged onboard computers in around 11 million cars so they switched on pollution controls during lab tests and switched them off again in the real world. While the cars appeared clean and green, they were, in fact, belching out three times the legal limit of nitrogen dioxide. The flames of scandal engulfed two other firms in the VW group, Audi and Porsche, and several senior bosses, including former chief executive Martin Winterkorn (who was charged with fraud in Germany and accused, by the US Department of Justice, of authorising a cover-up). To date, Dieselgate has cost Volkswagen something like $30 billion – several years' worth of profits. It's also spread to other companies, including Jaguar, affecting 43 million cars in total. Extensive, recent testing has revealed that 97 per cent of diesel cars launched in the last decade perform far worse in the real world than in contrived lab tests, typically exceeding legal pollution limits by about five to ten times. Only

continued

diesels that meet the latest standards (Euro 6) are anywhere near as 'clean' as their petrol equivalents.

But who was really to blame? Was it the engineers? Their managers? A conflicted, faceless corporation geared to rewarding shareholders, that could never ultimately embody values like 'honesty', no matter how hard the admen tried to pretend otherwise? The profit-hungry petroleum industry, looking to open up markets for the 'waste' bits of crude oil that it couldn't otherwise use? Or was it something much more insidious? As we'll see in this chapter, there's no such thing as a non-polluting car and there are no safe levels for some of the toxic chemicals they give out. So was Dieselgate really a sign of the fundamental conflict between our desire to have clean cars and the ultimate impossibility of engineering any such thing? Our desperate desire to carry on, business-as-usual style, butting up hard against the realisation that, where things like air pollution and climate change are concerned, that just isn't possible? In the end, was Dieselgate about car makers not being honest with us ... or about us not being honest with ourselves? [17]

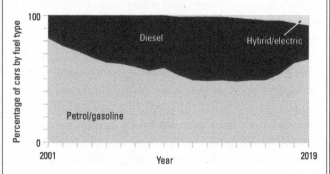

Figure 25. The rise and fall of diesel. The 21st century saw a radical shift in how we fuelled our cars, with a massive move to diesels, which are more efficient and economical but also more polluting. Since the Dieselgate emissions scandal in 2015, there's been a sharp shift back to petrol: less than a third of new cars are now diesels compared to around half at the peak of the market, from 2011 to 2015. Despite the hype about hybrid/electric cars, they represent only a tiny fraction of sales. Source: Percentage of cars registered for the first time by fuel type, Gov.uk [18]

The vicious circle of car culture

Pollution is a problem of scale: a drop, however toxic, swiftly disappears in the ocean. But what if the drops multiply? What if the ocean isn't as vast as we thought? In 1920, there were something like 10 million cars in the United States (and not so many more in the world as a whole). By 1925, Ford's assembly line was churning out a new car every ten seconds. In 1950, there were 50 million cars in the States and today there are over a billion in the entire world – a 100-fold increase in 100 years. Thanks to explosive growth in Asia, the world's car population is predicted to reach 2 billion around 2040. [19]

You can almost see this particular tragedy of the commons scaling up before your eyes. In the country where I live, in 1985/6, 38 per cent of households had no car, 45 per cent had one and 17 per cent had two or more. Thirty years later, in 2015, only 25 per cent had no car (dramatically fewer), 42 per cent had one (slightly down) and 33 per cent had two or more (almost twice as

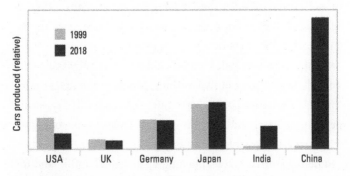

Figure 26. Explosive car growth in Asia. While Western car production has stagnated or declined for the last two decades, there's been a huge increase in production in Asian countries, especially India and China, which now make many of the cars driven in the West. Drawn using data from International Organization of Motor Vehicle Manufacturers. [http://www.oica.net/]

many). Let's indulge the architects of the fictitious Great Manure Crisis of 1894 for a moment, and consider what would have happened if the world's horse fleet had grown so fast. A billion horses, each dumping 22 kilograms (50 pounds) of muck a day, would generate a mass of manure equal to the weight of the world's entire human population every single month. A billion horseless carriages arguably make as big a mess; traffic *pollution* now kills more people than traffic *accidents*. [20]

Car culture is a vicious circle that seems to grow more vicious by the day. Advertising (which underwrites the programmes we watch and the articles we read) is heavily dependent on the car business – including car dealers and oil firms (General Motors and Ford are two of the top six advertisers in the United States). Car advertising lures us into buying more new cars at a hefty price. It adds an astonishing average of $1,000 to the cost of each new vehicle sold in the United States (if you buy a Jaguar, $3,325 of what you pay is squandered on advertising). This seems even more outrageous if you consider the finding that people are more likely to seek out car ads *after* they've bought a car to confirm they've spent well. More robot-built cars being sold mean more traffic, and more traffic means more congestion and pollution. More congestion prompts calls for roadbuilding, which might solve the immediate problem but makes things worse in the longer term through what transport experts call 'induced traffic': releasing pent-up demand and prompting more journeys, encouraging trips to places we couldn't so easily get to before, making longer commutes more credible, opening up so-called 'infill' land for things like out-of-town shopping centres you can only reach by car ... and more besides. Building roads to tackle congestion is like buying bigger clothes to 'solve' your weight problem and ending up morbidly obese; it scales up the problem without solving it.

Buying into car culture locks us into car culture, and the age-old solution – building ever more roads – is actually a big part of the problem. [21]

What kinds of pollution do cars make?

More to the point, why do cars make pollution at all?

Petroleum is a complex, messy mixture: the petrol we pump in our tanks is a cocktail of over 150 different chemicals: apart from the fuel itself, there are additives of all kinds, including anti-knock agents (to make combustion smoother and prolong engine life), antifreeze, rust resistors and detergents. Historically, one of the worst additives was a brain-stupefying antiknock chemical called tetra-ethyl lead (TEL), from which children were most at risk because their lungs sponge up four to five times more air-borne lead than an adult's. Since the 1980s, leaded car fuel has been phased out in every country of the world except Yemen, Algeria and Iraq, producing spectacularly welcome reductions in children's lead exposure.[3] I say 'spectacularly welcome' because the story is only just beginning to emerge of how much damage systematic lead poisoning may have done to society in the 50–60 years during which TEL was soaking into our air, water and land. [22]

Over the last two decades, eye-opening studies by US researchers Kim Dietrich, Rick Nevin, John Paul Wright and others have found strong correlations between lead levels in the environment and all kinds of social problems. Lead has been implicated in everything from juvenile delinquency and the

---

[3] Lead is still widely used in some kinds of aviation fuel. In the United States, small, piston-powered aeroplane propeller engines are now the biggest source of atmospheric lead emissions. [23]

incidence of burglaries to teenaged pregnancy, urban homicide rates and racial disparities in education. Nevin's startling work, for example, suggests that lead emissions from petrol and other sources explain 90 per cent of the variation in violent crime in the United States and at least seven other countries he's studied since. There's growing evidence that the effects of lead persist for decades – maybe life – and that some of the horrifying, age-related brain decline we currently attribute to dementia is, in fact, caused by the long, poisonous memory of deadly toxic lead. Every year, in all its various forms, lead pollution causes an estimated half a million deaths and costs 9.3 million lost years of life due to chronic ill health, according to the Institute for Health Metrics and Evaluation (IHME). When they finally emerge, years and decades too late, shocking statistics like these prompt drastic action – but not always for the best. Some countries replaced TEL with other hazardous chemicals, including benzene, toluene and xylenes. Another of TEL's hasty replacements, methyl tert-butyl ether (MTBE), promised better combustion and lower tailpipe emissions, but turned out to be carcinogenic and caused pollution of groundwater (and public water supplies) right across the United States. In 2008, a dozen oil companies agreed to pay 153 water companies and public agencies in seventeen US states some $423 million plus clean-up costs to rectify the problem, which is expected to take 30 years. [24]

Another problem with petrol engines is that, due to various technical and engineering limitations, they don't burn fuels completely. So the filth that vehicles make is also, quite understandably, a complex mixture of many different pollutants. If you're a child, strapped in a pushchair at tailpipe height trundling down the streets of Beijing or Madrid, you'll be breathing in what air pollution scientists call the 'invisible killer': a deadly modern mixture that includes particulates, carbon monoxide, nitrogen oxides and ozone. [25]

Where do these things come from? The finer (PM2.5) particulates drift (mostly) from the tailpipes of sooty diesel engines, but the coarser ones, which include toxic heavy metals like antimony, also come from vehicle wear-and-tear we tend to overlook: gradual brake and tyre disintegration and the scraping away of the road surface when cars, trucks and buses whizz along it. (This is an important point and one we'll return to in a moment.) The nitrogen oxides are compounds fused from varying proportions of the air's two major gases, nitrogen and oxygen. Most is nitric oxide (NO), converted by oxygen in the air into nitrogen dioxide (NO_2), a lung irritant, which, according to the European Commission, causes some 71,000 premature deaths in Europe each year – or three times the toll from traffic accidents. (Italy scores worst with about 21,000 early deaths, followed by 12,000 in the UK and 10,000 in Germany.) In the real world, a typical diesel car produces about *ten times* as much of these nitrogen oxides as a comparable petrol car, according to the European Environment Agency. Nitrogen dioxide is converted in the atmosphere into acid rain (which, as we'll explore in Chapter 9, kills forests and poisons lakes) and ozone (O_3), which causes a further 17,000 early deaths in Europe alone and about 5,000 each year in the United States. [26]

Multiply the imperfection of every internal combustion engine by the number of imperfect engines in your chosen town, city or country and what you get is a planet-sized problem. A 2013 study by MIT found that road transport accounts for 39 per cent of nitrogen dioxide pollution in the United States: over twice as much as power plants and ten times more than factories. When the British Parliament's Environment Select Committee last studied the issue, it concluded that road transport is 'the biggest single contributor to two of the most harmful and widespread sources of air pollution – nitrogen oxides (NO_x) and particulate matter (PM) ... [and causes] 42 per cent of carbon monoxide, 46 per cent of nitrogen oxides and 26 per cent particulate matter in England'. The recent shift to bigger, bulkier, less aerodynamic cars has made matters worse; according to the Sierra Club environmental group, SUVs produce 47 per cent more air pollution than average cars and 43 per cent more greenhouse gases. [27]

Still, you might say, so what? We're not all going around choking to death, are we? Well, it turns out that 'infernal' combustion of all kinds *is* horribly correlated with premature death. The MIT study, by Steven Barrett and colleagues, calculates that pollution from road transport causes 58,000 early deaths each year in the United States alone (compared to 52,000 from power generation and 41,000 from industry). Over in the UK, transport emissions are believed to cause 7,500 early deaths a year (three times more than power generation and nine times more than industry). The same influential researchers have concluded that air pollution delivers a double whammy: if it's going to cause your death, it will shorten your life by about a decade first. [28]

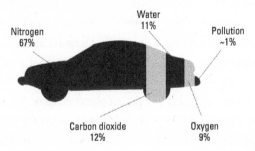

Figure 27. What's in diesel exhaust? Perhaps surprisingly, only 1 per cent of a typical diesel's exhaust is actual air pollution. That 1 per cent consists mostly of carbon monoxide, hydrocarbons, nitrogen oxides, sulphur dioxide and particulates. Based on figures from İbrahim Aslan Reşitoğlu et al, January 2015. [29]

Safe inside?

If you live in a smog-choked city, perhaps you feel like 'doing your bit' and making a difference: how about swapping the car for a bike or running or walking to work instead? Your first thought is probably: 'Not so fast! What about all that pollution?' And it's true: according to recent research by Dr Marko Tainio and colleagues, there are now at least fifteen cities in the world where as little as 30 minutes of vigorous outdoor exercise does you actual harm by accelerating the flow of toxic pollutants into your body. Thankfully, in an overwhelming majority of places, including capitals like New York City, London and Paris, these researchers concluded that the 'benefits of [physical activity] by far outweigh risks from air pollution even under the most extreme levels of active travel'. (Wherever you are, try to make sensible choices about where and when you exercise to minimise the risk.) [30]

Nevertheless, just as misplaced fear of traffic has more parents driving their children to school, scare stories like these help to power the vicious circle that puts more cars on the road. It comes as no surprise to hear that commuting cyclists and walkers – the very people we should be encouraging, the ones doing their best to make our dirty cities cleaner – give up altogether and seal themselves back inside their cars. That, however, can be a big mistake: hunched behind the wheel, inching forward through the jam, you're far from safe even with your windows shut.

Pollution can get trapped inside a vehicle (especially a poorly maintained one), where it slowly builds up over time, so you might actually be at more risk driving than cycling or walking alongside. With noses pressed, metaphorically, to the tailpipes of the trucks and buses in front, drivers and their passengers sometimes breathe levels of pollution significantly higher than those outside. Up to half of the pollution inside a car comes from the vehicle in front – and obviously that's a bigger deal if you're riding in the slipstream of a dirty diesel bus instead of a moderately clean hybrid or electric car. An imaginative study by Dr Ben Barratt from King's College London compared the air pollution exposure of an ambulance driver and a cycle courier to find out who suffered most. Surprisingly, it was the driver trapped in her vehicle, lungs sponging pollution for hours on end, hurtling faster towards her own death even while she raced to prevent other people's. Other researchers found consistent results when they drove the 'Smogmobile' (a small truck fitted with sampling equipment, which we met briefly in Chapter 1) down a busy highway, comparing its indoor air quality with that outside. It turned out that nitrogen dioxide levels were 21 per cent higher inside the vehicle and, at times, almost twice as high as permitted legal limits. But the results differ for different types of pollution. Other studies suggest walkers and cyclists, out in the open and breathing hard to move their muscles, are at much more risk from particulates than car drivers (especially ones who keep their windows closed) or bus and train passengers. [31]

Outside or in, it's not just how much *time* you spend in traffic but how that traffic is moving. Not surprisingly, your lungs will absorb significantly more pollution if you drive through lots of stop-start traffic lights and roundabouts. You might spend a mere 2 per cent of your time at the lights, but you'll soak up 25 per cent of your pollution dose while you're there. Sitting at a red light drumming your fingers, research shows you could be inhaling up to 40 per cent more coarse particulates (PM10s) and 16 per cent more fine ones (PM2.5s) than you will nipping along in free-flowing traffic. Frightening though these studies are, they're still contrived experiments and one-offs. We have no real idea how much cumulative pollution ambulance drivers, cycle couriers, lorry or cab drivers,

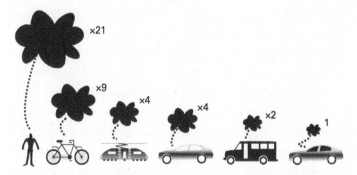

Figure 28. 'Active' commuters (who walk and cycle) breathe in more harmful particulates than 'passive' ones (car drivers or passengers on buses and trains) when they make exactly the same journey. Figures show the relative amount of particulates inhaled by pedestrians, cyclists, light-rail users, car drivers with open windows and bus passengers compared to car drivers with closed windows, who inhale least. Drawn using rounded data from Robert Chaney et al, 2017. [32]

city commuters or anyone else soaks up from week to week, year to year or decade to decade; the research has never been done. [33]

None of this will come as any great surprise to motorists or make much difference to whether they drive or not. We can maintain jarringly dissonant attitudes as our cars breathe out and suck in pollution at exactly the same time; you might fret about the car in front, but what about the one behind? The problem is not unique to pollution; we're deeply ambivalent about most environmental issues and unable to connect their causes with their effects, even when we're responsible for both. Pollution, we tend to feel, is always caused by other people.

Taxi drivers are a good example. In Leeds, a deceptively populous English city with a big pollution problem, cabbies have spoken out fiercely against plans to introduce a daily congestion charge, which would slash traffic pollution but also (they fear) their livelihoods. Councillor Javaid Akhtar of the local taxi association told

the *Yorkshire Evening Post*: 'On the one hand we do care about the
health issues, but on the other hand we also need to be thinking
about the ordinary person who is trying to make a living as a
professional driver.' [34]

What about the health risks to the drivers themselves? That
issue doesn't seem to occur to them. Typically, taxi drivers are
uninformed about pollution, unconcerned or both. A recent study
of cabbies in New York City found their awareness of the issue
'limited': only 56 per cent believed themselves to be at greater risk
than non-drivers. That's frightening, because air-quality measurements taken in cabs has found them likely to exceed safe limits on
particulates after a mere 24 hours of exposure. In Beijing, a study
by Greenpeace found cabbies were exposed to three times the
level of the harmful fine particulates (PM2.5s) as average Chinese
citizens and five times the WHO's guideline. [35]

Will full-time drivers ever wake up to reality? Researchers
have been red-flagging the problem for at least two decades with
little impact. As far back as 2000, a medical study of Parisian
cabbies found them 'highly exposed to automobile pollutants';
they still are today. Unfortunately, taxi drivers have never been
forward-looking: way back in 1801, horse-driven cab drivers pelted
cabbage stumps, rotten eggs and onions at Richard Trevithick as
he chuffed past in his steam-powered *Puffing Devil*. But the problem
isn't intractable. While the world's eyes were trained on Beijing
for the 2008 Olympics, the government tightened air pollution
controls in the country and China's cabbies found themselves
breathing significantly less PM2.5s than usual. And the issue of
how pollution affects professional drivers does belatedly seem
to be tunnelling through to wider consciousness. When the UK
held its first ever National Clean Air Day in June 2017, it prompted
a group of drivers to set up Cabbies for Clean Air to highlight

the issue of urban traffic pollution, the growing problem of less-regulated Ubers being used as taxis and the unaffordability of eco-friendly vehicles. [36]

Going nowhere fast

From steam engines and nuclear energy all the way to the Internet, it's a highly uncomfortable fact that our most far-reaching technologies have caused new problems as well as solving old ones; it's illogical, if tempting, to believe that tomorrow's innovations will sweep away the mess we're making today. Those of us gazing to the hopeful, sunny horizon of electric cars need to remember that 'zero-emission vehicles' (ZEVs) is a misnomer. The electricity that powers them causes air pollution, if it comes from conventional, fossil-fuelled power plants (as about two thirds of electricity currently does), and they still produce *substantial* amounts of particulate pollution. Manufacturing their bulky batteries takes lots of energy and causes all kinds of environmental damage we conveniently ignore; a typical battery-electric car has to be driven an extraordinary 125,000 kilometres (80,000 miles) before it breaks even with a diesel car on carbon dioxide emissions. [37]

Remarkably and somewhat depressingly, even if every motorbike, car, bus and truck were completely electric, air pollution from traffic would still be a major public health issue, as a recent book by Spanish researcher Fulvio Amato and his colleagues makes clear. What they discovered was that vehicles generate at least as much coarse particulate dust (PM10s) and a third as much fine particulate dust (PM2.5) from brake and tyre wear, road surface disintegration and the disturbance of dust already lying on the road as they do from their exhausts. The amount of waste rubber that slowly disintegrating car tyres deposit on our

roads is also astonishing: in the United States, it amounts to an
average 6.8 kilograms (15 pounds) of rubber per vehicle per year.
According to Birmingham University's Professor Roy Harrison, an
advisor to the World Health Organization on air pollution, within
a few years only 10 per cent of the particulates produced by traffic
will be coming from vehicle tailpipes. [38]

These sorts of hidden emissions apply to electric cars too –
sometimes even more so, since current models are up to 30 per
cent heavier than comparable fossil-fuelled ones and need far
harder braking to stop, which kicks out much more dust. Another
expert on vehicle pollution, Professor Frank Kelly, argues in a
recent *Guardian* article that: 'Our cities need fewer cars, not just
cleaner cars ... electric vehicles will not sufficiently reduce particulate matter.' Unlike exhaust gases, these sorts of emissions
are completely uncontrolled and unregulated, so this promises
to become a major issue in future. [39]

Supposing, just supposing, we could control these non-
exhaust emissions too, with technologies like regenerative and
eddy-current braking (which slow wheels electromagnetically,
without any contact, instead of using frictional brake pads as in
conventional cars). Could we breathe easily at last as a global fleet
of electric cars shuttles us back and forth? Not really; where cars
are concerned, there's simply no escaping pollution. Even with the
engine silent and the car going nowhere, even before the horseless
carriage has left the showroom with a single centimetre on the
clock, you're still – remarkably – at risk.

Have you ever yanked open the door of a car on the forecourt
and breathed in that captivating new car smell? It might seem
entrancing, but it could prove fatally polluting too. When Ann
Arbor Ecology Center studied the chemicals inside new cars, they
identified a rogue's gallery of 300 plastics, vinyls, foams, adhesives,

flame retardants and solvents, many of them toxic volatile organic compounds (VOCs), known carcinogens or harmful to health in other ways. Polish researchers found a similar thing when they measured air samples in cars that had just rolled off the production line: an alarming cocktail of 250 different VOCs. Sunlight liberates these chemicals so they dance with the dust you see in the air, and fill your lungs when you open the door. Now some of these may be quite benign, and it's very hard to prove that in-car chemicals directly damage our health, though they can certainly affect us in other ways. American comic Rita Rudner once joked that she could attract men by wearing a perfume called 'New Car Interior' – and the same trick works just as well on buyers. There are marketing companies who specialise in creating ambient aromas, constantly dreaming up subtle perfumes for different brands that are quietly pumped through the air conditioning ducts of savvy showrooms; you can even buy air fresheners called 'New Car' to make your tired old jalopy smell clean again. [40]

New or old, all cars pollute, even the ones you play with as a child. While I was researching this chapter, I stumbled across an obscure medical paper looking at the emissions from, of all things, toy cars. Toy cars pollute? They do if they're electric. If you've ever played with an electric train set, you might remember the heady smell of the carbon brushes (the pencil-lead-like contacts that press against the electric motor), especially if you sniffed up close; that was particulate pollution. In much the same way, toy cars with miniature electric motors make *toy amounts* of pollution from wear and tear (less than cooking or smoking but still significant) – mostly copper emissions (again from the moving motors), with some organic pollutants thrown in for good measure. [41]

There's nothing children like more than realistic toys; might as well start them young.

TESTING TESTING

Train strains

You can't always see modern pollution, smell it or taste it; wander around the car-free centre of a modern city with an air monitor and, if you're lucky, you might even struggle to measure it. On several different days when I wandered up and down the streets of Birmingham, one of Britain's busiest cities, hunting for traffic pollution, I completely failed to find any.

Head for the train, however, and it's a different story. Birmingham's huge New Street Station, located in a cramped and dingy underground vault, is one of the busiest in Europe, with anything up to a quarter of a million passengers a day served by 600 diesel trains. For as long as I can remember, it's also been one of the dirtiest.

But how dirty? I knew a recent study by Birmingham University researchers had found that NO_2 and particulate levels at this station were 'very high, and significantly in excess of' legal limits. My informal measurements with the Plume Flow found exactly the same thing. Walking into the station, the Plume's pollution indicator lights flashed orange (moderate), then red (high) and finally purple (very high). Sitting on the train as it filled with fumes and (to a lesser extent) on the train home, my lungs enjoyed half an hour of filth well above the WHO's one-hour limit. You'll certainly be helping the environment by taking public transport, but you won't always be doing your health any favours. If I made this journey twice a day as a commuter, I'd be quite concerned. [42]

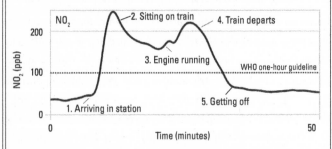

Figure 29. Chart shows: Y axis: NO_2 concentration in parts per billion; X axis: time in minutes.

What to do?

There's no such thing as a clean car; there's no way to escape vehicle pollution. If you're a non-driver living in a big city like New York or Madrid – a selfless cyclist or otherwise earnest devotee of no-frills public transportation – you might resent the breathless-ness inflicted on you by all those 'selfish car drivers'. Much like the politically savvy gun lobby in the United States (a vocifer-ous minority, expert at misrepresenting the moderate majority who don't unequivocally share their views), the motoring lobby is politically well connected and highly effective at convincing governments the world should continue to spin around car cul-ture. When President Ronald Reagan made his famous 'Tear Down this Wall' speech at the Brandenburg Gate in 1987, he praised the Germans for their 'abundance [of] food, clothing and automobiles – the wonderful goods'. His friend, British Prime Minister Margaret Thatcher, was another notable catch in the 1980s, famously talking up 'the great car economy' to justify 'the biggest road-building programme since the Romans'. But the wheels have long since fallen off that kind of rhetoric; shifting attitudes and hard statis-tics simply don't support it anymore. [43]

Though levels of car ownership continue to climb when we average across the world, if we drill into the statistics for different countries, continents and demographics, a very different pat-tern starts to emerge: many of us seem to be falling out of love with the car. In the United States, overall car ownership fell by an incredible 15 per cent between 2005 and 2015; in Europe and Japan, it essentially stagnated; only in Asia (notably China, India and Indonesia) and Latin America were there really big gains. [44]

We're not just buying fewer cars: we're showing less interest in driving them. Take the UK as a typical example. Some 39.9 mil-lion Britons hold full driving licences out of a total population of

65.6 million, so only six out of ten people *have* licences (including people who live overseas); far fewer drive regularly. Many people with licences simply can't use them (if they don't own a car, if they're in hospital or prison, elderly or infirm), and many don't use them or use them only rarely (in London, for example, only 39 per cent of adults have both access to a car and a licence, while 60 per cent have either a licence but no car, or neither). Some who *do* drive do so only from necessity, not choice; how many would happily ditch their cars given viable alternatives? We don't know, because transport surveys, sponsored by government departments hooked on the great car economy, never ask the leading question. More significantly, of course, even among the fraction of the 70 per cent who do drive regularly, only a smattering sit behind the wheel all day. In the UK, most people drive less than 16 kilometres (10 miles) to work, while in the United States, the average travel-to-work time is 25.4 minutes. Driving, in short, is a much smaller part of our lives than we're led to believe. [45]

We do know that there are significant demographic differences. Still considering the UK, no children drive, few very elderly people do, poorer households (and non-whites) are much less likely to own cars and in virtually every age group (from seventeen to 106), men with licences outstrip women by at least 10 per cent. Although there was a huge overall increase in the numbers of people holding licences between the mid-1970s and the mid-2010s, there's been little or no increase for males since the mid-1990s and, in fact, fewer males in all age groups under the age of 40 now hold licences than in the 1970s. Even in the supposedly gas-guzzling United States, car licences are in steady decline. According to a 2016 study by Michael Sivak and Brandon Schoettle, the number of people holding a licence has declined across almost every age group in the last few years by anything from 5 per cent (for ages 40–54) to as much as 47 per cent (for age sixteen). Only older people (55 and above) are driving more, so perhaps Hunter S. Thompson was right when he wrote: 'Old elephants limp off to the hills to die; old Americans go out to the highway and drive themselves to death with huge cars.' Exactly why motoring has fallen out of fashion is uncertain. The high 'cost of entry', growing use of technology to avoid travel, rising concerns about road safety, improved public transportation (including real-time travel planning with smartphone apps) and growing congestion on roads may all be playing a part. [46]

In fairness, it's important to remember that even people who don't drive depend on those who do. Non-drivers take buses, taxis and Ubers, rely on food shuttled back and forth by truck and enjoy door-to-door Amazon deliveries; all these things depend on others hitting the road while you stay safe and cosy at home. But it's equally unfair to assume non-drivers are a minuscule and irrelevant minority of eco freaks. While they share the benefits of a collectively motorised economy, they also share the costs of selfish motoring that bring them no benefit. If your children make the effort to walk or cycle, or bus themselves to school, they are directly *harmed* – not benefited in any way – by the parents of other children who insist in chugging up in the diesel SUV. If we're ever to scrub the air clean in our modern towns and cities, non-drivers (who make up 100 per cent of some demographics) need to be as savvy at politically articulating their interests as non-smokers became in the late 20th century.

Millions of dead and lives curtailed, the long shadow of lead poisoning, the evidence stacking up that medical problems like asthma and dementia are linked to airborne chemicals in the environment, cities that grow more polluted as they grow more congested – traffic pollution is an ongoing tragedy, certain to worsen in parts of the world like Asia, where car ownership is soaring. All this might sound like a pact with the devil – the fair price we pay for a 'great car economy' – but there's no reason why any of it should continue in the future. Environmentalists have spent the past four decades crowing about 'peak oil': when we start to hear the tell-tale sucking of the empty carton as we drain down the planet's last supplies of petroleum. But perhaps, given the epidemic levels of deaths and chronic illness, the universal filthy urbanisation, periodic petroleum wars and the dwindling interest in driving, it would be more fitting to talk about 'peak car'. Time to make fresh air, clean cities and urban health our starting points; *autogeddon* not for society, perhaps, but for the car itself.

CHAPTER 6

Made in China?

How we cleaned our air by exporting pollution overseas

When Santa Claus comes to town in the 21st century, he swaps his one-horse open sleigh for something more befitting a world of nearly 8 billion people: a 400-metre (1,300-foot) container ship (five times longer than a Jumbo Jet). In Western countries, it's become a ritual to welcome at least one of these vast vessels, hauling 165,000 tonnes of China-made presents, in the run-up to Christmas each year. Any of the 18,000 truck-sized containers on board, stacked 10–12 high, can carry 40,000 rechargeable batteries or 13,000 iPhones; together, they're big enough to shift a billion tins of baked beans or 36,000 cars from one side of the planet to the other. [1]

Bulging container ships are the visible proof of our globalised world – and there's no better example of conspicuous consumption. Worldwide retail sales are nudging $30 trillion a year, which is all the evidence you need that we live to consume. But the environmental cost of all the stuff we buy, use and toss away – filth-belching factories, stinking stagnant rivers and miserable Asian faces packed into sweatshops supposedly to escape poverty, to say nothing of the ticking time-bomb of climate change – has no price tag. Bewitched by brands, seduced by their ability to bestow instant appeal, it doesn't occur to us there might be a hidden price, let alone that someone else – the people in developing countries making *our* stuff in *their* factories – might be paying it. As long as we can recycle the packaging (a relatively recent but not unwelcome concern), all is well. No dirty factories, no smoking power plants – just solar farms and wind turbines as far as the eye can see. [2]

What's wrong with this picture? We've made our pollution someone else's problem. It looks like we've cleaned up our act since the dark Dickensian days when factories dirtied the sky, but the reality is different: consumption and production now happen on opposite sides of the globe. We've exported ('outsourced') our manufacturing industry to places like China, India, Mexico and Indonesia, brushing the eco-problems out of sight, under the developing-country carpet.

Cleaning up our act?

'Honey, I shrunk the pollution!' makes a great story for politicians. In 2018, following impressive air-quality tests that revealed a drop in most pollutants of about a quarter to a third over the previous decade, New York City Mayor Bill de Blasio couldn't wait to crow that: 'Since the dawn of the industrial revolution, New Yorkers have not been able to breathe air this clean'. Thanks to Google, it's easy to see that this particular green claim has been recycled many times over by eager politicians and environmental watchdogs, industry moguls and the gullible media. Back in 2005, an article published by the American Enterprise Institute made a similar assertion that 'Western cities enjoy cleaner air than at any time since the dawn of the industrial revolution'. Today, ALEC (the American Legislative Exchange Council) still boasts on its website that the US has, 'by any measurement, some of the cleanest air and water in the world post-Industrial Revolution'. [3]

At face value, the statistics seem impressive: perhaps the days of factory filth really are gone? In countries we still speak of as 'industrialised', industry now contributes only modestly to most chronic forms of air pollution (see Figure 30). Indeed, levels of particulates are generally three times higher in developing nations than in highly industrialised ones (for various reasons, not all connected with industry). Part of the explanation is just what we've longed for: there has certainly been a steady shift, worldwide, to 'cleaner and greener'. Take power stations, for example. In 2003, the United States had 629 coal-fired power plants; by 2018, that figure had fallen by 47 per cent to just 336. As recently as 2007, coal was making about half the electricity in the United States; a decade later, it was contributing just 30 per cent. Perhaps we really have cleaned up our act? [4]

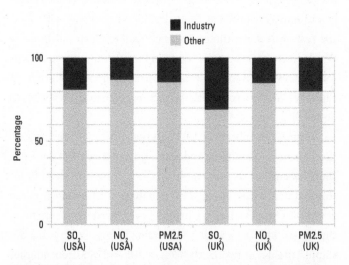

Figure 30. Industry (black bars) makes relatively little outdoor air pollution in nations such as the United States and the UK, compared to other sources (grey bars). But is that because it's so well regulated or because much has been exported overseas? Data sources: UK: DEFRA; USA: F. Caiazzo et al./Atmospheric Environment 79 (2013). [5]

Economists would certainly like us to think so. In the typical, hard-headed analysis of free-market economics, pollution and prosperity are tightly coupled: pollution is the price countries must pay for attaining economic prosperity, which allows them to shake off poverty and (eventually) eliminate the pollution, leaving the prosperity intact. That's the theory, anyway. It's borne out by Himalayan charts (technically known as 'environmental Kuznets curves') showing how emissions of sulphur dioxide (the gas belched out by the steam engines and power plants that electrified our industrialisation) soared in areas like Europe and the United States between the Industrial Revolution and the mid-20th century, before plummeting in recent decades. For less-developed parts of the world, the same graphs are lagging by at least a century: sulphur dioxide emissions are still steeply rising in Asia and Africa. But the economists are quick to reassure us that that's just a temporary problem: soon, developing countries will follow the rest of us down the green-brick road to clean, 'sustainable development'. Swapping production for consumption and goods for services, they too can have prosperity without pollution. Or can they? What's wrong with *this* picture? Someone always has to do the dirty work. [6]

For now, globalisation still holds the answer. Beyond the cultural nuances of branding and marketing, in a world of one-click shopping and just-in-time delivery, countries have no meaning for transnational corporations. They can make stuff wherever in the world it's cheapest, pay tax in whichever territory grants them the biggest breaks and sell goods online in one country that are shipped in a day or two, by the likes of DHL and UPS, from another country entirely; geography, to them, is an irrelevance.

Take Ford, the quintessential American company founded in the United States in 1903. It pioneered assembly-line mass production with its famous Model T, opened its first overseas plant (in Manchester, England) in 1913, and a little over a century later, has 77 plants and offices and a presence in over 200 countries (pretty much the whole world). In recent years, like General Motors, Toyota, Honda, BMW and Volkswagen, it's shifted significant amounts of car production out of the United States and into Mexico and China. Back in the 1920s, a Ford Model T would have been 100 per cent 'Made in the USA', maybe at the company's 800-hectare (2,000-acre) River Rouge plant in Dearborn, Michigan. Once the world's most integrated factory complex, it boasted its own coal power station, blast furnace, steel mill and glass-making plant. A century later, however, an American Ford Focus is still made in Michigan, but gets only 40 per cent of its parts from the United States, 26 per cent from Mexico and the rest from elsewhere in the world. (Many rival cars are far worse: General Motors' Buick Envision sources a mere 2 per cent of its parts from the United States.) [7]

So, when it comes to issues like air pollution, it makes no sense to compare country-wide emissions in the late 19th century, when companies like Ford were largely based in single countries, with the early 21st century, when no one is really tied anywhere. The countries and the companies aren't the same, the apples-and-pears comparison breaks down and the graphs charting dwindling emissions are misleading. You can't crow that New York is cleaner than at any time since the Industrial Revolution if New Yorkers are driving round in Chinese-made cars and the clean-up has been achieved, in part, by making cities in China dirtier or more dangerous – at least, not if you're being honest.

If air pollution is more than an abstract issue, if we're really interested in improving people's health and saving lives, we have to look at the world as a whole. It's not as if we're consuming any less now; quite the opposite. As we saw in the previous chapter, a century ago, the global population of cars numbered something like 10 million; today, it tops a billion – it's 100 times greater. They may be more efficient cars, more efficiently made and using lighter materials such as aluminium and plastics, but the idea that their total environmental footprint could somehow be slighter – that a billion cars could magically be better for the planet than 10 million – is a complete delusion.

And that's just cars. What about all the other stuff that arrives in those 'Made-in-China' shipping containers that didn't exist 100 years ago? We have more efficient materials now and we have greener power plants, but there are four times more people on the planet today than there were a century ago. Between 1700 and 1900, the average person on Earth tripled their energy use (for food, power and transportation), and tripled it again between 1900 and 2000. Drill down to individual homes and it's easy to see why. According to the US National Association of Homebuilders, the average size of an American family home increased by about 2.5 times between the 1950s and the 2000s. And the people inside consume twice as much as they did back then. The idea that we've scaled up our lives to this extent and simultaneously done away with pollution is simply not credible. [8]

When we look at a chart of sulphur dioxide pollution for North America, and note that emissions have declined from 26.50 million tonnes to 11.79 million tonnes over the last half century or so, we could certainly pat ourselves on the back and smile. Or we could check out the chart for Asia and note how emissions of the same pollutant, over the same period, increased from 10.10 million tonnes in 1950 to 51.73 million tonnes. Now quite a bit of that increase is clearly down to China's own, massively growing afflu-ence. And it's also true that there's been some cleaning up in North

America and a lot of things are done more efficiently now. Even with these qualifications, however, it's clear that we've shifted a huge amount of our pollution to other parts of the world – and to China, in particular. [9]

Over to you, China

Although the environment has a bumpy ride on the political rollercoaster, green issues have probably never been higher in the public consciousness than they are today; there's enormous pressure on governments to deliver on climate change, renewable energy, plastic waste – and air quality. Paradoxically, however, what public pressure achieves is often just empty 'greenwash', the illusion that serious problems are being properly tackled, which could be hampering real solutions in the longer term. (I argued in the last chapter that this is how we ended up with the Dieselgate scandal.) Official figures that show progress in reducing air pollution, tackling carbon dioxide emissions, improving the rate of recycling and other environmental goodies often don't stand up to scrutiny. In New York City, for example, Bill de Blasio's comment about air quality never being better referred particularly to the dramatic reduction in atmospheric sulphur dioxide from changes in how people heat their homes. As in virtually all the world's major cities, parts of New York still have problems with particulates, nitrogen oxides and ozone from traffic – issues that kicked in long after the Industrial Revolution. [10]

Apparent cuts in greenhouse gases (mostly carbon dioxide emissions) have often turned out to be a good example of creative environmental accounting. According to some estimates, a quarter to a third of China's total CO_2 emissions come from making goods for export, so those emissions should really be counted in the

countries where the goods are consumed. Take Britain as a typical
example. In the world's original industrial powerhouse, the official
line is that carbon dioxide emissions were about 40 per cent lower
in 2017 than in 1990. But what about emissions from all those
container-ship goods the UK imports, that are counted in China's
debit column instead? In 2009, when Professor David MacKay[1],
the late Cambridge University physicist, was appointed chief
scientific advisor to the UK's Department of Energy and Climate
Change (DECC), he was quick to point out that apparent reductions
in British carbon dioxide emissions were largely 'an illusion'. As
the BBC reported, MacKay observed that: 'Our energy footprint
has decreased over the last few decades and that's largely because
we've exported our industry. Other countries make stuff for us
so we have naughty, naughty China and India out of control with
rising emissions but it's because they are making our stuff for us
now.' His argument focused on greenhouse gas emissions, and it
seems to ignore the growing importance of China's own internal
market: 'they' are making their own stuff as well. Even so, he
was right to point out that a certain amount of China's emissions
are really ours – and that applies to other forms of air pollution,
too. [11]

Among the first to highlight this issue was Oxford University's
Professor Dieter Helm, who discovered (at the time he made his
analysis, in 2009) that about half the energy Britain was using (and
the carbon emissions and pollution it was making) was really overseas: 'If carbon outsourcing is factored back in, the UK's impressive

[1] David MacKay will be remembered for his book *Sustainable Energy Without
the Hot Air*, which sets out the stark choices society must make to tackle
climate change. MacKay's book buries the environmental truism that 'every
little helps'; where energy is concerned, it's more a case of 'every big helps'.
Similar logic applies to air pollution solutions like machines that claim to
clean the air and tree-planting schemes.

emissions cuts over the past two decades don't look so impressive anymore. Rather than falling by over 15 per cent since 1990, they actually rose by around 19 per cent ... No doubt, recalculating the figures for other European countries and the US would reveal a similar pattern.' More recent analysis confirms that 'offshoring' has been responsible for a great deal of the UK's apparent emissions cuts. From 1990 to the mid-2000s, the emissions the UK claimed to have cut were actually offset by increases in emissions through imported goods. (In the last decade or so, however, there have been genuine cuts in the UK's emissions, largely thanks to more efficient use of energy and a steady switch to renewables such as wind power.) [12]

The same argument does indeed apply to other countries. When two scientists from the US National Center for Atmospheric Research ran through the numbers, they found that US CO_2 emissions would have been 6 per cent higher if imported goods from China had been made in the United States instead, while China's emissions would have been 14 per cent lower. In other words, we can't always believe the official figures or the interpretations that politicians spin around them. And the upshot is that tackling problems like air pollution, energy demand and climate change is a much bigger task than we think – we've been cooking the books to make it look like we've achieved more than we actually have. [13]

MacKay and Helm's arguments are echoed in the international scientific consensus. According to the Intergovernmental Panel on Climate Change (IPCC, the UN-sponsored international committee of scientists who are studying global warming), greenhouse gas emissions have grown rapidly in the early 21st century, more than doubling in China and the other fast-growing nations since 2000 alone. Although domestic energy use is substantially to blame, the IPCC notes that: 'A growing share of CO_2 emissions

from fossil fuel combustion in middle-income countries is released
in the production of goods and services exported, notably from
upper-middle-income countries [such as China and Mexico] to
high-income countries [such as the United States and European
nations]'. So far, most of the discussion about climate change
– who causes most damage, so who needs to take most action
– has focused on where carbon dioxide is *emitted* (produced).
Increasingly, however, scientists and economists are taking the
global view and realising that we need to look at where things are
ultimately *consumed*, so the emissions linked to making a car or
some shoes are counted against the country where those things
are bought and used, not where they're made. Focusing on production overestimates the emissions of middle-income countries
such as China by about a fifth, and underestimates the emissions of
richer countries, such as the United States and European nations,
by a broadly similar amount. Interestingly, while China now produces about twice the overall carbon dioxide emissions of the
United States, its per-capita emissions are only half (though both
are increasing rapidly). [14]

To repeat, these arguments are based on carbon dioxide emissions, but broadly the same argument applies to air pollution. That
much is clear if we look at China and its air quality more specifically, which is officially monitored in some 338 of the country's
biggest cities. Back in 2010, roughly two thirds of those places were
considered polluted; that year, an estimated 1.2 million Chinese
died early thanks to air pollution (about 40 per cent of the global
total). By 2017, there had been a considerable improvement, but
days when the air was clean were still recorded only 75 per cent
of the time for these cities as a whole (and a mere 55 per cent of
the time in Beijing). Although air pollution isn't specifically listed
among China's leading causes of death, it's unclear how many of

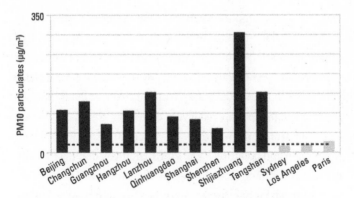

Figure 31. Most of China's big cities (black bars, left) remain grossly polluted, compared to major cities elsewhere in the world (grey bars, right) and the World Health Organization guideline (dotted line). Chart shows levels of PM10 particulates in µg/m³. Data source: World Health Organization Ambient Air Pollution database.

the country's deaths linked to cancer, heart disease, stroke and so on were really caused by chronic dirty air (a topic we'll return to in Chapter 8). [15]

To what extent China's dirty air is caused by Western consumers isn't clear, though a few estimates have been attempted. According to one international team, led by Jintai Lin of Beijing's Peking University, somewhere between 17–36 per cent of the country's total air pollution comes from the factories where 'Made in China' takes place. About a fifth of these 'foreign emissions' were produced on behalf of the United States alone. [16]

And who's to blame? Is it the corporations who outsource their factories, jobs and pollution – or the unthinking consumers who snap up jeans and shoes at bargain prices, without taking time to think about the 'Made in Somewhere Else' labels? Is there any credible alternative to this particular game, now the world has shifted so far? Is there any going back on globalisation, for consumers or producers? If 'ethical consumers' suddenly cry foul and turn on the producers, what are you supposed to do if you're a transnational corporation like Gap, H&M, Nike or a hundred others, competing on illusory, internationalised brand values – so your products essentially differ only by their label? Do you make your shoes in the United States, trumpet that fact loudly and sell fewer at a higher price, even if your customers are in 200 different countries around the world? Or do you continue to offshore your production and pollution – knowing that, if you don't, your competitors will still do so – and steal your customers? The numbers seem to speak for themselves. According to a study by Yue Maggie Zhou and Xiaoyang Li, the share of goods imported into the United States made in low-wage countries rose from 7 per cent in 1992 to 23 per cent in 2009. Over the same time period, air pollution from manufacturing industries in the United States fell by 50 per cent. Though offshoring isn't the whole explanation, it seems too much to believe that these things are completely unconnected. [17]

One more point is well worth noting. While we think of China when it comes to outsourcing, similar arguments apply to India, Brazil, Indonesia, Mexico, Vietnam, Cambodia, the Philippines and numerous other 'Made in...' countries to which Western factories have migrated en masse. In some ways, India is in far worse shape than China – and has a worse prognosis. The world's ten most polluted cities are all in northern India, and more Indians than Chinese live in densely populated, heavily polluted areas. Some 77 per cent of the entire Indian population breathes dangerous, fine particulates (PM2.5s) at levels four times greater than World Health Organization guidelines; meeting those guidelines would add 4.3 more years to the life expectancy of the average Indian (even more in heavily polluted hotspots like Uttar Pradesh and Delhi). Interestingly, China lies 'downwind' of India, so any worsening of the air over India could potentially undermine China's own efforts at clean-up in the future. Without a more drastic shift to renewables, China's and India's growth paints a frightening picture of a highly polluted future. According to the International Energy Agency's 2018 World Energy Outlook: 'To meet rising demand, China needs to add the equivalent of today's United States power system to its electricity infrastructure by 2040, and India needs to add a power system the size of today's European Union.' [18]

Poverty or pollution?

Free-trade economists would be quick to point out that China has gained hugely by importing industry from, and exporting cheap goods to, the rest of the world. For three full decades between 1978 and 2008, a period of major economic reform, it achieved GDP growth of over 10 per cent a year (roughly three times the rate of the United States, Britain and the world as a whole). As a direct result, China improved from 108 to 72 on the UN World Development Index (an aggregated measurement of things like income, education levels and life expectancy) and household incomes in China rose by over 5 per cent, lifting (by different estimates) some 250–400 million people out of poverty. Among rural Chinese, absolute poverty fell from 41 per cent of the population in 1978 to just 4.8 per cent in 2001 – making a major dent in overall world poverty. Before the economic reforms kicked in, China was a much more self-contained country: just 10 per cent of its wealth was earned from imports and exports; after the reforms, in 2005, almost two thirds of its wealth came from the international import-export trade. Today, China is widely recognised as the 'engine of the world economy' (Google returns a quarter of a million hits for that phrase). From steel, cotton, tobacco and cars to renewable energy and coal, China dominates many of the world's most important industries – ones where the United States now trails, tiredly, in second or third place. [19]

Not surprisingly, such rapid industrialisation carries a heavy environmental price. Chinese energy consumption, for example, increased by about 70 per cent between 2000 and 2005 alone, and 75 per cent of that increase came from coal. Burning coal means mining it as well, which also comes at a cost: the death rate for Chinese coal miners is about 37 times that of the United States. By 2002, a quarter of a century after its major economic reforms began, two thirds of Chinese cities had PM10 particulate levels pushing three times the World Health Organization guideline values. Although average sulphur dioxide levels managed to fall by 44 per cent between 1990 and 2002, China still exceeded its targets for SO_2 and PM10 soot production during this period. [20]

Today, China appears to be making great strides towards a clean-up. It has the largest solar farm in the world, more wind-farm power capacity than any other nation and twice that of the United States (although it ranks only about 20th in the world for wind power measured per capita). It planned to spend at least $361 billion on renewable energy by 2020 (creating 13 million green jobs in the process). And it's instituted a rigorous process of targeting its most polluting factories: some 80,000 plants have been fined, charged or closed completely for not meeting the standards. [21]

Even so, the country has a long, toxic legacy to shake off – and other figures reveal a firm commitment to coal. China grew its coal plants by a factor of five in the 21st century alone, it currently operates half the world's total coal power plant capacity and is home to a third of all the new coal capacity currently in the pipeline. While the rest of the world was congratulating itself on killing off 8.1 gigawatts of dirty old coal power in 2018, China unhelp-fully added 43 gigawatts back to the global tally, simultaneously approving 45 billion yuan ($6.64 billion) of new coal mines in the process. All this bodes ill for air quality. According to the 2018 State of Global Air (SOGA) report, coal-burning is still China's big-gest source of air pollution, causing an estimated 370,000 deaths a year. Industrial sources (many powered by coal-fired electricity) were one of the greatest causes of Chinese deaths attributable to fine, PM2.5 particulate pollution (about 27 per cent of total PM2.5 deaths). [22]

China is a great illustration of a point Naomi Klein made in her 2014 international bestseller *This Changes Everything*: 'Forced to choose between poverty and pollution, these governments are choosing pollution, but those should not be their only options.' Given the economic rhetoric that paints pollution as a price worth paying to escape from poverty, it's also critically important to note that air and water pollution tend to hit the poorest hardest. A few years ago, a World Bank report noted that: 'environmental pollu-tion falls disproportionately on the less economically advanced parts of China, which have a higher share of poor populations ... Ningxia, Xinjiang, Inner Mongolia and other low-income prov-inces are more affected by air pollution on a per capita basis than high-income provinces such as Guangdong and other provinces in the southeast.' [23]

When it comes to poverty and pollution, there's no shortage of statistics, but which ones should we believe? Which numbers matter most? Is it the roughly one million people who were dying each year from air pollution during China's economic reforms or the several hundred million who were lifted out of poverty? Does one really offset the other? If you're a Western consumer, do you feel a tingle of satisfaction striding along in shoes made in China, happy in the knowledge that your exported money made some poorer people slightly richer ... or a shudder of shame that you might have contributed to those million deaths from dirty air? Chances are, like me and most other people, you have absolutely no idea of the environmental and social costs you're causing.

Thankfully, some researchers have been attempting to find out. One intriguing recent study has attempted to figure out how particulate pollution 'Made in China', directly attributable to Western consumption, causes different numbers of deaths both in China itself and (because pollution blows with the wind) in other parts of the world, too. Inspecting historic data for the year 2007, the researchers, led by Qiang Zhang of Tsinghua University, discovered that about 22 per cent of the 3.45 million deaths (762,400 deaths) caused by fine PM2.5 particulates could be attributed to goods and services produced in one region and consumed in another. Looking at China more closely, they found 108,600 deaths in the country could be linked to consumption of Chinese-made goods in western Europe and the United States, while Chinese pollution carried by the wind caused 64,800 early deaths outside the country. The interesting finding is that international trade causes greater health impacts, through PM2.5 pollution, than the long-distance transport of pollution through the air. [24]

One of the traps in this kind of analysis lies in assuming that losses of one kind in one place are neatly compensated by gains of other kinds in other places – that we're dealing, in other words, with a zero-sum game. It might sound morally dubious to wonder whether reductions in poverty offset deaths from pollution, or whether pollution made in China is preferable to that produced in the United States, for either party – but it's more complex than that. These sorts of environmental-social-economic balancing acts sometimes lack the most basic logical validity because they're not like-for-like comparisons. China, in short, is not the United States: it's much more coal dependent, its factories were, for a long time, much less efficient and its worker protections more lax. Outsourcing a factory making a certain product from the United States or Europe to China could therefore produce greater emissions and pollution than if that product had been produced, to an identical specification, in the West.

About a decade ago, a British analysis by the New Economic Foundation discovered that Chinese factories produce roughly a third more carbon-dioxide emissions (and, we can assume, significantly more pollution) than European factories making identical products. A more recent analysis of steelmaking by Lawrence Berkeley National Laboratory found that a tonne of steel made in China produces 1.25 times the carbon dioxide emissions of a tonne of steel made in Germany or the United States, and twice as much as a tonne of steel made in Mexico. And none of this includes the emissions or the pollution from transporting globalised goods around the world. (That currently accounts for about 5 per cent of global greenhouse emissions – and it's predicted to double or quadruple over the next two to three decades.) [25]

Beyond the air

Air pollution isn't the only thing we export when we ship factories and the power plants that drive them to the other side of the Earth. Back in the early 1990s, Greenpeace was quick to highlight how little attention countries like the UK were paying to the pollution they were pouring out at home and – thanks to impressively tall smokestacks – spreading overseas. Famously, it branded Britain 'The Dirty Man of Europe' for its wilful failure to tackle wholesale air and water pollution. Around the same time, Greenpeace and others popularised the concepts of 'toxic colonialism' and 'garbage imperialism' for another growing trend; dumping rich-world waste in poorer nations, which continues to this day. More recently, Greenpeace has focused on China's crippling water pollution – and how it stems partly from 'Made in China' manufacturing for Western companies. [26]

China's rapid push to industrialisation from the late 1980s onward hit its rivers hard. By the early 2000s, just over half the water in the country's seven main rivers was regarded as unsafe for human use; in the industrial north, water quality was particularly badly hit. By 2009, Greenpeace was pointing fingers at Western consumption and its impact on the Pearl River Delta in Southern China, the world's biggest urban area (often nicknamed the 'world's factory floor'), which produced almost a third of the entire country's exports at that time. According to the group's Chinese campaign manager, Edward Chan: '"Made in China" products used by consumers worldwide are being manufactured at a high cost to the Pearl River. If the results of our sampling are any indication of what factories in general are doing in China, then China's waters are in deep trouble.' [27]

When we're finished with our Chinese-made clothes and shoes, smartphones and computers, nylon toothbrushes and PVC washing-up bowls, what do we do with them? We shunt quite a lot of them straight back where they came from – sometimes on the 'empty' return journeys of the very same container ships that bring us those goods in the first place. Despite the existence of an international law called the Basel Convention, supposedly designed to halt the global trade in hazardous waste, industrialised nations still export vast amounts of trash to the developing world. Old smartphones, laptops and other electronic gadgets are particular offenders. According to the United Nations, something like 7 kilograms (15 pounds) of electronic waste *alone* is now generated each year for every single person on the planet. The total weight of the world's old e-junk is equivalent to eight Egyptian pyramids, and it comprises 1,000 different substances, from relatively benign iron, plastics and glass to highly toxic lead, mercury and cadmium. And that's just the electronic waste. [28]

While Western countries congratulate themselves on their impressive recycling rates, developing nations struggle with the problem of what to do with the world's steadily accumulating junk. Some of it is indeed recycled; much is landfilled or incinerated, causing land, air and water pollution. Meanwhile, the developing nations are growing wiser to toxic colonialism – and are finally making a stand. For over 25 years, during its period of huge economic growth, China ran a profitable sideline importing and recycling almost half the world's plastic trash. But in 2017, it abruptly changed tack and banned a wide range of waste imports 'to protect China's environmental interests and people's health', promptly throwing recycling programmes around the world into chaos. Taking a stand is catching on. In the Philippines, President Rodrigo Duterte earned environmental kudos by insisting that his 'right-on' Canadian counterpart, Justin Trudeau, take back 69 container loads of trash (supposedly plastics for recycling, but allegedly contaminated with other household waste) that had been illegally dumped in his nation (according to the Basel Convention) six years earlier. [29]

Feel-good 'recycling', exported from the West, that arrives in developing countries as useless trash is another example of greenwash – the token appearance of environmentalism – that doesn't benefit the planet or its people in any way. And there are plenty more examples where that came from. Take our sudden Western enthusiasm for electric cars. If you buy one of these, persuaded by the argument that it's a zero-emission vehicle, most likely you're selling an old, fossil-fuelled car in its place. Where does that go? If it's not bought by someone in your own country, chances are it's exported to somewhere like Uganda (where the average age of an imported car is over sixteen years) or Kenya (99 per cent of whose imported cars are second-hand rejects from places like Europe, Japan and the United States). So your switch doesn't really take a dirty old car off the road: it shifts the old car somewhere else and adds an extra electric car on top. It's another example of exported pollution. And it's worsened by a dubious, interlinked practice through which cars exported to Africa are filled up with filthy, low-quality diesel or leaded fuels in ports along the way, that would never pass muster in places like Europe. [30]

One reason Western power plants, factories and waste incinerators pollute the air much less than they used to is because their chimneys are fitted with 'scrubbers' that catch the smoke and ash that would otherwise stream out into the air. That sounds like an excellent advance until you remember that the captured particulates still have to be disposed of somehow. What happens to things like incinerator ash? At one time, some was simply shipped overseas. A particularly notorious case happened back in August 1986, when a ship called the *Khian Sea* was dispatched from Philadelphia in the United States with a toxic cargo of 14,000 tonnes of ash. A whole series of countries – Bermuda, the Dominican Republic, the Dutch Antilles, Guinea-Bissau, Honduras, Morocco, Senegal, Singapore, Sri Lanka and Yemen – refused it entry before the ash was finally (it's believed) dumped in the ocean instead. Professor David Naguib Pellow of the University of California at Santa Barbara, an expert on 'toxic colonialism', describes the incident as 'an unbridled example of international environmental racism and a case that became an early training ground for the movement for global environmental justice'. [31]

It was episodes like this that provided the impetus for the 1992 Basel Convention (full title: The Basel Convention on the Control of Transboundary Movements of Hazardous Wastes and Their Disposal). But while that treaty may have reined in some of the most egregious forms of waste dumping, it's clear from the other examples we've considered that richer nations continue to export all kinds of pollution in all kinds of sneaky ways. Do you know where all your 'recycling' goes, or where your last trashed computer finally ended up? I'm ashamed to say that I don't have a clue. [32]

Import-export

China can't turn its back on Western trade, even if it has been trying to turn back Western trash. Officially, as we've already seen, it's doing its best to switch to renewable energy, and policing air and water quality more vigorously than ever before. All that's just as well, because the impacts of 'Made in China' pollution extend far beyond the country itself: in a variety of different ways, China also exports pollution overseas.

As we've noted in previous chapters, air pollution knows no boundaries; it blows not just from one region to another but between entire continents. One of the greatest ironies of Western consumer nations exporting their factories and pollution to China is that prevailing winds blow some of it straight 'back' across the Pacific in the opposite direction. Research by a team of scientists from China, the US and the UK has shown that, over the western United States, as much as 11 per cent of sooty particulates and a quarter of sulphates in the air were originally emitted in China.

Meanwhile, Los Angeles experiences an extra day of smog each year thanks to carbon monoxide and nitrogen oxides that were 'Made in China' with our sneakers and jeans. Another recent study has discovered that one of the reasons dangerous ozone pollution persists on the West Coast of the United States, despite concerted local efforts at cleaning the air, is because a significant amount of it travels across the Pacific from China. [33]

Some of China's pollution exports are more questionable. One of its most polluted provinces, Hebei, in the north-west of the country, is home to seven of the country's top-ten polluted cities, which is no big surprise given that this region alone produces twice as much steel as the entire United States. China's long-term strategy for cleaning up Hebei includes relocating steel-, glass- and cement-making plants overseas to Africa, eastern Europe, other parts of Asia and Latin America. In other words, having imported

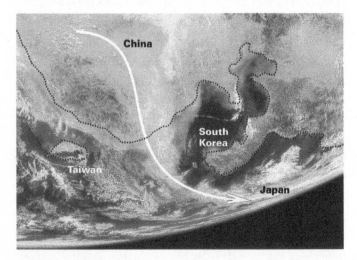

Figure 32. How China exports its pollution. In this image from the NASA SeaWiFS satellite, you can see a huge band of haze sweeping out from East China past South Korea, across Japan and out into the Pacific. Photograph courtesy of NASA. [34]

the world's pollution for the last few decades, it's now going to try exporting it instead. [35]

Earning money by making goods for other countries has lifted millions of Chinese out of poverty, but it's also left cash for long-term overseas investments in poorer, developing nations. Here, too, there's a risk that China may, in effect, be exporting pollution to other countries. According to a recent opinion piece in *The New York Times* by Paulina Garzón of the China Latin-America Sustainable Investments Initiative and Leila Salazar-López of Amazon Watch, China has provided something like $250 billion in development loans to Africa, the Caribbean and Latin America. Unfortunately, despite China's apparent green commitment back home, Garzón and Salazar-López claim much of this investment has gone to fund environmentally dubious projects like coal mining, oil drilling and highway construction – and financing at least 50 new coal-fired power plants in Africa alone. Chinese companies are currently building coal plants in seventeen other countries. [36]

Coming clean?

The industrial shift from West to East is an ongoing trend, which means the problems we've explored above could well get worse in the decades to come. By 2040, world energy consumption is expected to increase by about a third, with two thirds of that growth happening in the fast-developing economies of Asia. China is the biggest issue today (a third of the world's energy growth in 2018 happened there); India is expected to be a bigger problem tomorrow. While China is taking important steps to decarbonise its energy system, it continues to use about as much coal as the rest of the world put together. And it won't really be using that much less in future: rather, renewable energy will be supplying most of the *extra* new energy the country will be consuming. Ambitious plans to shift the Chinese economy from products to services, export factories to other nations and supply investment funds for 'dirty' infrastructure projects overseas could see China's current pollution problems effectively exported to other parts of the world. [37]

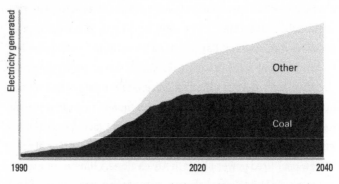

Figure 33. The end of coal? Not so fast. Almost three quarters of China's electricity came from coal in 2015; by 2040, that figure is expected to fall to just under half. But that doesn't mean China will be using half as much coal: it means the country's vast *extra* energy will largely be coming from renewables. In absolute terms, China will still be burning almost as much coal in 2040 as it does today. Source: US Energy Information Administration (2017). [38]

Long-term critics of globalisation see problems like this as an inevitable consequence of free trade that prioritises race-to-the-bottom economics over social and environmental concerns. It's all too easy to highlight apparent absurdities in the international trade system. The New Economics Foundation noted, one year, how the UK imported 47 tonnes of vacuum cleaners from Canada, but exported 34 tonnes of similar cleaners in the opposite direction, while no one but the planet's future generations pays the environmental costs of back-and-forth transportation. On the other hand, strident free-market economists have often argued for even greater exporting of the world's pollution to developing nations. In his capacity as Chief Economist of the World Bank, former President of Harvard College Larry Summers wrote a notorious memo arguing that 'the economic logic behind dumping a load of toxic waste in the lowest wage country is impeccable and we should face up to that ... I've always thought that countries in Africa are vastly under-polluted; their air quality is probably vastly inefficiently low compared to Los Angeles ... Just between you and me shouldn't the World Bank be encouraging more migration of the dirty industries to the Least Developed Countries?' [39]

While attitudes like this prevail, the problem of exported air pollution is unlikely to be cleaned up any time soon. Spreading pollution around the world raises the same moral problem as 'carbon offsetting' (compensating for the environmental damage of something like a long-haul flight by planting trees in Africa). Instead of taking responsibility for the problems we're causing, we're trying to fiddle the books to conceal those problems (by counting emissions in the countries where they're produced), brush them under someone else's carpet (by exporting dirty factories around the world) or disguise them with greenwash (by highlighting China's enthusiasm for renewables, while forgetting to mention its long-term commitment to coal). To many environmentalists, 'sustainable development' is an oxymoron; it's an inherently flawed compromise that legitimises business as usual – including the 'Made in China' consumption we all take for granted. Ultimately, though, 'Made in China' pollution isn't made in China at all: it's made in *our* minds through our own actions and choices. Until we address that, we will never entirely resolve the problem of air pollution in developing countries and the millions of deaths it causes.

BLUE-SKY THINKING?

Exactly how bad China's air had become after 30 years of relentless economic revolution was essentially a state secret. The arrival of the Olympic Games in Beijing in 2008 put paid to that. How would the city's famously dirty air affect the performance – and, more importantly, health – of the world's top athletes? The Chinese invested huge effort in cleaning up their capital (including, briefly, closing factories in six nearby provinces) while all eyes turned their way. Particulate pollution fell by around a third during the Games themselves, though much of that improvement was down to helpful changes in the weather. And it was still, according to research published in 2009, the most polluted Games ever.

Despite frantic attempts to clear the air, it didn't stay that way for long. Between 2010 and 2017, the world's media still found cause to run endless variations on headlines with the words 'Beijing' and 'airpocalypse'. Then, in 2017, China declared a full-scale war on air pollution – with Premier Li Keqiang vowing: 'We will make our skies blue again.' By the end of that year, even Greenpeace marvelled at how Beijing's PM2.5 particulates had fallen by 'a whopping 54 per cent', noting: 'Nationwide, about 160,000 premature deaths were avoided in 2017 due to the reduction in pollution.' That was an amazing achievement.

What made the difference? Lazy Western media love to credit the American Embassy in Beijing and its public Twitter feed, @beijingair, which has posted crude, hourly measurements of the city's pollution levels since 2008. On one occasion in 2010, it famously posted a reading of 'Crazy Bad', prompting international amusement and considerable Chinese embarrassment. In truth, of course, most of the credit is due to the efforts of the Chinese themselves, who don't enjoy breathing dirty air any more than anyone else.

Many things have made a difference, from both the top down and the bottom up. The Chinese government has gone for tougher laws,

continued

better air monitoring, crackdowns on thousands of the worst factories, traffic bans and national air quality plans. From the bottom up,
there have been grassroots campaigns like the Institute of Public and
Environment Affairs (IPE), run by activist Ma Jun, which has published
live data on air and water polluters since 2006 and now works closely
with government agencies and foreign corporations. Meeting in the
middle – mutual trust and effective two-way cooperation between
the government and the people – will be key to the success of China's
long-term pollution-busting efforts.

So far, those efforts have really paid off. Between 2013 and 2017,
average concentrations of most of the major pollutants fell by between
a quarter and a half in 74 of China's major cities. Although these gains
are compromised by the country's huge ongoing commitment to coal,
they're incredibly impressive nonetheless. Environmental economist Thomas Stoerk, from the European Commission and the London
School of Economics, recently analysed China's clean-up and compared it to the post-Industrial-Revolution equivalent in Britain. Both
countries started from similar peaks of pollution. But where Britain
took most of the 20th century to make a significant dent in its filthy
air (from a high point around 1900), China has made serious strides
in repeating that achievement in just the few decades since its own
peak in 1980. With major investments in cleaning up industry, energy
and transportation, clear skies over China will save millions of lives.
That should be justification enough, but the economic data stack
up too. One Chinese government estimate put the cost of the clean-up
between 2013 and 2017 at an enormous 1.75 trillion yuan (£176 billion),
while the benefit would weigh in at an even more impressive 2 trillion
yuan (£202 billion). Whichever way you look at it, China's new, blue-
sky thinking makes very good sense. [40]

CHAPTER 7

Safe indoors?

Why air pollution indoors can be worse than it is outside

Andrew Marvell famously described the grave as a 'fine and private place' and most of us see our homes that way too. When we think of air pollution, typically we imagine filthy clouds billowing from smokestacks or puffing from the tailpipes of cars; it's a problem that doesn't affect us as long as we're sealed away, safe indoors. What we don't realise, however, is that the pollution *inside* our homes, offices, schools, factories and all kinds of other indoor spaces can be equally lethal and sometimes more so. Roughly half the world's total air pollution deaths are caused by dirty indoor air. While most of those are due, very specifically, to burning crude fuels for cooking and heating in developing countries, indoor air pollution is also a big problem in richer, supposedly cleaner parts of the world like North America and Europe.

Think about it. Unless you happen to work outdoors, you'll spend about 90 per cent of your time in a completely enclosed indoor environment. What do you do there? Maybe you huddle around a wood burner (a source of indoor and outdoor particulates) eating food you've heated on a gas cooker (a rich source of both nitrogen oxides and particulates). Perhaps you pad around in your socks on new wooden floors and carpets that typically 'off-gas' (give off volatile organic fumes from manufacturing) for months after they're installed. Maybe – despite endless nagging from your friends and conscience – you're still a smoker: a pint-sized, personal chimney breathing out (as we'll discover in a moment) more particulates than a diesel engine. Perhaps you have a badly maintained gas boiler that's leaking out dubious amounts of carbon monoxide? Maybe you're keen on DIY? All those paints, varnishes, waxes and glues give off heady fumes that amount to toxic pollution. Perhaps you're house-proud? Cleaning products, 'anti-bac' sprays, moth repellents and even air fresheners fill your home with chemicals you'd be better off not breathing. And when it comes to keeping yourself clean, deodorants, perfumes, laundry detergents, dry-cleaning fluids and even your new shower curtain are all things that pollute the air. If you can smell it, and it's been made in a factory, there's a good chance it's pollution. [1]

Worldwide, for all ages and sexes, household air pollution is the eighth leading cause of death, after things like high blood pressure, smoking and outdoor particulate pollution (which comes in at number six). It ends 3.8 million lives too soon, each year, in a variety of ways. As you might expect, the majority of these early deaths are breathing-related (27 per cent from pneumonia, 20 per cent from COPD and 8 per cent from lung cancer). Of the rest, 27 per cent are heart-related and 18 per cent are due to strokes. Surprisingly, toxic indoor air is more harmful than the things we're warned about more often, like poor diet, alcohol and lack of exercise; in Europe alone, it's estimated to cause close to 100,000 early deaths a year. Why exactly is *indoor* pollution such a big deal? What counts is our total exposure, so (aggregating across the entire world), that high death rate comes from the huge number of people who live in polluted homes (around 3 billion of us burn fuel indoors), the high levels of pollution in places like developing-nation dwellings (which can be 10–20 times greater than WHO guidelines) and the fact that modern humans spend almost all their time indoors. [2]

Having said all that, beyond creating impressive-sounding statistics, lumping together every single form of indoor air pollution isn't necessarily that helpful. Let's tease apart some of the different kinds and delve into their problems in a bit more depth.

Fuel for the fire

In an age when most of us walk no further than the car, 'try walking a mile in my shoes' – see things from my perspective – is a pretty glib suggestion. But what if the person who said it to you was a Maasai woman? Then it's likely you'd find yourself trudging not 'a mile', but three to four times further to fetch up to 45 kilograms (100 pounds) of firewood at a time, before walking the same distance back again. That's after you've milked ten to fifteen cows by hand (at 5:30 in the morning), walked some more miles to collect your water, made and sustained the fire, tended to your husband and family and mentally ticked off all the other boxes on your daily to-do list. In many parts of the world, it's quite common to spend more than twenty hours a week collecting firewood or other biomass fuels to keep the home fire burning. [3]

Of course, not everyone in developing countries lives a life that, by spoiled Western standards, is so austere and extreme. But 30–40 per cent of the world's population (up to 2.5 billion people) still rely on burning dirty fuels indoors (around 80 per cent of them burn biomass, such as wood, peat, crop waste and dung and the rest, mostly in China, burn coal or charcoal). In some countries, indoor fuel-burning is ubiquitous and universal: in poorer African nations, for example, well over 90 per cent of the population live this way. People mostly cook and heat using simple stoves or three-stone fires (where cooking pots are balanced on three large rocks with the flames burning in between – a simple idea that dates back to Neolithic times). Such crude combustion can belch out fine, sooty, PM2.5 particulates at anything up to 100 times higher than WHO guidelines (though it's usually six to twenty times higher). And those smoky fumes, which might seem a quaintly charming backdrop to TV documentaries about indigenous tribes, kill around three people a minute (between 2–4 million people worldwide each year). [4]

The statistics are sobering. Smoke from burning solid fuels is one of the top four biggest causes of death or disease in poor countries. It kills *over a million children*, mostly under the age of five, each year, many of whom die a particularly unpleasant death from pneumonia (half of all childhood deaths from that illness are down to sooty indoor air pollution). In poorer countries, the under-fives are 60 times more likely to die from air pollution (mostly the indoor kind) compared to children of the same age in richer nations. In the quarter century from 1990 to 2013, there were great improvements in many countries – household air pollution deaths among the under-fives fell by about 60 per cent, for example. Even so, thanks to factors like the ageing global population, the total number of deaths remained pretty much constant at a scandalous 3 million or so a year, while the economic cost of household air pollution rose by about 60 per cent over the same period. These figures come from recent research by the World Bank and the Institute for Health Metrics and Evaluation at the University of Washington, who calculate that household air pollution costs low- and middle-income countries about $1.5 trillion a year in welfare losses, and $94 billion in lost labour. [5]

The trouble with statistics like these is that they lump together a huge number of very different countries, smearing details in the averaging process and making it harder to understand where a complex problem is better or worse. Suppose we break the figures down a bit further, with the help of the Health Effects Institute's State of the Global Air Report. Then we can see that of the 2.5 billion or so people who suffer from household air pollution, about a billion of them are in India (560 million) and China (416 million) alone. Despite being the smaller country, India clearly has the bigger problem, with 43 per cent of its people exposed to toxic indoor air (mostly produced from biomass burning) compared to just 30 per cent in China (where coal is an increasingly popular fuel). Among poorer and smaller developing nations, far fewer people are affected, but the percentage of the population exposed is much higher. In Nigeria, for example, 71 per cent of the people are exposed to dirty indoor air and in Ethiopia, Tanzania and the Democratic Republic of the Congo, the figure hits 96–97 per cent. [6]

Just as it's misleading to lump different countries together, it's equally unhelpful to talk about millions of 'people' having their health or their lives compromised by indoor air pollution, because the burden falls more heavily on some than on others. The Maasai women who are collecting firewood and keeping the pot boiling are also the ones who crouch by the stove with their young children, breathing in the choking smoke: women and younger children in poorer parts of developing countries are at much greater risk. According to Hugh Warwick and Alison Doig, authors of a groundbreaking report about the problem of indoor smoke pollution in developing countries published some years ago: 'A child is two to three times more likely to contract acute lower respiratory infection if exposed to indoor air pollution. Women who cook on biomass are up to four times more likely to suffer from chronic obstructive pulmonary disease, such as chronic bronchitis. Lung cancer in women in China has been directly linked to use of coal burning stoves.' [7]

While we're busy disentangling averages and aggregates, it's also worth pointing out that home fuel burning makes more than one kind of pollution. Fine sooty particulates are the cause of greatest concern, but they're far from the only problem. Burning dirtier kinds of coal at home produces sulphur dioxide; that's essentially how the Great London Smog happened. Carbon monoxide, hissing out from under-ventilated or otherwise faulty stoves, is another insidious risk. In the first two months of 2018, 400 Chinese died from CO fumes leaking out of badly fitted natural-gas stoves; tragically, they'd switched to gas from coal- and wood-powered stoves because of the perceived health benefits. Even in richer countries, CO poisoning from poor indoor fuel combustion is a big issue. In the United States, carbon monoxide poisoning kills around 400–500 people a year and sends 10,000 more to hospital. Unfortunately, their symptoms are often confused with other illnesses, prompting them to be discharged back to their homes where they quickly suffer a relapse. [8]

Even if you don't cook your supper on a three-stone fire in Malawi and you have a sensible little carbon monoxide alarm, don't assume you're completely safe from the risks of indoor fuel burning. According to studies by smoke pollution expert Martine Dennekamp and her colleagues, a gas cooker, like the one you probably have in your kitchen, can whack indoor levels of nitrogen dioxide up to 1 ppm. That might not sound much, but it's around 50–100 times background levels and about twice the level you'll find in dense outdoor traffic. Love the lush, cosy smell of baking a cake? Just remember that you could be generating nitrogen dioxide levels almost the same as those in smog. And that's not all. A similar study by Marina Vance and colleagues from the University of Colorado Boulder found that roasting meat and vegetables could produce PM2.5 levels in a kitchen that are (for the duration of your cooking) higher than those you'll find in the most polluted industrial cities of India and China. Finally, if you get a bit carried away and scorch your pan while you're frying, watch out for something called 'Teflon flu' (polymer fume fever). As the name suggests, high temperatures can break down the non-stick coating in a pan, releasing chemical fumes that can give influenza-like symptoms in humans and even prove toxic to pets. All this might sound scary; in practice, it just means you need to get into the habit of cooking with plenty of ventilation, especially if you use a gas stove. [9]

The good news – indeed, it's excellent news – is that the problem of indoor air pollution from solid-fuel burning seems certain to improve in coming years and decades. According to the annual State of Global Air reports from the Health Effects Institute, the percentage of people burning indoor fuels has been in marked decline in many regions over the last quarter century. In South Asia, for example, about 90 per cent of the population were breathing toxic air from indoor fuel burning in 1990, but the figure has fallen to below 50 per cent today. There have also been improvements in East and Central Asia, Latin America and North Africa and the Middle East. Yet in many parts of sub-Saharan Africa, there's been little or no change in the proportion of households using solid fuels in home fires and stoves. [10]

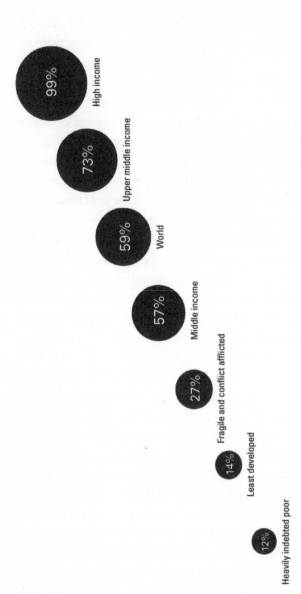

Figure 34. Indoor smoke is the biggest single cause of death from air pollution, but people in many countries still lack safe fuels. This chart shows the percentage of the population in various country groupings who have access to clean fuels for cooking. The world average is just 59 per cent, ranging from 0.57 per cent in Rwanda to 100 per cent in the United States. Drawn using 2016 data from World Bank, Sustainable Energy for All (SE4ALL) database/WHO Global Household Energy database, published under a Creative Commons (CC BY 4.0) Licence. [11]

TESTING TESTING

Gas cooking

Cooking with (natural) gas can release surprising amounts of nitrogen dioxide, which is certainly bad for your health: if you have asthma, for example, numerous studies have shown that gas cooking will make it worse.

I thought I'd run my own quick test with the Plume Flow to see how my cooker compared. I fired up all four burners and let them roar away on max for about fifteen minutes. You can see from the graph below how that was enough to send NO_2 levels well above the WHO's one-year guideline (the most you can safely breathe, on average, for a whole year) and, since I deliberately didn't open a window, they stayed that way for a couple of hours. Now fifteen minutes of gas cooking is a very small risk for me and not something I'm going to worry about. (The NO_2 levels I'm breathing here are about five times lower than the ones I encountered sitting on a train in Chapter 5.) But what if you work in a restaurant and you're breathing these sorts of NO_2 levels all day long? Make sure there's an extractor fan and check that ventilation levels are adequate. [12]

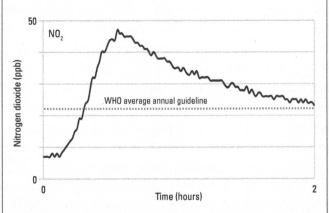

Figure 35. Chart shows: Y axis: Nitrogen dioxide level in parts per billion (ppb); X axis: time in hours.

The trouble with keeping clean

If cleanliness really is next to godliness, our places in heaven
must surely be secure. Just check our under-sink cupboards and
bathroom cabinets: deodorants, shampoos, soaps, shaving foams,
perfumes, anti-wrinkle creams, sunblocks, hair gels and waxes,
face peels, air fresheners, washing liquids, laundry detergents,
disinfectants, toothpastes, mouthwashes, cream cleaners, mould
and mildew sprays, limescale zappers, bleaches, baby-friendly
wet wipes, anti-bacterial sprays, fly killers and toilet blocks – to
name just a few. Many household products assure us that they
kill '99.9 per cent of germs and bacteria', nailing the lie that
cleaning is an act of genteel house pride and prettification. In
reality, it's an interminable, domestic Vietnam; it's an ongoing, misguided war against sometimes imaginary foes – and one
we can never win. Thanks to all the chemicals packed in products like these, it's also a war in which our health – alongside
dirt, germs, mould, old-age and body odour – may be one of the
chronic casualties.

Focusing purely on air pollution, the biggest problem with
home cleaning, DIY and personal care products is that many of
them give off high levels of VOCs (volatile organic compounds,
the ones that readily evaporate in the air, making our heads spin).
Outdoors, VOCs often dissipate quite quickly – although, by taking
part in chemical reactions with other things in the air, they also
help to form longer-term pollution such as ozone, smog and fine
particulates that stick around much longer.

Inside, it's a different story: there's really nowhere for VOCs
to go. Polish your shoes in the kitchen and, depending on ventilation, you might find the stink lingers there for the rest of the
day. Paint a radiator with gloss and you'll be dealing with
the heady stench of VOCs for days or even weeks. According to

the US Environmental Protection Agency, levels of VOCs are 'consistently' two to ten times higher indoors than out, which is bad enough. But if you use something like paint stripper inside your home, you'll bump indoor VOCs up to 1,000 times their normal, background level for hours afterwards. While you might expect things like the petrol and diesel from the world's billion cars to make the most VOC emissions, that turns out not to be true. When Brian McDonald and his team from the Cooperative Institute for Research in Environmental Sciences in Boulder, Colorado compared petrol VOC emissions to those from VOC-emitting home products, they were shocked. We use about fifteen times as much petrol and diesel (by weight) compared to household products, but the household products make 38 per cent of all VOC emissions, compared to just 32 per cent from petrol and diesel, and household VOCs contribute just as much to secondary pollution (ozone and particulates) as the ones in fuel. All this matters because some of the VOCs come with a raft of short- and long-term impacts on our health, ranging from headaches, nausea, memory loss and brief spells of dizziness through to permanent liver, kidney and nerve damage and – though you'll struggle to make the connection to the radiator you painted 20 years before – various kinds of cancer. [13]

Now we expect things like gloss paint to stink and we can take simple precautions to minimise our exposure and risk. (After years of terrible DIY headaches, I try very hard now to buy water-based, low-emission paints whenever I can.) But household air pollution isn't always so easy to spot and, because home products are usually laced with artificial fragrances, the harm they're doing is often masked by a compelling smell. Clothes, for example, act like sponges in the presence of everyday pollution, which gets boiled off into the air when we wash and dry them at high temperatures, even if we use nothing more harmful than water. Laundry detergents and tumble-dryer sheets, deliberately designed to deceive us with floral fragrances, are often adding VOCs to the mix. When Professor Anne Steinemann of the University of Washington studied a range of household detergents, cleaners and other personal care products – including some described as 'green' or 'natural' – she found they emitted an average of seventeen VOCs, including up to eight toxic or hazardous chemicals with no safe levels of exposure. Does the smell of clean clothes still sound so appealing? What about when you get your clothes back from the dry cleaners? What you can smell as you tear off the bag isn't reassuring cleanliness; it's perchloroethylene, a known animal carcinogen. If that doesn't worry you, spare a thought for the people who clean your clothes, whose exposure to these chemicals puts them at up to nine times greater risk of bladder, kidney and other cancers, and almost twice the risk of heart disease. [14]

Even without the stink of household cleaning and personal care products, your home still harbours plenty of potential air pollution. For example, pet hair and dander (animal dandruff) can trigger asthma and a raft of allergies. The same applies to dust mites, which you'll find wriggling through your bedding, carpets, stuffed furniture and even in your teddy bear, grazing on your old skin. A mere gram of dust contains about 1,000 mites and, on that basis, all the dust in your mattress will be a cosy home for a few million of the creatures. Moulds, another source of allergic reactions, thrive in warm and humid places like kitchens and bathrooms and other parts of your home if you do silly things such as drying your wet socks on the radiators. According to my calculations, drying an average load of washing inside your home is like spraying a couple of litre bottles full of water into the air in very slow motion. One recent study found 87 per cent of Scottish homes dried their washing indoors in winter; a quarter of the houses tested were home to a mould that causes lung infections and immune system damage. [15]

If you find the thought of indoor air pollution too much to cope with, don't, whatever you do, sit down to de-stress in the company of a scented candle. According to a quick study by *The Sunday Times* newspaper, burning one of those things will fill your room with dangerous PM2.5 particulates, pushing household levels to something like four times WHO guidelines, with peak levels not far shy of those in the choking streets of Delhi. [16]

TESTING TESTING

Candles

Candles look cosy, but how bad are they for your health? I've read a few lab tests but decided to do my own. I set up my air monitor in my kitchen, lit an ordinary (unscented) church candle and waited. Within minutes, the Flow was registering significant levels of fine PM2.5 particulates at around 50 $\mu g/m^3$, which is nearly as much as the annual, urban level in Hyderabad, India – five times the level in Madrid and about three to four times the level in London.

Dangerous? Not really. I inhaled the smoke for about 30 minutes; people in Hyderabad breathe it all day, every day. On the other hand, a person I once shared a house with used to relax every evening by lighting about ten candles around her bath and lazing in the water for a couple of hours. I'd really think twice about doing that: you're making the air in your home far dirtier than the stuff you'll breathe on the street. That person eventually died of dementia, an illness exacerbated by air pollution. Now I'm not suggesting candle smoke killed her – she lived all her life in a busy city – but, who knows, it might just have been a factor in her decline.

continued

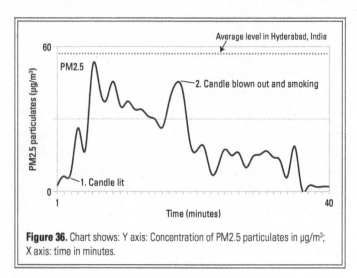

Figure 36. Chart shows: Y axis: Concentration of PM2.5 particulates in μg/m³; X axis: time in minutes.

Built-in pollution

Trying to banish air pollution from our homes is bound to be a losing battle when it's built into their fabric from the start. Just think of all the brilliant building materials people have used over the years that turned out to be not so wonderful in the end. Lead, as we saw in Chapters 3 and 5, is probably the most notorious example, variously blamed for everything from high rates of homicides and teen pregnancies to the decline and fall of the Roman Empire. Or how about asbestos? In ancient times, that rocky mineral fibre was considered such a marvellous insulator and flame-retardant that, over 2,000 years ago, the Buddhist King Ashoka proudly presented his friend the King of Ceylon with a fireproof asbestos towel as a gift. Today, the King of Ceylon would take that as an insult and get straight on the phone to his personal-injury lawyer. (You can't type 'asbestos' into a search engine without being bombarded by advertisements for mercenary law firms who'll help you sue for compensation.) Left alone, asbestos is perfectly fine;

once disturbed, it releases dusty fibres that will scar your lungs if you breathe them, increasing the risk of more serious illnesses such as lung cancer and mesothelioma (a cancer that attacks the linings of body organs). [17]

It's not just our homes and the things we use to clean them, but the furniture and fittings we pack inside them. Hands up if you're addicted to flat-pack furniture? Build-it-yourself, pressed-wood bookshelves, cabinets, laminate floors and similar products (made from particle board, fibreboard and plywood) are held together by resin-type glues that are based on (and give off) for-maldehyde – a pungent chemical used to preserve dead bodies that can hasten the decay and departure of still-living ones. At best, it provokes teary eyes and nausea; at worst, at unusually high levels of exposure, it causes cancer. Fortunately, though levels of for-maldehyde can be high for a week or two after wood products are made, they fall away fairly rapidly after that (great news – unless you work in a furniture store). [18]

Whether you're spending thousands on a new carpet or swap-ping your mouldy old shower curtain for a new one, the pleasure you get from your purchase could bring you real, long-term pain. New carpet smell is something we all instantly recognise, and while it might have connotations of affluence and luxury, it's really nothing more than systematic indoor VOC pollution. Technically, this is called 'off-gassing': the toxic chemicals used to manufacture the carpet slowly diffusing into the room. They include controversial stain repellents like Scotchgard; dubious antimicrobial preservatives; plastic backings such as polyurethane and PVCs made with highly unpleasant isocyanates, organotins and phthalates; and a whole raft of unpleasant adhesives. If you think carpets are made of lovely things like lambswool, think again. Up to 40 per cent of the filling in some carpets and carpet tiles is filthy fly ash from coal-fired power plants, which contains toxic substances like arsenic, lead and mercury. [19]

By contrast, jumping into the shower sounds like the cleanest thing you could possibly imagine – but if you use a shower curtain, it's certainly not. A blast of hot water flushes VOCs from its plastic and vaporises them, while the curtain itself (by definition) seals them in the column of soggy air you're standing inside, so you're obliged to inhale them. A study by the Center for Health, Environment and Justice found that new PVC shower curtains are 'potentially toxic', releasing no fewer than 108 different VOCs over the first month of use alone and levels over sixteen times greater than those in recommended green building codes. One widely available superstore curtain proved such a potent source of VOCs that the chemicals it gave off jammed the scientists' equipment and brought their tests to a premature halt. [20]

While we're talking about household products, it's worth remembering they're not merely polluting while you're using them; they have cradle-to-grave air pollution impacts. In the previous chapter, we looked at the hidden cost that 'Made in China'-type pollution imposes on rapidly developing countries, where cheap disposable household goods are manufactured for the rest of the world. There's an unknown health cost to builders, joiners, carpet layers and other construction workers who fit out our homes with gleaming new products (that are at their most polluting when they've just been made). And there's a cost to those of us who live in homes with off-gassing furniture and fittings; surprisingly, it starts from the very moment we're born. One recent study discovered that the popular practice of painting and renovating nurseries in preparation for a new child is a significant cause of indoor air pollution for infants who are much more susceptible to its effects. Two thirds of the parents questioned had spruced up the nursery before their child's arrival – but maybe they wouldn't have bothered if they'd read the results of the survey first. A similar study by Japanese researchers suggested children are also potentially at risk in newly built and recently renovated school classrooms, where levels of formaldehyde and VOCs can pose a danger for up to two years after building work has been completed. [21]

In and out

Buildings are leaky boxes at the best of times, so the difference between indoor and outdoor pollution can be somewhat arbitrary. You might spend little of your time outdoors, but if your windows are wide open, you're essentially breathing outdoor pollution *inside* your home. On the other hand, if your ventilation passes through an air conditioning system, or a heat- or energy-recovery ventilator (one that warms the cool, incoming air with the stuffy, outgoing air using a heat exchanger) it's likely to trap a significant amount of outdoor pollution in its filters (a good thing), though it can also harbour dust mites and increase your risk of breathing difficulties (a bad thing). Even if your building is well sealed and ventilated, some pollutants will still work their way inside. Fine particulates (PM2.5s) are so small that they can easily worm their way in from the outdoors, whereas bigger, coarser particulates (PM10s) are more likely to be trapped on the way, and reactive pollutants such as ozone and nitrogen dioxide will transform themselves into other things before they get inside. Indoors, you might find two thirds the concentration of fine particulates as outdoors, but significantly lower concentrations of coarser particulates, sulphur dioxide, ozone and nitrogen dioxide – as long as the windows are closed. (If you happen to share your building with a laser printer or a photocopier, expect to find significantly higher amounts of ozone and particulates, however.) [22]

Ventilation – how much and how often your building refreshes its air – makes all the difference. It's hardly surprising that one US study found people who open their windows roughly three quarters of the time have twice the exposure to fine, outdoor particulates as those who keep their windows almost permanently shut; that's bad news if you live in a city, near a busy road and you don't have the luxury of air conditioning. It's not just how much pollution there is in your home but how long it stays there that matters (your exposure, in other words). The rate at which your building's air changes determines whether indoor pollution builds up or dies away, which, in turn, governs the likelihood of it causing health problems. One of the difficulties here is that the need for ventilation means you're unwittingly striking a balance between indoor and outdoor pollution. So if you resist opening your windows in your city apartment or office block to minimise your exposure to outdoor particulates, you could be increasing indoor levels of gases like carbon dioxide. At moderate levels, that will lead to sluggish thinking (at best) and a variety of much more serious health risks such as bone and kidney problems (at worst). [23]

Of course, just as outdoor pollution travels inside, so indoor pollution travels outside – and when we're talking about problems like smoke from primitive indoor stoves, shifting pollution outside the home where it can dissipate in the air sounds like a good plan. On the other hand, if many people are blowing indoor pollution outside at exactly the same time, that's going to cause significant ambient pollution, some of which could return indoors to other buildings. The Great London Smog of 1952 was caused partly by people burning coal inside their homes, but the lesson of that terrible episode is one we've already forgotten. Outdoor air pollution caused by *indoor* wood burners is now a growing problem in many cities around the world (including London) over half a century later. According to a report by the Danish Ecological Council, a new, eco-certified wood burner (made since 2015) will produce almost 30 times more PM2.5 particulates than a diesel truck, while an older (c.1990) stove will produce 170 times more. (Other studies give different figures, but there's broad general agreement that wood burners are significantly more polluting than diesel engines.) One of the buildings I work in has an old-fashioned, gas central-heating boiler that draws air from the room it's in and from the garden outside through a ventilated 'air brick' on the wall. Unfortunately, as the boiler sucks its air inside, it also pulls in diesel-engine quantities of *outdoor* pollution from our neighbours' wood-burning stoves. (That's why I described wood burners as a source of indoor pollution: your wood burner will pollute other people's homes, even if it doesn't pollute your own.) [24]

Some forms of outdoor pollution that steal their way indoors are much less obvious. Radon gas, for example, which causes about 10 per cent of lung cancer deaths, seeps up into buildings from the ground beneath and accumulates in places like basements and lower floors. It's a naturally occurring pollutant, so you can't make it go away altogether, but you can install a pump in your home to stop it rising to dangerous levels or use a building technique called radon-resistant new construction (RRNC) to 'vacuum' the gas out of the soil and pipe it harmlessly around your home. Once you're aware of radon, it's relatively easy to fix it.

Thank you for not smoking

By far the biggest improvement in indoor air quality most of us will have noticed in our lifetimes has come from the huge social shift away from smoking. If you're old enough to remember the 1970s and 1980s, you might recall having the bad luck to sit in restaurants where flirting neighbours were constantly blowing smoke in one another's faces (how romantic!) or, perhaps worse, finding yourself trapped like a lab beagle in the smoking compartment of a train, an unwitting participant in a long-distance experiment in passive choking. Did you ever stop to think what you might be breathing in? Did you know, for example, that one of the many dangerous chemicals in cigarette smoke is a radioactive element called polonium-210 (^{210}Po), famously used in the assassination of Russian dissident Alexander Litvinenko, which gets into tobacco from fertilisers? Maybe you didn't. But cigarette makers knew about it way back in 1959. [25]

Thankfully, the days of forced passive smoking are just about gone – but they took a disgracefully long time to go. The connection between cigarettes and lung cancer was definitively established in 1950 with the work of British epidemiologists Richard Doll and Austin Hill. Doll famously stopped smoking two thirds of the way into his research after finding that cigarettes, and not road-traffic pollution as he'd supposed, was the most likely cause of a 'phenomenal increase in the number of deaths attributed to cancer of the lung' after World War I. Up till that point, cigarettes had even been advertised on the basis of supposed health benefits. In 1949, the year before the Doll study came out, one leading brand ran a survey of 113,597 health professionals so it could claim, outrageously, that: 'More doctors smoke Camels than any other cigarettes.' Despite mountains of evidence pointing to the health risks, brands like that continued to be advertised as 'hip' throughout the 1960s and early 1970s. Thanks to decades of intense brand-building, by 1990, six-year-old children could recognise Joe Camel (the mascot of Camel cigarettes) as easily as Mickey Mouse. [26]

By the end of the 20th century, it was widely accepted that smoking was bad for you; but passive smoking (also known as environmental tobacco smoke or ETS) was another matter entirely. Today, we know that smouldering cigarettes in enclosed spaces can produce ten times the particulate pollution of an idling diesel engine; even so, controversy over passive smoking rumbled on well into the new millennium. Respected scientific and medical bodies such as the World Health Organization, the US Environmental Protection Agency, the French Institut National du Cancer and many others argued a very persuasive public-health case for wholesale indoor smoking bans (by highlighting links between passive smoking and illnesses such as lung cancer). Meanwhile, the wealthy tobacco industry, fearful of further dented profits, sponsored a raft of studies seeking to undermine the idea that non-smokers could be harmed, backed by vociferous libertarians who resented any and all curbs on their freedom (including their freedom to kill themselves and the people around them with their toxic cigarette smoke). [27]

According to the WHO, around 8 million people a year die from tobacco-related illnesses, with 1.2 million deaths due to passive smoking alone. Frightening numbers like these proved an irresistible argument for widespread bans on smoking in indoor places, which swept across much of the world from the 1990s to the 2010s. Most countries now restrict indoor public smoking in one way or another. To the delight of epidemiologists, all those bans kick-started a grand, global and ultimately successful before-and-after experiment on the health effects of passive smoking: all the medics had to do was wait. In country after country, and study after study, doctors found significant improvements in public health that were directly attributable to people no longer having to breathe tobacco smoke in public places. A 2016 'Cochrane' review (a meticulous analysis of all the different medical evidence on a particular issue) of 77 different studies from 21 countries found a significant reduction in cardiovascular disease and other tobacco-related illnesses, with the biggest effect among non-smokers, and concluded that smoking bans were easy to justify. [28]

Figure 37. Smoking in public places was recognised as a nuisance for well over a century before it was banned or restricted in many countries from the 1990s onward. Artwork from the 1880s, courtesy of US National Library of Medicine. [29]

Are you sitting comfortably?

Most of the time, we live, work and breathe our lives away in almost perfectly sealed boxes, shared with chemicals that are, in high enough concentrations, no good for us at all. And perhaps, for most of us, that really doesn't matter. But it will matter very much for some.

If you can smell it and it's a chemical, it's probably doing you no good when you breathe it in – and that's a decent enough rule of thumb to live by: our noses can smell things for a reason. The cleaner I use to blast the mould from my fridge ('Anti-bacterial multi-surface spray: kills bacteria all around the home') carries a whole series of warnings on the back, including: 'Do not breathe mist. Use only outdoors or in a well-ventilated area. If inhaled, remove person to fresh air and keep comfortable for breathing.' The air freshener I just found in the bathroom warns: 'Use only in a well-ventilated room.' My limescale remover tells me: 'Do not inhale spray. Use only in well-ventilated areas.' My clothes-washing detergent carries similar warnings.

All this might leave you speechless, as well as breathless. We pity people in poorer countries who suffer the self-inflicted effects of household air pollution, but at least they have a sensible excuse for killing themselves softly with dirty indoor air: they have to cook and keep warm somehow. What excuse do the rest of us have for poisoning ourselves with chemicals we don't need and can easily avoid? What would people in poorer countries make of the way we squander our relatively clean air on such frivolities?

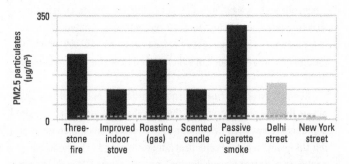

Figure 38. What you might be breathing indoors. Left (black bars): Three-stone fires, improved developing-country cookstoves and even gas cookers in Western countries all make levels of PM2.5 particulates comparable to the average outdoor levels in some of the world's most polluted cities. Scented candles and passive cigarette smoke are also much worse than you might think. Right (grey bars): Average outdoor PM2.5 levels in Delhi and New York City for comparison. The dotted line shows the World Health Organization's recommended guideline limit. (All measurements in µg/m³). [30]

DUST TO DUST

The pollution 'locked' inside buildings can reappear in dramatic ways when, suddenly and unexpectedly, they reach the ends of their lives.

New York City's World Trade Center was 25 years in the planning and took four years to build. But it collapsed within two hours of the most audacious terrorist attack the world had ever seen. No one alive in 2001 will ever forget the horrific sight of the twin towers blazing and smoking like tall chimneys, before finally thundering down in terrible, rolling clouds of ash. Especially the half a million people who were nearby, unlucky enough to be breathing in that dust at the time.

Almost 3,000 people lost their lives in the four attacks that day and 6,000 more were injured, but that was just the start. An unknown number have died since then from the effects of breathing in the toxic cloud that roared across lower Manhattan when the twin towers tumbled down. According to *Dust to Dust*, a documentary about the aftermath of the disaster directed by Heidi Dehncke-Fisher, the cloud that heralded the transformation of the towers and their contents into 1.8 million tonnes of debris spread a toxic cocktail of 2,500 contaminants across New York City, including 400 tonnes of asbestos, 90,000 tonnes of jet fuel (producing 2 million tonnes of potentially toxic hydrocarbons), 90 tonnes of lead and cadmium and 420,000 tonnes of pulverised concrete (much of which turned to deadly fine particulate dust).

Keen to avoid any further panic at a time of near hysteria, city mayor Rudy Giuliani insisted at the time that 'the air quality is safe and acceptable'. Meanwhile, Christine Todd Whitman, then head of the US Environmental Protection Agency, claimed: 'The good news continues to be that air samples we have taken have all been at levels that cause us no concern', later reassuring New Yorkers that the air was 'safe to breathe and their water is safe to drink'.

Gradually, however, a different story emerged. Five years after the attack, around 70 per cent of some 10,000 or so emergency workers

continued

Figure 39. An emergency responder, wearing only a simple face mask for protection, searches a squad car buried under toxic dust and rubble near the World Trade Center in Manhattan on September 11, 2001. Thousands of 9/11 first responders have since developed cancer. Photo courtesy US Library of Congress.

and other responders examined in one medical study had developed respiratory illnesses. Ten years further on, some 37,000 of the estimated 75,000 workers involved in the aftermath of the attack had been declared sick, while over 1,100 had died from their exposure. By 2016, *Newsweek* was reporting that some 5,441 of these workers had developed at least one cancer. No one knows exactly how many of the 400,000 or so people estimated to have been exposed to the 9/11 dust – everyone from courageous first-responders to terrified, fleeing passers-by – has been affected or will be affected in the decades it can take for illnesses like cancers to make themselves known.

Though New York residents eventually sued Christine Todd Whitman for misleading the public, she was found 'not liable' by a federal court of appeals in 2008. Even so, New York congressman Jerry Nadler insisted she was to blame in a statement he released

continued

soon after: 'By falsely assuring the public that the air was safe to breathe – when all the evidence indicated that it was in fact extremely hazardous – she caused thousands of residents, workers, and first responders to suffer injury and, in some cases, death due to unnecessary exposure to toxic chemicals released by the collapse of the World Trade Center buildings.' Almost ten years on, and some fifteen years after the attacks, Whitman finally offered an apology of sorts in an interview with *The Guardian* newspaper. 'I'm very sorry that people are sick,' she said. 'I'm very sorry that people are dying and if the EPA and I in any way contributed to that, I'm sorry. We did the very best we could at the time with the knowledge we had.'

Even so, the lesson of toxic air pollution from dramatic building fires doesn't seem to have been learned. When a terrifying blaze broke out in Grenfell Tower, a high-rise residential skyscraper in west London in June 2017, 70 people died and a similar number were injured. But concerns about huge concentrations of toxic residue from the fire – both air and land pollution – were downplayed by the authorities or ignored. The same thing happened when flames ripped through the roof of Notre Dame cathedral in April 2019, releasing an estimated 300–460 tonnes of highly toxic lead into the air above Paris. Police insisted there was no danger to local residents, despite reports of lead in the ground nearby reaching up to 1,300 times the French safety guidelines. As with 9/11, it could take many years before we know whether the authorities' assurances were sound – or if many people's lives were put in jeopardy. [31]

CHAPTER 8

Killing us softly

How air pollution harms our health

A t least smokers can choose; the rest of us don't get to pick
our pollution – indeed, we might not even know it's there. If
you're a pregnant woman, you probably wouldn't dream of smoking, but if you happen to be having your baby in Salt Lake City,
air pollution will be increasing your risk of miscarriage by just as
much. If you're a twelve-year-old growing up in London, dirty air
(largely from traffic) is making it significantly more likely that
you'll suffer from depression by the time you hit eighteen. Maybe
you're whiling away your retirement in Ontario? If you're breathing the typical urban mix of particulates, nitrogen dioxide and
carbon monoxide, numerous studies have shown you're already at
greater risk of mental decline and dementia. Even a trip to the hospital puts you in more danger, simply because most are in towns
and cities where pollution is higher than the norm. The closer
you study the evidence, the more you're likely to conclude that
breathing is a loaded game of Russian roulette with something evil
lurking in every single barrel. [1]

Air pollution and health make for some horrible headlines;
here's a small selection from around the world. Every year, in
China, dirty air ends 1.1 million lives too soon; in India, pollution lowers average life expectancy by a whopping 1.7 years; the
European toll is 400,000 early deaths and the economic bill that

goes with them is €1.6 trillion ($1.43 trillion) a year. In Africa, household pollution causes 581,000 early deaths a year (including 7.4 per cent of all deaths in South Africa alone). By comparison, in Australia, the figure is a third as much – 2.3 per cent of early deaths – but that's still twice the toll from road accidents. Most of the world's children will see twenty months chopped off their lives, on average, by breathing filthy air – almost three years in sub-Saharan Africa but still several months in richer countries. Deaths, obviously the worst part of air pollution, account for the bulk of the economic impacts you see in news reports ('Air Pollution Costs Global Economy Trillions...') – but they're only the tip of the iceberg when it comes to our suffering. [2]

If this all sounds gloomy, it needn't be. The other side of this dark and dirty air pollution coin is a lot of very optimistic research

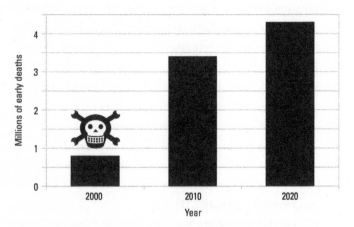

Figure 40. The World Health Organization (WHO) has repeatedly increased its estimate of how many people die early from outdoor air pollution. The current figure (4.2 million early deaths a year) is over five times higher than it was two decades ago. This doesn't mean the world is five times more polluted or that the death toll has risen five-fold; it means we're getting better at understanding the true, deadly impacts of dirty air. [3]

showing how many lives and how much suffering will be averted, some almost immediately, when we finally get round to cleaning up our act.

What harm do air pollutants do to us?

The toxic cocktail of pollution we sip varies from place to place and from indoors to out, but the base ingredients in the mix – particulates, nitrogen oxides, ozone, sulphur dioxide, carbon monoxide and VOCs – remain more or less the same. We've explored these things from various angles already; now let's look in more detail at what they do to our health.

Particulates

Microscopic particles of dirt, dust, soot, sand and more are thought to cause over 90 per cent of air pollution deaths in the 21st century. That's why many statistics about the impact of dirty air focus purely on the impact of PM (taking it as a proxy for pollution as a whole); it's also why those same statistics are a conservative estimate of air pollution's overall death toll. In developing countries, most PM comes from indoor burning of biomass for cooking, heating and lighting; in developed countries, it's more likely to come from traffic, industry, farming or wood burners. [4]

A fraction the diameter of a human hair, particulates are light enough to zip through the air; the smallest ones stay airborne longer, travel further and burrow deeper into our lungs, where they cross into our bloodstreams, just like oxygen, and lodge in our hearts and brains. Minuscule though they are, they're still vastly bigger than atoms, the building blocks of our world (a PM2.5 particle is about 25,000 times bigger than the smallest, hydrogen atom or 250 times bigger than a typical protein). The best way to think of them is probably as sinister, microscopic delivery trucks, ferrying things like toxic heavy metals, specks of contaminated soot and all kinds of other things you'd prefer not to think about to any and every part of your body.

What harm do they do? A couple of decades ago, two landmark pieces of medical research (the Harvard 'Six Cities' and American Cancer Society studies) helped to establish that increasing amounts of outdoor PM pollution lead to more early deaths, particularly from cardiovascular problems (which cause the majority of PM deaths) and lung cancer. But PM pollution has also been linked to many other health problems in every stage of life, including miscarriages and low birth weight, childhood asthma and pneumonia and later-life diabetes and dementia (much more about all these things in a moment). Frighteningly, fine PM2.5 particulates have been found to harm people's health at levels far below the guideline (even the most ambitious WHO guideline, that's exceeded in almost every major world city). It's now widely accepted by researchers that there is no lower threshold for PM2.5s below which people are completely safe. It's also been discovered that health effects can occur after relatively short exposures to PM: you don't have to be breathing diesel exhaust for 20 years to suffer very real harm. [5]

Nitrogen oxides

Understandably, given their huge impact on global health, and particularly since the Six Cities and American Cancer Society studies, there's been a major focus on particulates in medical research, to the extent that some of the other poisons in everyday pollution have become a little neglected by comparison. A recent experiment by Denise Wooding from the University of British Columbia and her colleagues suggested that focus might be leading us astray. They tested how people with allergies responded either to ordinary diesel exhaust (particulates and other pollutants) or carefully filtered exhaust (with all the pollutants significantly reduced except for nitrogen dioxide, which was deliberately increased). Surprisingly, the subjects in this experiment were significantly more affected in the second case, leading Wooding to conclude that 'particulates are not necessarily the sole or main culprit responsible for all harmful effects'. [6]

As we've already seen, nitrogen oxides aren't just produced by diesel engines; generally speaking, they're made whenever we burn fuels in air (a mixture of nitrogen and oxygen), which covers everything from car engines and power plants to camping cookstoves and even the Sunday roast. Like particulates, nitrogen dioxide is strongly implicated in many different health conditions throughout life. One recent study suggests it could be responsible for some 4 million new cases of childhood asthma a year, 64 per cent of them in towns and cities. Disturbingly, 92 per cent of these happen in places where the levels of NO_2 are within WHO guidelines. [7]

Ozone

Less well known than most other major pollutants, ozone creeps in at number 33 on the hit parade of global risk factors for death, well below general outdoor air pollution (number six) and indoor pollution (number eight). Even so, it's still a major killer, contributing to almost a quarter of a million deaths a year from lung disease alone, according to the Health Effects Institute's annual *State of Global Air* reports. Ozone doesn't just cause chronic breathing problems: it's implicated in a variety of short- and long-term health conditions, including generally reduced lung function, childhood asthma and atherosclerosis (clogging of the arteries, which leads, in turn, to heart attacks and strokes). One major study of deaths recorded in 95 urban areas in the United States between 1987 and 2000 found a connection between relatively short-term ozone exposure and early deaths. Significantly, unlike other major pollutants, ozone levels are on the rise in many parts of the world, in both developed and developing countries. That's partly due to greater nitrogen dioxide emissions from increasing traffic (ozone is largely formed from NO_2 and hydrocarbon VOCs) but also due to climate change (warmer temperatures favour ozone production). [8]

Sulphur dioxide

Up until the middle of the 20th century, SO_2 produced by burning coal was generally regarded as the most lethal everyday air pollutant. Unhappily, the Great London Smog of 1952 provided the first scientific evidence of a connection between smoky sulphur dioxide pollution (which reached about five times normal levels and ten times those levels in the worst areas) and the death rate (which was also being closely monitored). Analysis carried out in 1953 and 1954 by Dr Ernest Wilkins of the British government's Department of Scientific and Industrial Research makes the potent power of sulphur dioxide very obvious. Wilkins plotted graphs of the smoke and sulphur dioxide concentrations in London during December 1952 when the episode took place, and added a third graph of the number of deaths each day. This produced three sharp peaks, all lined up, and all centred on 7 December 1952 when the disaster was at its worst. [9]

How did all these unlucky Londoners die? One theory is that brief exposure to high levels of sulphur dioxide has effects similar to chronic bronchitis (tightening of the airways and coughing or wheezing, as experienced by emphysema and asthma sufferers). There's another theory, too. In the second half of the 20th century, when clean air laws were slowly bringing air pollution under control in countries such as the UK, sulphur dioxide returned to public prominence as one of the major causes of acid rain. And that gives another clue to its potential health impacts. During the London Smog, high humidity and high levels of sulphur dioxide would have produced significant concentrations of sulphuric 'acid fog'. Inhaling this, as well as the black smoke and sulphur dioxide, could have been responsible for some of the thousands of deaths in London in 1952. [10]

Carbon monoxide

Thanks to effective public information campaigns, many of us have electronic carbon monoxide detectors screwed to the wall to warn about faulty cookers, gas boilers, wood burners and other sources of 'incomplete combustion' (burning fuel in too little oxygen). Carbon monoxide is one of the simpler and better-understood pollutants. With the chemical formula CO, it bears a strong resemblance to carbon dioxide, CO_2, but it's much more harmful. Oxygen is carried around our bodies by binding to an iron-rich protein in red blood cells called haemoglobin. Carbon monoxide interferes with this process: it snatches up haemoglobin about 200 times more readily than oxygen, making it harder for your blood to carry oxygen to your brain and other organs. While we're all pretty clued up about the risks of indoor CO pollution, most of us won't be aware that it's also lurking outdoors, thanks largely to petrol and diesel engines. In different countries, road transport blows anything from 40 per cent (France) to 86 per cent (Delhi, India) of all carbon monoxide into the air.

You can easily brush that thought aside, but spare a thought for any city-dwelling, pregnant friends you might have: the developing foetus is particularly susceptible to high levels of carbon monoxide. [11]

VOCs

Volatile Organic Compounds (VOCs – readily evaporating carbon-based chemicals) are often glossed over in discussions about air pollution, and because 'volatile' and 'organic' covers such a broad range of different substances, it's no surprise there's confusion over the harm they cause.

At one extreme, breathing even large amounts of relatively innocuous VOCs such as limonene (a natural fragrance found in citrus fruits, used in many household cleaners and detergents) produces little or no irritation of the airways. The US EPA regards limonene as safe and essentially non-toxic (although it's been registered as an insecticide in the United States since 1958 and as a dog and cat repellent since 1983). At the opposite extreme, dangerous VOCs include chemicals like benzene and naphthalene. Benzene was once merrily swilled around in school science labs; it's now known to cause blood cancers such as leukaemia. Naphthalene is a possible carcinogen that can cause everything from eye irritation and headaches to eye damage and kidney shutdown. In developed countries, as benzene is a petrol additive, about 80 per cent of the benzene in the atmosphere gets there from car exhausts, petrol station fumes, breaker's yards and so on. But, given that most people spend most of their time *indoors*, until the recent global clampdown on smoking in public places, most of us would have received the overwhelming majority of our benzene dose from second-hand tobacco smoke. [12]

How are everyday health problems related to air pollution?

Most people understand that air pollution can cause breathing problems – that's pretty obvious – but it's also just the beginning: when toxic particles ferry into our bloodstreams, and chug their way round our bodies, they can do all kinds of internal harm. Who would have thought that dirty air had anything to do with diabetes, for example, or dementia? According to the World Health Organization, air pollution is a 'critical risk factor' in many non-communicable, everyday diseases (ones you don't catch from other people). Indeed, the catalogue of health issues linked to air pollution runs on for many pages. [13]

It's easy to make a list of the ingredients in air pollution, and a list of the health problems pollution causes, but it's much harder to map from one to the other. Each pollutant can cause multiple problems and it's often very difficult to pin down the exact cause of a particular health issue among all the toxic things we're breathing in. We just don't live in a neat and simple chemical lab; the science is so much harder to disentangle in the messy real

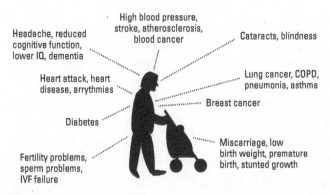

Figure 41. Under attack: air pollution has been linked to many different health conditions.

world. If it were that easy to link causes and effects, tackling pollution would be a whole lot simpler. Smoky indoor cooking, for example, releases particulates, carbon monoxide, polycyclic aromatic hydrocarbons (PAHs), sulphur dioxide, nitrogen dioxide and more, and can result in (or complicate) everything from breathing problems, birth difficulties, heart disease and strokes to asthma, sleep disorders, depression and headaches. The same is true of traffic pollution, a noxious cocktail that can cause many different health problems. Tobacco smoke, meanwhile, contains a reputed 7,000 different ingredients – maybe more, if you have equipment sensitive enough to detect them. We still don't know exactly what they all do, alone, in combination and mixed up with other indoor and outdoor pollutants; the real challenge is to home in on the needles in the chemical haystack that pose greatest risk. [14]

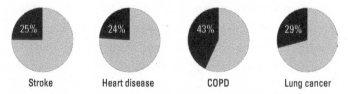

Figure 42. Air pollution causes a significant proportion of deaths we attribute to other things: roughly a quarter of deaths from strokes and heart disease, almost half of deaths from breathing-related diseases (COPD), and just under a third of all lung cancer deaths. Drawn using figures from the World Health Organization.

By the same token, most serious health complaints – from heart disease to breast cancer and from diabetes to dementia – are highly complex and poorly understood: we still don't know the exact mechanisms behind them. That's why medical scientists carefully refer to 'risk factors' rather than causes. Air pollution is increasingly seen as an important risk factor for many different illnesses, but that doesn't necessarily mean it's the main cause or that it works alone: it might exacerbate some mechanism involving one or more other risk factors. We know, for example, that it doesn't *cause* hay fever – but it certainly makes it worse.

Breathing problems

Although air pollution can sneak into your body through your skin, most breezes in through the open front door – your nose or mouth. According to the American Lung Association, we suck in about 9,000 litres (2,000 gallons) of air a day (enough to fill a car fuel tank about 150 times over) and there are 2,400 kilometres (1,500 miles) of airways in our bodies (about the distance from Moscow to Brussels or Los Angeles to Houston). There are something like 100 trillion trillion molecules a day buffeting in and out of our bodies, some of which are downright toxic – and, given how far they travel, there are plenty of opportunities for them to make mischief en route. [15]

The harm they do varies from simple irritation of your airways, to asthma and respiratory infections and even to COPD, pneumonia and respiratory cancers (including nasopharyngeal and lung cancers). In poorer countries, inhaling wood smoke from cooking and heating is likely to lead to the infections, while burning dirty fuels like coal and charcoal is more strongly linked with the cancers. Most of us automatically connect lung cancer with cigarettes – and with good reason: tobacco causes 90 per cent of lung cancers and 22 per cent of all cancer deaths. But smoking is on the wane in most countries, while household air pollution is seen as a growing menace: some 17 per cent of all lung cancer deaths happen through breathing dirty indoor stove smoke in developing countries. And, dangerous though it is, we do need to keep the risks of tobacco in proportion. In the UK, where I live, it's illegal to smoke outdoors in a completely open bus shelter for even a few minutes; if you dare to try, you'll be reprimanded with a

harsh stare from anyone nearby. Yet you can drive a diesel bus up
to the same shelter and leave it there as long as you like, chugging
out clouds of pollution, and no one will even blink. Outdoor air
pollution kills far more people than passive smoking – especially
outdoor passive smoking – but there are no warnings about it and
few laws that tackle it immediately, at source. [16]

Worldwide, pneumonia is one of the biggest causes of death
from household air pollution (accounting for about 27 per cent of all
indoor pollution deaths or just over a million people a year). That's
because it's the single biggest (infectious) cause of death in children
under five (with 90 per cent of those deaths occurring in low- and
middle-income countries). Although it's caused by bacteria, viruses
and fungi, it's greatly exacerbated by dirty indoor air. According
to the World Health Organization, household pollution practically doubles the risk of developing pneumonia and leads to about
45 per cent of all pneumonia deaths among the under-fives. [17]

Growing up in a richer country, you'll get off more lightly,
but you won't escape entirely. A huge, long-term study of children in polluted areas of southern California found the growth
of their lungs stunted by between 3.4 and 5 per cent – the kind
of alarming medical impact that would generally go unnoticed.
(How, ordinarily, would you discover that pollution is shrinking
your child's lungs?) Harder to miss is childhood asthma. Although
the causes of asthma are very complex and varied, exposure to
traffic pollution in early life is now known to play a key part.
Asthma can prove fatal, and though it's very hard to link traffic
exposure to any specific death, people are increasingly trying to
make that connection. In London in 2013, when nine-year-old Ella
Kissi-Debrah died after an acute asthma attack, her family began
a brave and very determined legal campaign to find out if high
levels of air pollution near their home were responsible. (Ella lived

just 25 metres/80 feet from London's busy South Circular road and
had suffered with seizures for three years, prompting 27 hospital
visits.) In a media statement, her mother Rosamund said: 'If it
is proved that pollution killed Ella then the government will be
forced to sit up and take notice that this hidden but deadly killer
is cutting short our children's lives.' [18]

The heart of the matter

Perhaps surprisingly, breathing-related health issues don't cause
the majority of outdoor air pollution deaths. According to the
World Health Organization, most (some 80 per cent) are actually caused by ischaemic (blood-flow-related) heart disease and
strokes. Given that a million people a year also die early from
ischaemic heart disease caused by *indoor* air pollution, it's easy
to see that the heart is incredibly significant when it comes to
understanding why dirty air is such a prolific global killer.

Worryingly, high exposures to pollution aren't necessarily
needed to cause heart problems. One recent study of women in
Cape Town, South Africa found that exposure to even low levels of
nitrogen dioxide and VOCs such as benzene increased other risk
factors for cardiovascular problems. Air pollution can also trigger sudden problems like arrhythmias (irregular heartbeats) and
heart attacks. In one ingenious study, scientists monitored people
with defibrillators implanted in their chests as they breathed in
different kinds of pollution, including nitrogen and sulphur diox-
ides, ozone and PM2.5 particulates. They discovered that steady
increases in PM2.5s – equivalent to worsening city air quality –
produced corresponding and relatively sudden increases in atrial
fibrillation. Worryingly, the levels of PM2.5 particulates tested in
this (American) study were significantly lower than levels recommended by the US Environmental Protection Agency. [19]

The exact mechanisms by which dirty air damages healthy hearts aren't fully understood, but studies have found links between household air pollution and a variety of cardiovascular risk factors, including inflammation, high blood pressure and arterial stiffness. One recent study of 63 young people who died in traffic accidents in polluted Mexico City discovered a possible mechanism linked to iron-rich magnetite nanoparticles (smaller than 200 nanometres in diameter, which is the size of typical bacteria or the transistors in a computer chip). Researchers found the particles lurking deep inside the mitochondria of heart muscle tissue – twice as many as they found in control subjects living in less-polluted places – and suggested they were linked to 'early and significant' heart damage. Is air pollution planting tiny time bombs in our hearts? [20]

Like heart disease, strokes are among the world's biggest killers: over 6.2 million people die from them each year. According to the World Health Organization, 12 per cent of those deaths are caused by household air pollution, mainly from cooking with solid fuels and kerosene. Some recent studies have found relatively modest increases in traffic pollution (nitrogen dioxide and particulates) can significantly increase your chances of dying after a stroke. A recent study of over 3,000 stroke victims in London found that a modest increase in particulates produced a 52 per cent increase in the risk of death, while the same increase in nitrogen dioxide produced a 28 per cent increase. In other words, if you have a stroke in the city, it's probably a good idea to recuperate in the cleaner air of the country. [21]

The cancer connection

One of the most startling and persuasive studies of the harm air pollution can do was published by the leading American epidemiologist Arden Pope and colleagues in 2002. Popularly known as the American Cancer Society study, it compared questionnaire data from roughly half a million adults with air pollution records for the places where those people lived. Pope found that each 10 μg/m³ increase in PM2.5 particulates (which is a bit like moving from less-polluted Los Angeles to more-polluted Moscow) increased risk of death from lung cancer by 8 per cent. [22]

Now it's no surprise that there's a connection between lung cancer and air pollution, given that the link between lung cancer and tobacco smoke has been known for decades. Yet other, more surprising cancers are also now being linked to the air we breathe. Many things put women at greater risk of breast cancer, including age (and DNA damage), family history, alcohol, smoking, lack of exercise and obesity – but these things still don't explain the majority of new cases or the fact that a high number of victims live in urban areas. Another explanation comes from growing evidence of a connection with air pollution. A major study of almost 75,000 women in nine European countries found 'suggestive evidence' of a link between breast cancer and PM2.5, PM10 and nitrogen dioxide, though the evidence wasn't strong enough ('statistically significant') for that link to be persuasive. At least a dozen other recent studies have found connections between passive smoking and colorectal cancers, which suggests there might be links between other forms of air pollution (containing similar chemicals to tobacco smoke) and those cancers too. [23]

Brain drain

Is air pollution making us stupid? Could it be blunting our brains to the risks we face from toxic chemicals in dirty air? That was one of the slightly tongue-in-cheek questions I posed in the introduction to this book. Lots of medical researchers are now looking into how pollution affects the brain. They do indeed seem to be establishing a connection between air pollution and the slowly imposed stupidity of what they'd politely term 'reduced cognitive function' or, in plain language, poor memory, impaired IQ and lower test scores.

One large recent study of 25,000 Chinese people of varying ages, in 162 widely spaced counties, found a link between air pollution and worse performance on verbal tests. The longer the exposure to air pollution (nitrogen dioxide, sulphur dioxide and particulates), the bigger the effect, with more damage to verbal than maths skills, men at more risk than women and older, less-educated men (aged over 64) most affected. The study's authors discovered that high amounts of air pollution were tantamount to cutting people's schooling by a year, but in the oldest, least-educated men, the brain harm from pollution was equivalent to losing several years of education. Although the authors believe pollution may contribute to mental decline, itself a risk factor for Alzheimer's and other forms of dementia, the explanation isn't yet known. As we saw above, the recent discovery of toxic nanoparticles of magnetite lodged in people's hearts may signal a mechanism linking pollution to a wide range of cardiovascular problems. The same particles have also been found in people's brains, so that might offer a clue as to how dirty air is making us stupid. Nanoparticles of air pollution have also been linked to higher incidence of brain cancer. [24]

Some intriguing new research has moved beyond basic tests of cognition (how our brain processes information like a computer) to exploring whether the impacts of air pollution could be harming our mental health. Several recent studies have found links between exposure to air pollution and the most serious psychotic mental illnesses, including depression and schizophrenia. It's unclear, however, whether the connection is biological (something toxic in pollution produces, perhaps, inflammation

of the brain or interferes with neurotransmitters), psychological
(polluted urban environments leading to more stress and anxiety,
which then leads to mental health problems), or both. [25]

And what happens in the brain – in the shape of poor mental
health – doesn't always stay there; mental health problems can
cause major social problems, too. As we saw back in Chapter 5,
economist-researcher Rick Nevin has spent years teasing out his
theory of a connection between environmental lead pollution
(from things like vehicle fuel and paint additives) and a wide
range of social problems. More extensive academic studies have
explored other general explanations of how air pollution could
cause social problems by impairing people's mental health. One
recent study of almost 9,500 US cities found patterns of air pollution could reliably predict six different types of major crime,
suggesting that pollution causes greater anxiety, which in turn
leads to unethical and criminal behaviour. In the authors' words:
'Air pollution not only corrupts people's health, but also can con-
taminate their morality.' [26]

HOW DOES AIR POLLUTION MAKE US SICK?

*What's the fundamental biological mechanism connecting dirty gases
and particulates to such a huge range of everyday illnesses?*

How, for example, do particulates contribute to heart or lung
diseases? As we've already seen, PM10s are filtered out in the
upper airways, but PM2.5s and smaller particulates get past these
defences, break into the blood and travel deep into the brain and
other organs. From there, things are more uncertain. We know, for
example, that particulates can damage the blood-brain barrier, opening up the nervous system to other kinds of attack, and raising the risk

continued

of illnesses such as Alzheimer's and Parkinson's. We also know that nanoparticles of magnetite, from pollution, have been found deep in people's brains and hearts. But quite how a slow and steady invasion of toxic particles could ultimately trigger heart disease, lung cancer, depression, dementia, or countless other things remains something of a mystery.

It's perhaps easier to understand the process through which pollution worsens breathing problems like pneumonia, an infectious disease mostly caused by bacteria, viruses and fungi. What pollution seems to do in this case is weaken the immune response in our airways, making it easier for invaders to attack, increasing the risk of pneumonia and other respiratory infections.

How, though, are individual body cells actually damaged by pollution? One likely mechanism is oxidative stress, the process by which invasive chemicals effectively overwhelm a cell's defences to cause toxic effects that include DNA damage, genetic mutations and then illnesses such as cancer. Recent research suggests metal-rich particulates, such as those thrown up by traffic, can indeed work in this way.

A number of other mechanisms are also being explored. Some research teams have been investigating whether particulates and pollution gases cause damage to telomeres ('caps' on cell chromosomes). The length of telomeres is believed to play a key part in ageing – shorter telomeres seem to be linked to chronic disease and early death – and numerous studies have found that people subjected to air pollution have shorter telomeres than expected. If pollution accelerates biological ageing, that might explain why some of its victims die early. [27]

Who suffers most?

So far, we've examined the triangle of how air pollution harms health from two sides: we've looked at the ingredients in pollution and the harm they do, and we've looked at common health conditions and related them back to different pollutants like nitrogen dioxide and particulates. We now need to look at the people that pollution tends to harm and see if that tells us anything more. The short story here is that pollution affects everyone – but, cruelly, those most affected are least able to do anything about it. According to Dr Tedros Adhanom Ghebreyesus, Director-General of the WHO: 'The poorest and most marginalised people bear the brunt of the burden.' [28]

The most vulnerable and powerless of all are the innocent unborn. Pollution begins its deadly work on the foetus nine whole months before birth – and maybe even sooner, since there's evidence that ozone messes up the quantity and quality of men's sperm. Despite what you might think, a baby is far from safe in the cocoon of the womb: its mother sucks in pollution, which passes from her lungs into her bloodstream and placenta, and from there to the baby's body and brain. Dirty air raises the risk of miscarriages as much as smoking and increases still- and premature births. It also heightens the risk of low birth weight (LBW), which is a major risk factor for all kinds of lifelong conditions including heart disease, diabetes and other serious illnesses. A huge recent study of over half a million British babies concluded that air pollution from road traffic is stunting their growth, with about 3 per cent of LBW cases linked to significant PM2.5 particulate pollution. Other studies have confirmed this, noting how steadily increasing concentrations of pollutants such as NO_2 lead to low birth weight, reduced baby length and reduced baby-head circumference. [29]

Some children will show no ill effects of their polluted journey through pregnancy; others will be damaged into childhood and – outrageously – for the rest of their lives. Parents will be alarmed to read the results of two studies of children in Poland and New York City who had been exposed to toxic polycyclic aromatic hydrocarbon (PAH) pollution in the womb (from everyday sources, including traffic fumes, power plants and various forms of indoor pollution, including passive smoking), and were found to have a four-point drop in IQ by age five. The really alarming thing is just how many children are affected. According to UNICEF, the global children's charity, some 17 million babies under the age of one breathe toxic air that is six times more polluted than WHO guidelines, with the vast majority of them (12 million or 70 per cent) in South Asia. But children in rich countries are affected too, often in truly scandalous ways. Way back in 2001, the US environmental group NRDC discovered that millions of American children travelling on school buses were breathing four times as much toxic diesel exhaust as they would riding in a car in front, and eight times more than they'd breathe in the open air. It took over a decade (until 2013) for the EPA to launch the Clean School Bus programme that funds replacements. Even so, an estimated 250,000 dirty old school buses are still on the road today in America. [30]

The WHO itself tells us that 90 per cent of the world's children are breathing toxic air, 93 per cent are exposed to those especially harmful PM2.5 particulates and 98 per cent of under-fives – effectively, all of them – are exposed to PM2.5s, too. That really matters because children are much more vulnerable to air pollution than adults. When they're young, they spend a lot of time with their mothers (who, in developing countries, will be spending a lot of *their* time choking over indoor stoves); when they're a bit older, they spend more time outdoors (where ambient outdoor pollution becomes a bigger risk). Their tiny lungs will still be growing until they're teenagers, so they breathe at higher rates and take in more polluted air for each unit of bodyweight than adults: very loosely speaking, we can think of the pollution they take in as being more concentrated in their smaller bodies. Also, their immune systems aren't fully formed or properly able to defend them against pollution (or against germ invaders, which are given an easier ride into their bodies with the help of pollution). When adults take time off sick with breathing problems like asthma, they might lose out financially or their companies might pick up the bill; when children take time off school, however, their education suffers – and that could have a serious knock-on effect for their entire lives. [31]

Of course, pollution doesn't stop when childhood ends; the older you get, the more susceptible you become: among the people most at risk from PM2.5 particulates are the elderly and the middle-aged. We've already seen that pollution is linked to classic later-life health problems like heart disease, heart attacks, diabetes, COPD, lung cancer and strokes. Dirty air is seen as an increasingly important health risk for older people, not just because some forms of pollution are on the rise and not just because we understand it better, but because the world's population is ageing, older people have less effective immune systems and the risk of most communicable diseases (like malaria) is starting to fall – even despite the COVID-19 coronavirus outbreak. In terms of global public health, epidemiologists have noted a fascinating shift from decades ago, when communicable diseases in young children (such as malaria and smallpox) dominated the death statistics. Today, noncommunicable diseases in the elderly (such as heart disease and strokes closely correlated with air pollution) are the world's growing menace. We still know very little about how air pollution affects older people. The evidence that it contributes to things like Alzheimer's and other forms of dementia grows stronger by the day. One recent study of 131,000 British patients aged 50–79 tracked what happened to them over a period of seven years: those in the top fifth of polluted areas were 40 per cent more likely to develop dementia than those in the bottom fifth. Another recent review of thirteen studies from Canada, Taiwan, the UK, the USA and Sweden concluded that greater exposure to air pollution (PM2.5 particulates, nitrogen oxides and carbon dioxide) produced a bigger risk of dementia, though exactly why is unclear. [32]

Much of the world, unfortunately, still discriminates on the basis of sex, so it should come as no surprise that air pollution discriminates this way too, even though neither sex is biologically more susceptible than the other. In developing countries, the burden of cooking with biomass and childcare still falls mostly on women, and that's where the burden of air pollution falls too. This is why a number of studies have found women in poorer countries are at significantly greater risk of breathing-related diseases and lung cancer compared to men the same age, which can have a knock-on effect on their children's health and well-being, too. Surprisingly, some types of indoor air pollution discriminate against Western women for exactly the same reason. As we saw in the last chapter, gas stoves (which burn natural gas in oxygen) produce significant NO_2 pollution in the room where you're cooking, which is why, in countries where women still prepare the food, they're also more likely to show linked symptoms of respiratory illnesses. [33]

GOING VIRAL

When the COVID-19 coronavirus locked down the global economy in 2020, air pollution experts looked at their spreadsheets and breathed a sigh of relief. Eager for good news, newspapers around the world reported 'huge' drops in air pollution. There were novel blue skies in Delhi, birdsong was clearly heard in London, and in Kathmandu, Mount Everest was visible for the first time in decades. Among the apocalyptic gloom of a global pandemic, all this seemed rather wonderful. One pollution expert, Professor Paul Monks of Leicester

continued

University, told *The Guardian* newspaper: 'Are we looking at what we might see in the future if we can move to a low-carbon economy? Not to denigrate the loss of life, but this might give us some hope from something terrible. To see what can be achieved.'

Others were less optimistic, noting that air pollution wasn't down in its entirety; while some pollutants plummeted (like nitrogen dioxide and PM2.5 particulates from traffic), others stayed the same or even increased (notably ozone). There was no improvement in indoor pollution, ammonia from agriculture or particulates from wildfires. All around the world, thousands of power plants were still blowing sulphur dioxide and carbon dioxide high into the sky. And the spectre of a sudden 'pollution rebound' preoccupied many. At Australia's University of Melbourne, chemist Dr Gabriel da Silva noted: 'A subsequent emissions surge as economies recover is likely to leave the environment … in even worse shape than ever.'

Scientists also started to uncover much more complex and worrying connections between the virus and air pollution. Curiously, dirty air seemed to be a major contributor to COVID-19 infections, hospital admissions and deaths: separate studies in Europe, the United States and China found pollution exposure could increase COVID-19 deaths by anything from 6 to 15 per cent. What could explain an apparent connection between a *biological* virus and what is, in effect, *chemically* dirty air? Was there really a causal link, or was our determination to find one just a specious throwback to the ancient miasma theory – that bad air spreads disease?

Though the science is unlikely to be settled for years, three possible mechanisms were rapidly identified. As we've seen elsewhere in this chapter, long-term exposure to air pollution can wreak havoc on pretty much every part of our bodies, especially our hearts and lungs; it's no coincidence that around a third of deaths from COVID-19 involved existing cardiovascular or respiratory illness. Alongside that essentially 'long-term' effect, there appeared to be two short-term ones. Dirty air can inflame your respiratory system, weakening your

continued

defences and potentially making it easier for something like a virus to take hold. Finally, and most intriguingly, scientists found evidence that air pollution particles might be helping to ferry floating, tiny droplets of the COVID-19 virus over long distances, well beyond the 2 metre (6 foot or so) 'social-distancing' boundary assumed to keep people safe.

Could air pollution also help to explain the finding that black and minority ethnic (BAME) communities were significantly more at risk from COVID-19? It is well demonstrated that air pollution discriminates against some ethnic communities; if you're black or Latino and living in the United States, for example, you're more likely to breathe air pollution for a lengthy period of your life by growing up in deprived urban neighbourhoods with dense populations – and that could explain why people in your community are ultimately more at risk from a deadly virus. Some argue that social factors like this are a kind of latent environmental racism.

It will take years of rigorous science to tease out all of these complex connections. In the meantime, the question is whether the world can sustain any of the environmental improvements it made during 'lockdown', when hundreds of millions across the planet were simultaneously confined to their homes. That, too, is a complex issue. Some cities improvised bold plans to encourage walking and cycling; others were forced to put ambitious clean-air zones on hold. While many people were able to work from home, those who had to travel shunned buses and trains, leading car traffic to soar.

What lessons were learned from 'going viral'? Three stand out. First, though the world was shocked and stunned by the scale of the COVID-19 pandemic, we seem to have become desensitised to the staggering problem of air pollution, which ultimately kills far more. Second, directly or indirectly, air pollution might be having grave, global effects on public health far beyond the obvious impacts we already know about. Third, and much more positively, it has shown that if we put our minds to it, we can very rapidly and dramatically clean the air. The challenge is how to do that proactively – without waiting for 'help' from a deadly virus. [34]

Coming back to life

There are hundreds if not thousands of epidemiological studies of air pollution and health; the US National Library of Medicine's definitive 'Pubmed' database lists over 36,000 medical papers and journal articles that mention pollution in passing or tackle it head-on. Individually, they're all pieces of a jigsaw that has slowly resolved into a shocking but fairly clear picture over the last few decades. Air pollution harms not just the lungs, as many of us have long suspected, but pretty much every organ in the human body.

But don't despair. Much that you've read in this chapter – outrageous and depressing though it can certainly seem – is surprisingly good news. Pollution kills millions, but cleaning it up could *save* millions. We have a great opportunity to make life better for many of the world's people. Remember that something like 10 million people die early from air pollution each year. Some of those people could live years longer and far more lives could be substantially improved. Wonderfully enough, just as stopping smoking brings immediate benefits, so the health benefits of some of these 'public health interventions' (such as reducing PM2.5s) are practically immediate to society.

What are we waiting for?

POINTS OF LIGHT

Among the often bleak wastelands of air pollution research, there's a huge amount of optimism about what we could achieve. Here are just a few examples:

- The World Bank estimates that its $130 million investment in clean cooking and heating over recent years has benefited something

continued

like 11 million people in thirteen countries, including China, Ethiopia, Kenya, Indonesia, Senegal and Uganda.

- If the whole of South Africa complied with the country's existing air quality standards, it would save 14,000 early deaths a year, with economic benefits of $14 billion, equivalent to 2.2 per cent of its GDP. Meeting WHO guidelines would save 28,000 lives and more than double the benefits.
- In China (as we saw in Chapter 6), a recent air-cleaning investment of around $226 billion brought benefits of over $257 billion and saved 160,000 early deaths in 2017 alone.
- For England and Wales, it's been estimated that a significant (10 µg/m^3) reduction in PM2.5 pollution would save more lives than eliminating all road traffic accidents or passive smoking. In Wales alone, simply reducing urban speed limits from 50 km/h (30 mph) to 30 km/h (20 mph) would save about 120 deaths a year from PM2.5 particulate pollution.
- In highland Guatemala, adding chimneys to homes cut carbon monoxide exposure in children by 50 per cent and led to a major reduction in pneumonia (the single biggest killer of young children).
- In the United States, one positive of Arden Pope's American Cancer Society study (confirming a link between fine particulates and lung cancer) was the observation of a major reduction in PM2.5 particulates between 1980 and 2000. That translates into people living, on average, two to three years longer.
- Also in the United States, clean-ups brought about by the Clean Air Act have been saving something like 200,000 or so early deaths a year.
- A European study found reducing PM2.5s to WHO guidelines would be equivalent to extending people's lives by anything from two months (in Malaga) to almost two years (in Bucharest).
- Cutting pollution to those same WHO levels would stop over 66,000 new cases of childhood asthma in Europe each year.
- In São Paulo, Brazil, cutting PM2.5s to WHO levels would save over 5,000 deaths a year, worth an estimated $15.1 billion. [35]

CHAPTER 9

Down to Earth

What happens when air pollution comes back down to land?

O ur biggest concern about dirty air is obviously the impact it has on human health. Gazing down from space, however, what astronauts see isn't billions of bobbing human heads but a greeny-blue smear of land and ocean. Seventy per cent of the globe is covered by water and, despite our very best efforts with steel and concrete, much of the rest is still home to a staggering 3 trillion trees. As we've already seen, air pollution isn't just gas: there's plenty of dusty particulate matter (PM) swept along in it too. 'What goes up ... must come down' (the law of gravity) applies to much of the air pollution we hurl into the atmosphere. Beyond the direct harm that dirty air does to our own health, there's also the impact on oceans, lakes, rivers, trees and food crops to consider – all of which may affect our own food and drinking water, and indirectly our health as well. [1]

Scientists use the word 'deposition' for the way in which air pollution deposits itself back down to Earth. Doctors even talk about 'pulmonary deposition' as a way of describing how human lungs can clog like grimy kitchen sponges as they suck on the air. Deposition, arriving through dry airborne dust and snow, fog or rain, contributes to all kinds of environmental harm, from the white-dusty leaves you see on roadside plants to 'dead zones': vast areas of lifeless ocean, the biggest of which (in the Baltic Sea) is now the size of Ireland. By far the best known example of deposition is acid rain – so let's start there. [2]

Purple rain

Back in the 1840s, Henry David Thoreau sat by the shore of Walden Pond in Concord, Massachusetts, musing on how 'A single gentle rain makes the grass many shades greener'. How was he to know that industrial-scale air pollution was already changing 'gentle rain' to acid and turning the grass brown? During the 20th century, pesticides, pesky swimming tourists, invasive fish stocks and climate change all took a toll on the water that Thoreau described as 'so transparent that the bottom can easily be discerned at the depth of twenty-five or thirty feet'. By the early 1990s, when ecologist Dr Marjorie Winkler from the University of Wisconsin sampled Walden Pond, she found the water less clear, and notably more acidic and eutrophic (over-fertilised) than in Thoreau's time. Despite various attempts to put things right, it still hasn't recovered. [3]

'If it turns pink, it's acid, I think' is one of the first bits of chemistry you probably learned in school. Acids make neutral litmus paper blush to a shocking pink or purple, while alkalis (which somehow sound more friendly than acids but can be just as harmful) bleach it blue instead. You'll also have learned that we measure the strength of different acids and alkalis on a pH scale. Traditionally, it stretches from 1 (battery acid) to 14 (lye, a vicious alkali you might use to unblock your drain), with pure water theoretically balanced in between on a neutral pH of 7. Although the pH scale is useful, it's also deceptive because it's *logarithmic* rather than linear. On a ruler, which is linear, every centimetre (half inch or so) you step up the scale is just another centimetre, but on a logarithmic scale every step represents a ten-fold leap (10, then 100, then 1,000 and so on). For pH, each step down the scale is a ten-fold increase in acidity, while each step up is a ten-fold increase in alkalinity; vinegar with a pH of 3 is 10,000 times more acidic than pure water with a pH of 7.

What, then, to make of rain or snow tumbling from the sky that's acidic enough to turn litmus paper pink? Normal rain trickles through carbon dioxide in the air, and so has been lightly acidic since pre-industrial times, creating weak carbonic acid with a pH of about 5.6 (the acidity of milky coffee or tea). But when the air is rich in sulphur dioxide and nitrogen oxides, from power plant smokestacks and traffic tailpipes, rainwater picks these up as well to make sulphuric or nitric acid. That's significantly higher up the scale on a pH of around 4, which is about as acidic as orange juice. It might not sound so bad, but undiluted orange juice is not something you'd want to swim around in all day if you were a trout. A pH much below 5 is too acidic for most fish and other freshwater plant and animal life (lightweight snails bail out at 6, while hardcore frogs are robust down to about pH 4). [4]

Acid rain *was* actually known in Thoreau's lifetime. It was discovered way back in 1852, two years before his book *Walden* was published, by Scottish chemist Dr Robert Angus Smith, a government 'alkali inspector' (pollution monitor) who wrote the first book on the subject, *Air and Rain*, two decades later. Collecting and comparing samples from different places around the famously rainy English city of Manchester, Smith noted a simple connection between the acid in the rain and urban pollution: 'All the rain was found to contain acid in proportion as it approached the town,' further observing that 'the presence of free sulphuric acid in the air sufficiently explains the fading of colours in printed and dyed goods, the rusting of metals and the rotting of blinds', as well as erosion on stone buildings. [5]

But it was another century before the concept of acid rain gained currency following extensive scientific studies by Gene Likens and his team at the Hubbard Brook Experimental Forest in New Hampshire in the early 1960s. It was here that the explicit connection was first made between large-scale urban pollution, travelling across countries and sometimes continents, and rain that had turned acidic enough to obliterate entire ecosystems. The very first rain sample taken at Hubbard Brook on 24 July 1963 had a pH of 3.7, which, from an acidity viewpoint, is approaching vinegar. By comparison, Likens and his colleagues estimated that before the Industrial Revolution, rain would have been much more weakly acidic (with a pH of around 5). [6]

Exactly what happens when acid rain falls is more complex and nuanced than shaking vinegar from a bottle. In a lake, the highly interconnected web of plants and animals (the freshwater ecosystem) will be completely adapted to the local environment, including the geological makeup of the local rocks and soils, the amount of nutrients they receive and so on. The amount of rain-fall is obviously critical too. The key word here is ecosystem: once acidification starts to diminish some species, other parts of the food chain will gradually be affected too, even if they're less sensitive to the acidifying water itself. Meanwhile, in some circumstances, acidification will also leach out aluminium, magnesium and other metals, which dissolve in the water and are likely to be directly toxic to fish and other species.

The simple band-aid for acid rain is liming – shovelling alkaline limestone into lakes and ponds to neutralise some of the acid and lift the pH closer to neutral. But freshwater bodies aren't sealed up and self-contained, like garden ponds, so liming is a process that has to be repeated over and over again at intervals ranging from every few weeks to every few years, depending on how often the water refreshes itself. Of course, liming doesn't stop more acid rain from arriving, but it's a decent temporary fix to prevent the complete collapse of freshwater ecosystems. And it buys time for longer-term fixes – cutting sulphur dioxide emissions from power plants – to take effect.

Given the number of freshwater lakes, ponds and rivers affected, liming has been a vast and hugely expensive operation for the worst victims of acid rain, such as Norway, where the problem came to light in the early 1970s. At one time, something like a third of that country was degraded by acid rain; by the mid-1990s, 'vinegar' falling from the sky had wiped out or seriously degraded the salmon population in almost 50 different Norwegian rivers. The huge scale of the damage helps to explain an extraordinary diplomatic spat between Britain (whose careless, coal-fired power plants were causing much of Scandinavia's acid rain) and Norway (on the receiving end). Back in 1993, the Norwegian environment minister Thorbjørn Berntsen famously called his British counterpart, John Gummer, a 'drittsekk' (shitbag) over the UK's failure to clean up its sulphur dioxide emissions. It was a sign of Norway's huge pent-up frustration: almost two decades earlier, back in 1976, Brynjulf Ottar of the country's Institute for Air Research had warned how 'large amounts of [acid] can be transported over distances up to a few thousand kilometres' from fossil-fuelled power plants, causing 'severe damage to life in rivers and lakes'. [7]

Today, over a quarter of a century later, even though Britain has closed almost all of its coal plants and SO_2 emissions are a fraction of what they once were, nitrogen dioxide emissions from traffic mean that *nitric acid* rain continues to be a problem. Norway is still liming some of its rivers and lakes, notably those in the south of the country, to the tune of about 90–100 million kroner a year ($12 million or £10 million). Fortunately, though, there has been good progress in about half the affected rivers: twelve are now secure, while salmon stocks are being re-established in ten more.

Although Scandinavia was infamous for its acid rain, it was far from the only part of the world affected. Acid rain can fall wherever there are high enough sulphur dioxide and nitrogen dioxide emissions – and it's been a problem everywhere from the north-east of the United States (as the research at Hubbard Brook established) and eastern Europe to China, India and South Africa (industrialising countries with a heavy dependence on coal power). At one point, around half the forests in Germany and Poland and 30 per cent of those in Switzerland were damaged (although it was quite a complex problem and acid rain wasn't the only cause). At the height of the problem, back in 1979, *The New York Times* reported that: 'some 50,000 lakes in the Adirondacks and Canada have become acidified to the point that the fish population has declined or been destroyed' thanks to 'rainfall with an acidity level of vinegar'. Thankfully, rainfall in north-east America is now about ten times less acidic than it was in the 1970s. There was a huge improvement between the early 1990s and 2016, when the number of acidified lakes in the Adirondacks alone fell by 59 per cent, though around 6 per cent remain acidic even today – and, due to an unfortunate recent relaxation of pollution controls, the problem is now returning. [8]

Back in Europe, acid rain hardly registered as an issue in 1970, but by 1985 half of the forests sampled in scientific studies showed clear signs of leaf damage and about 14 per cent of all European forest was affected. Over in China, acid rain was estimated to be costing the country 30 billion yuan a year in crop damage by

2007 (something like $5 billion today) and 7 billion yuan a year in damage of other kinds. Even with the country's massive commitment to coal power, its SO_2 emissions have fallen dramatically – by about 75 per cent – since then. In India, it's a very different story. According to NASA, sulphur dioxide emissions in India have increased by over 50 per cent over the same period, which explains why rainfall measured throughout the country has become increasingly acidic over recent decades. India is now, by far, the world's biggest sulphur dioxide emitter. [9]

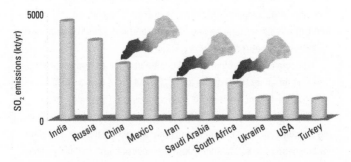

Figure 43. India leads the world in sulphur dioxide emissions – and, potentially, therefore, in acid rain. Chart shows SO_2 emissions in kt/year. Data source: Global NASA OMI Catalogue of Emissions 2005–2018. [10]

FROM METAL DUST TO PLASTIC RAIN

If air pollution contains toxic chemicals, so too does dust. Depending on where it originates and how it travels, the 'dust' sunning itself on your window ledge right now might contain toxic cadmium and mercury burned off in power plants; lead from sanding old paintwork; carcinogenic dioxins and furans from incinerators; pesticide and herbicide residues such as chlordane, dieldrin and lindane; and even

continued

faint traces of long-banned chemicals such as PCBs (polychlorinated biphenyls) and the notorious pesticide DDT. [11]

Heavy metals like mercury (transformed in the environment into particularly toxic forms called methylmercury and dimethylmercury) and cadmium, plus other toxic chemicals such as arsenic and fluorine, enter the air from things like coal-burning power plants and city waste incinerators. Their tall smokestacks hurl pollution hundreds of kilometres before it drifts back down to Earth, lacing crops or tainting rivers and lakes in the form of heavy metal 'deposition'. Somewhere between 50 and 80 per cent of the mercury arriving in North America's Great Lakes comes not from the land, as you might expect, but from this kind of air pollution. Meanwhile in New Zealand, natural pollution from active volcanoes like White Island and Mount Ruapehu is another major source of mercury. [12]

How big is the problem? Thanks to humans, there was over three times as much mercury in the air in 2000 as there was in 1900. Once it's entered the ecosystem, it bioaccumulates (becomes progressively more concentrated) the higher up the food chain it goes, posing a significant risk to humans and other animals at the top. The slow, steady seep of toxic chemicals into the environment, and their ability to persist for decades, explains why (for example) people in coastal parts of Florida are still warned against eating shellfish over 40 years after toxic discharges in the region came to an end. A killer whale that washed up in the Inner Hebrides in 2017 was found to have very high levels of toxic PCBs in its body, decades after they were banned. Emissions of this kind are less of a problem than they were in countries that have cut their dependence on coal power. But heavy metal deposition is still a major problem in countries as diverse as China, Korea, Russia, Poland, South Africa and Nigeria, where coal-burning, industry, transport, intensive agriculture and general urbanisation continue to dirty the air. [13]

Do you wash your fruit and vegetables before you cook and eat them? Most of us assume the reason for doing that is to scrub away

continued

pesticides, but even if you scrupulously eat organic, you could still be gobbling down residues of air pollution with your greens. Polycyclic aromatic hydrocarbons (PAHs) enter the air from forest fires, fossil-fuel burning in engines and power plants, garden bonfires, tobacco smoke, indoor cooking, home wood burners and more besides. Some of it comes back down to Earth as deposits on the food we eat. [14]

Much of the world's environmental attention is currently (and rightly) focused on the problem of plastic trash. But while everyday disposables (toothbrushes, pens, bottle tops and all the rest) are the most visible signs of that issue, tiny fragments of plastic – microplastic particles and fibres – are now being deposited into the environment, invisibly, from the *air*. In one recent experiment, when scientists in Hamburg, Germany set up metre-square-sized sampling areas to count pollution falling from the sky, they collected up to 512 bits of airborne plastic each day. Another recent survey, carried out by the US Geological Survey in Colorado, found plastic fibres, beads and other fragments in samples of snow and rain. This sort of 'plastic rain' is now cropping up everywhere; another German team has recently found traces of microplastic even in Arctic snow. [15]

Nitrogen blues

Acid isn't the only thing that arrives on land and water thanks to dirty air in the sky: there's also nitrogen and ammonia. At face value, nothing's more natural than nitrogen: it represents four fifths of the air you're breathing right now and it's an essential element in plant growth. In its ordinary gas form (N_2) it's largely unreactive, so it has little effect on plants and the wider ecosystem. In more reactive forms (as nitrate ions, NO_3^-, or ammonium ions, NH_4^+), it's a potent fertiliser; falling in sufficient quantities in rain, it essentially over-fertilises things causing a condition known as eutrophication (a Greek word meaning 'well-nourished' that, in this case, is something of a euphemism). In freshwater lakes and coastal areas, eutrophication starves the water of oxygen and causes massive growth in algae (producing the phenomena called 'harmful algal blooms' and 'red tides') or phytoplankton, which suffocate other forms of life. At the extreme, this can lead to what's known as a dead zone. One of the largest, in the Gulf of Mexico, grows to a vast area of about 14,000–21,000 square kilometres (5,000–8,000 square miles) each year, or roughly the same size as the US state of New Jersey. [16]

Most of this unwanted fertiliser comes from water pollution (things like nutrient-rich sewage and farm water runoff), but the nitrogen-based molecules in air pollution are another important source. A lot of it comes from farms, where nitrogen-rich fertilisers and animal waste waft ammonia up into the sky. Some comes from burning biomass and urban pollution – some even from things like nitrogen oxides belched out by traffic. You might think it's insignificant, but fossil-fuel burning of various kinds adds about a fifth as much reactive nitrogen to the environment as all the fertilisers we use. So while the connection between dirty diesel cars and the slimy green stuff floating on your local waterway might seem tenuous, nitrogen dioxide generated by things like city traffic can and does help to cause algal blooms in lakes and rivers far away. Car fumes really are, albeit indirectly, a kind of unwanted fertiliser. [17]

You might not worry too much about algal blooms or red tides; they're just more scary headlines – and they may seem quite remote and unrelated to your own inland, probably urban life. But anything that causes water pollution is, sooner or later, a much wider concern, because it's likely to impact the water we drink or use for things like crop irrigation. Over the course of the 20th century, levels of nitrogen in some US rivers rose by between three and ten times, greatly increasing the level of nitrogen in drinking

water, sometimes to dangerous levels. At the very extreme, the
health impacts of drinking over-nitrogenated water can include
various forms of cancer and even a rare condition called Blue Baby
Syndrome (methemoglobinemia). It's caused by excessive nitrogen
in the blood, which effectively starves the brain of oxygen and
sometimes leads to brain damage or death, generally in children
under the age of six months or so. [18]

Growing pains

One of the biggest concerns about air pollution returning to land
is that it will damage plants, especially the crops we all rely on
for our food. Acid rain, for example, changes the balance of the
soil it builds up in, drastically altering what will grow in particular places, reducing the diversity of species that can thrive and
lowering the productivity of any plants that manage to survive.
Sulphur dioxide, nitrogen dioxide, sooty particulates and ozone
can all harm plants, although different species are susceptible to
different pollutants to different extents. Wheat, beans, soybeans,
peanuts, cotton, grapes, lettuce, onions and potatoes are all very
sensitive to ozone, while alfalfa, barley and spinach are highly
susceptible to sulphur dioxide. [19]

Exactly how plants respond to air pollution varies from one
pollutant to the next, ranging from a slight blip in the plant's
nutrition to total leaf loss and death. If we consider photosynthesis to be somewhat analogous to the way humans breathe (plants
'inhale' carbon dioxide and 'exhale' oxygen), it's easy to imagine
how air pollution can cause health problems in plants as well as
in humans. Gases pass through stoma (openings in the leaf's outer
'skin' or epidermis layers) to the inner cells, and pollutants enter
the same way. Some pollutants cause lesions (rapid death of plant

tissue or sudden leaf damage). Others discolour leaves and stop them from photosynthesising properly or make them drop off altogether, which eventually kills the plant. Some affect transpiration (the movement of water from the roots to the air outside) or how plants reproduce.

What harm do different pollutants do? In the case of particulates, it's often simply a matter of sooty dirt landing on leaves and blocking out light so the plant can't photosynthesise and grow as it should. Ozone is more insidious. Absorbed directly into leaves, it causes cell damage and turns the leaves yellow through the loss of the chloroplasts where photosynthesis takes place (a process called chlorosis), reducing the effectiveness of the plant's roots and inhibiting its growth. Peroxyacetyl nitrate (PAN), another chemical linked with smog, glazes the outer epidermis of leaves or turns them a silvery white. Sulphur dioxide enters via the same route and harms plants in multiple ways, from blocking the stoma and cutting off their ability to take in gases and water to impairing photosynthesis. It also bleaches leaves and causes chlorosis and, in the concentrated form of sulphuric acid rain, may even burn holes right through them. In lower concentrations, however, sulphur dioxide is absorbed as an important plant nutrient. The recent curbs in SO_2 emissions in some countries now result in sulphur deficiency and, ironically, farmers have to add sulphur to the soil to compensate (just as they used to back in the 19th century). Nitrogen dioxide can be equally contrary: it will sometimes stunt the growth of a plant, but it can be transformed into nitric acid, which (in weak form) will act as a fertiliser and boost growth. Sometimes, a complex cocktail of pollutants will conspire to produce better plant growth in cities than in rural areas (where ozone concentrations, for example, can be much higher). [20]

Trees – bigger, bulkier, more robust – have a more complex relationship with dirty air than smaller, slighter plants. As we saw in Chapter 4, deployed correctly, they can help to solve some of the problems of urban air pollution, although they can also exacerbate those very same problems if the wrong species are planted in the wrong places. A typical tree might contain as many as a quarter of a million leaves, giving it an effective surface area several times the footprint of its own canopy. This makes it very effective at mopping up certain types of pollution, notably particulates. On the other hand, trees are susceptible to acid rain and other kinds of deposition, which can cause leaf and needle loss, damage bark or stunt growth, make it harder for them to suck up water from the soil and increase the risk of attack from the weather, diseases and predatory insects (such as bark beetles). [21]

Most of us marvel at how old trees battle on through the centuries, shrugging off droughts and disease, lightning strikes, insect infestations and even (for a while) the terminal nibblings of internal rot. But trees are much less successful when it comes to a systematic onslaught from concentrated acid rain, which works its way through the high leafy canopy to the forest floor, gradually changing the composition of the soil so the trees are simultaneously destroyed from both above and below. One of the perverse things about acid rain is that it typically affects pristine rural areas far from the places where the pollution originates, including forests at high altitudes bathed in acidic clouds and hill fog. (That's because it takes time for sulphur dioxide, the pollution that's emitted, to convert into the sulphuric acid that does the damage.) In the United States, for example, the forests of the Adirondack mountains were notable victims of power plants in the Midwest (and, indeed, are becoming so once more thanks to clean-air rollbacks by the Trump administration). [22]

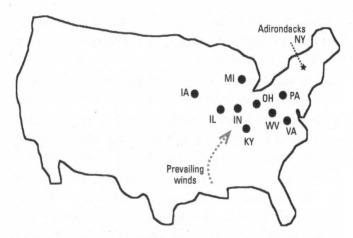

Figure 44. Forests and lakes in the Adirondacks of New York state (star) are affected by acid rain from power plant emissions, blowing in from a number of other states (dots) as far away as Iowa (IA) and Kentucky (KY). [23]

Cropped out

Although we worry about the direct effect of air pollution on our health, how it damages and degrades crops may prove to be a much bigger concern. For while the health impacts of air pollution are chronic, diffused across the whole population and may take years or decades to appear, the impact on the food that keeps us alive could be much more immediate and acute – and it will affect everyone. In a globally warming world with an ever-growing population, anything that puts pressure on the food supply could be enough to tip entire countries or continents into famine. [24]

As we discovered in Chapter 3, large-scale air pollution dates right back to the ancients, so it's no surprise to find the impact of dirty air on crops was a concern in earlier times. Way back in 1661, in John Evelyn's *Fumifugium* (his book about air pollution in London), he ranted at some length about 'this horrid smoke ... [which] ... kills our Bees and Flowers ... suffering nothing in our

Gardens to bud, display themselves, or ripen ... imparting a bitter and ungrateful taste to those few wretched Fruits, which never arriving to their desired maturity, seem, like the Apples of Sodom, to fall even to dust, when they are but touched.' Today, anecdotal observations like these have given way to meticulous studies of the effects of all the main air pollutants on the yields of major food crops. [25]

Not surprisingly, the world's most polluted places are causing greatest concern. In India, a recent study has estimated that air pollution and climate change, combined, are cutting wheat yields by about a third and rice yields by about a fifth, with the worst-affected, most densely populated Indian states losing about half their total wheat crop. Sooty black carbon particulates and ground-level ozone – generated by such things as biomass burning on home cookstoves, industrial emissions and traffic fumes – seem mostly to blame. The effects of global warming on the world's food supply have been flagged up by climate scientists for decades, but this study found that air pollution had almost ten times the impact on crop yields as climate change over the same period. Since the country's rapidly growing population will exceed China's within the next decade, the predicted effects of climate change have barely even begun and air pollution in India looks set to worsen significantly, results like this are a real concern. [26]

Ozone and soot pollution are also problems in China; it too will face growing challenges to food supplies in the future. As we've already seen, acid rain costs the country an estimated 30 billion yuan a year in crop damage (80 per cent of which comes from damage to vegetables). The economic impact of ozone pollution on food crops isn't known, largely because that pollutant isn't monitored extensively outside the country's main urban areas. We do know that China has achieved greater food security for its people by dramatically increasing food imports. According to an analysis of World Bank figures by China Power, the country's total food imports rose 50-fold in the decade from 2005 to 2015 alone, from $6 million to $300 million, while meat imports have risen by *several thousand per cent* since the 1970s as the Chinese diet increasingly resembles that of Americans. But its goal of achieving self-sufficiency in staples such as rice, corn and wheat could be seriously imperilled if air pollution starts to affect Chinese crops on anything like the same scale as seems to be happening in India. [27]

The fact that air pollution affects such bedrock crops is even more worrying. Rice, for example, provides up to half the calorific intake for people in many South Asian countries, which grow around a third of the world's total crop. Yields of rice are seriously affected by sulphur dioxide and fluorides (produced by coal power plants, domestic fuel burning and a wide range of industrial processes) and ozone and nitrogen dioxide (from traffic, power production and industry). All of them harm plants broadly by inhibiting photosynthesis; all of them are likely to increase in South Asian countries in future.

But the harm air pollution causes to food crops is far from just an Asian problem. In the United States, the famous photochemical smog of Los Angeles has long taken an economic toll on lucrative Californian crops such as grapes and citrus fruit. Way back in 1950, Dutch-born chemist Dr Arie Jan Haagen-Smit figured out the link between car pollution and smog after studying its effects on spinach, sugar beet, endive, alfalfa and oats. By 1978, the Californian damage alone was estimated at $100 million; in the 1980s, total crop losses for the United States stood somewhere between $1 billion and $5 billion. Ozone alone works out very expensive. In 2003, the US Environmental Protection Agency calculated that, all by itself, ozone damage to crops was costing the country $500 million a year. For the world as a whole, with total crop losses variously estimated at 5–20 per cent, the cost of damage from ozone is currently estimated at $20 billion a year. [28]

Of all the common air pollutants that affect plants, ozone gives perhaps the cause for greatest concern; its effects on crops have been documented since at least 1944. Four decades later, agricultural scientists in Greece noted how a major ozone episode wiped out a complete lettuce and chicory crop. One of the concerns about ozone is that it's much more of a problem in the countryside (where crops grow) than in towns (where high levels of nitric oxide help to destroy it). Another problem is ozone's ability to wreak havoc entire continents away from where it was produced. One recent study by scientists from the English universities of Leeds and York estimated that ozone produced in North America is responsible for the loss of 1.2 million tonnes of wheat each year in *Europe*, thousands of kilometres away. According to Dr Lisa Emberson, one of the authors: 'This study highlights the need for air pollution impacts on crops to be taken more seriously as a threat to food security; currently air quality is often overlooked as a determinant of future crop supply. Given the sizeable yield losses of staple crops caused by surface ozone, coupled with the challenges facing our ability to be food secure in the coming decades, further coordinated international efforts should be targeted at reducing emissions of ozone-forming gases across the globe.' [29]

Emberson estimates that ozone is cutting the global yields of staple crops like wheat, rice, maize and soybean by 5–12 per cent per year, which is a massive impact. But getting people to wake up to the problem is tricky, because ozone is a completely *invisible* pollutant generated *indirectly* from a complex mixture of other things – it's not something we can see or stop directly. And the trends are against us. While the original industrial pollutant, sulphur dioxide, has been brought substantially under control in many parts of the world, ozone is increasing virtually everywhere: in many places, the amount of ground-level ozone has doubled since the gas was first properly studied during the mid- to late-19th century. [30]

With wildfires on the increase, air pollution released by burning trees is another growing concern. Forest fires can release ethylene, for example, a gas used by the food industry for ripening fruits; this ripens fruit prematurely before it can be harvested, so much of it goes to waste. Smoke and ash deposits can dramatically reduce photosynthesis or render crops hazardous for human consumption, while ozone released by wildfires can drift and blow over huge distances, potentially harming crop productivity hundreds of kilometres away. According to Professor Nadine Unger of Exeter University, author of another recent study on air pollution and crop damage, 'the pollutants released by these fires impact plants in areas way beyond the boundaries of the disaster. Globally, over the past decade, fire ozone pollution reduced plant productivity substantially more than estimated drought losses ... We need to be concerned about [it] damaging forest and agricultural productivity downwind.' [31]

Feed the world?

What if we could see insidious forms of air pollution like ozone? What if we could sit back and watch them nibbling away at plants, trees and vital food crops? It would be like a time-lapse wildlife documentary where a plant grows from seed to maturity in a minute or two, except we'd be sitting through pretty much the opposite: a healthy green lettuce shrivelling and dying, perhaps, or the stalks and stems of a wheat crop slowly turning browny-yellow.

Just as with other complex environmental issues, such as climate change, we're several times removed from a hugely important problem that, by undermining the world's food security, has the potential to kill millions. Most of us don't understand where our food comes from – or the challenges involved in keeping it coming. We order a Chinese takeaway with rice; China grows a third of the world's rice crop and wants to be self-sufficient, yet it too relies on takeaway: it still imports more rice than any other nation. According to Colin Carter, professor of agricultural and resource economics at University of California, Davis: 'As ozone levels increase in China, this form of pollution threatens to not only decrease the nation's rice production but also affect the broad, global rice market.' [32]

Things are certain to worsen in the future. Acid rain might be coming under control in problem countries such as Norway, but ozone is on the rise. Thanks to problems like urbanisation, the world's ever-growing traffic fleet and even (ironically) the intensive agriculture that feeds the existing world population, the levels of key pollutants that lead to the formation of ozone (the so-called 'ozone precursors' – nitrogen oxide, carbon monoxide, methane and VOCs) are predicted to keep climbing over the next few decades. This is exactly the same time period when the world's population is predicted to grow from its current 7 billion to a daunting 9 billion or so around the year 2050. Climate change, meanwhile, will make matters worse: the hotter it is, the more harm ozone does to crops and other plants. The UN's goal is to reach 'zero hunger' worldwide by 2030, but 820 million people already fall short and the situation has worsened for three years in a row. The prospect of air pollution seriously eroding food production just at a time when there are ever more mouths to feed, and climate change is really starting to kick in, should truly alarm us. If pollution helps to push a warming world routinely into famine, it could kill significantly more than the millions who already die early each year from its direct effects. [33]

CHAPTER 10

Scrubbing up

Can better technology solve the problem of air pollution?

Suppose you could invent a machine to clean the air. What might it look like? It would need to be tall enough to pluck out the tiny (but fatal) concentrations of gases and particulates swirling all around us. Remember that many cities are massively polluted, so it would also need to be big enough to process lots of air, very quickly. A huge active surface area, spread evenly in all directions, would be helpful so it could suck in plenty of pollution at once. And since we're attempting to tackle one environmental problem, we don't want to create another by using electricity made from coal; solar would be an ideal power source.

Try sketching this thing out on paper and it will probably bear a distinct resemblance to a tree. Congratulations. You've just reinvented trees. Before you get too excited, however, remember that plants (as we saw in Chapter 4) aren't as dependable at cleaning the air as we often suppose. Apart from that, it's unlikely there's sufficient empty space in most cities to plant enough trees to make a difference.

Forget trees, then. Maybe what you drew looks more shiny and hi-tech – more like the giant smog-sucking machines that have started sprouting from the ground in polluted parts of China. The first one, built by Dutch artist Daan Roosegaarde, popped up in the middle of Beijing in October 2016. Roughly the same height as a mature tree, but more reminiscent of a cheese grater, the 7-metre (23-foot) tower claims to clean 30,000 cubic metres (1 million cubic feet) of air an hour, or roughly a football stadium's worth a day. Just how much difference it makes to air outside its own immediate surroundings isn't clear: you could squeeze about 300,000 tightly packed football stadiums into an area the size of Beijing and virtually all that space is already filled with things that are making the air dirty to begin with. That's why the Chinese are now testing much taller smog-busting towers. One of the latest, a giant 100-metre (328-foot) high chimney-like structure at Xian in Shaanxi province, claims to clean the air across a vast area of 10 square kilometres (3.86 square miles) and reduce thick smog to a lighter fog. Sounds great – but, even if it works, and that's a pretty big 'if', we'd still need over 1,600 of those to clean up the whole of Beijing. [1]

You could be forgiven for being sceptical about technology. The first use of fire, the steam engine, petrol and diesel engines, the jet engine, the atom bomb, the latest nuclear power plants – for all the good they've done, powering our progress through the centuries, human inventions like these really seem to have piled on the problems of pollution. Perhaps technology can help us solve those problems too? Search through records of recent inventions and you'll find hundreds devoted, one way or another, to cleaning the air. From the positive and practical to the wacky and weird, this chapter looks at some of the ideas people have come up with for cleaning polluted air – everything from catalytic converters in cars to a giant rooftop vacuum cleaner that plucks smog straight from the sky. Are technologies like these the solution to pollution? Can we really scrub clean the vast blanket of gas that's wrapped around our planet?

Cleaning up outdoors

The simplest, most effective way to clean the air is to make it less dirty to begin with. That means looking closely at emissions from transport, power plants, factories and many other sources of toxic urban pollution.

Taming the traffic

If you drive a car, it's already making a certain amount of effort to clean the air with help from the catalytic converter bolted underneath. You can't see it, but it's a bloated metal pipe that inhales dirty air from the engine, blows it over a honeycomb of expensive, chemically active metals such as platinum or palladium and then breathes out *relatively* cleaner air through the tailpipe at the back. In a typical gas/petrol car, even a half-decent converter will reduce hydrocarbons by about three to six times, carbon monoxide by perhaps two to seven times and nitrogen oxides by about a third to a half. Unfortunately, it won't do much good until it warms up (so it's not that helpful for short journeys) and it's likely to produce some nitrogen dioxide (a key component of smog) even while it's reducing other pollutants. What about diesels? If you're driving one that meets the latest emissions standards, it will still be throwing out about ten times more nitrogen oxides than a petrol-powered car. Though electric cars sound marvellous, as we saw in Chapter 5 there are still emissions from brakes, tyres and road dust to worry about – and the electric power, if it comes from fossil fuels, is also polluting. But let's be positive: with lead-free petrol and catalytic converters, and efficient lighter bodies and engines that go further on less fuel, today's cars are far cleaner than they were in the 1950s; the trouble is that there are vastly more of them, so vehicle pollution remains a problem. [2]

Tomorrow's highways full of silent, well-meaning electric

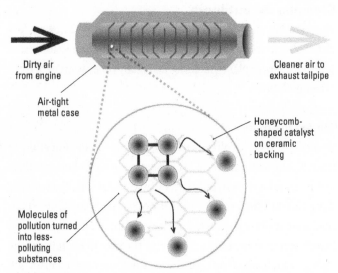

Figure 45. The catalytic converter under your car uses honeycomb-shaped catalysts to transform molecules of air pollution into less harmful things. In a typical gas/petrol car, even a half-decent cat will reduce hydrocarbons by about three to six times, carbon monoxide by perhaps two to seven times and nitrogen oxides by about a third to a half. [3]

cars will still be gridlocked and, if traffic levels increase much further, probably just as polluted. That's why environmental campaigners are fond of arguing that we need fewer cars, not cleaner ones. The broader, longer-term solution, they tell us, is more thoughtful urban planning (so we travel less), smarter use of technology (home working and video conferencing), clean-air and congestion-charging zones (to shift people from their cars) and better mass transportation (clean electric trains and buses) – a way of life geared to minimum travel rather than maxi-mum car. If only the planners were starting with a blank sheet of paper, and our minds were equally open, that would make sense. Unfortunately, we've already built the millions of homes, the vast 'just-in-time' warehouses that power next-day deliveries and the out-of-town shopping malls (accessible only from multi-lane highways) and many of us are fully paid-up members of car culture. [4]

As a sticking plaster, to reassure ourselves we're doing something about air quality, we eagerly seize on token solutions like 'greener' buses with built-in air hoovers. They suck in dirty air at the front, filter it and blow cleaner air out of the back – so, if you follow behind a bus like this, it's actually doing you a favour. But how much difference can these sorts of vehicles actually make? Take the UK, for example. When Britain's huge Go-Ahead bus group trialled such a vehicle in 2018, it was the only one of its kind; meanwhile the UK has 32,000 conventional, dirty diesel buses. Even in London, which probably has the most modern fleet in the country, only 2 per cent of the buses are low-emission vehicles. The average age of a bus in the UK is almost eight years, and the expected lifespan is thirteen to fifteen years, so even if we started replacing all the existing fleet today, it would still be ten to twenty years before the job was done. [5]

Perhaps we just need time and patience? But that can open up an opportunity for unscrupulous people to take advantage of our gullibility. A few years ago in China, fast-growing traffic congestion led engineer Song Youzhou to propose a 5 metre-high, hollowed-out 'straddling bus' that literally drives over traffic jams using 'outrider' wheels in the traffic lanes either side. Though the nutty project raised billions of yuan from credulous investors expecting huge profits, BBC News was soon reporting 'growing speculation that it was no more than an investment scam'. Some 32 people linked to the scheme were eventually arrested for illegal fundraising and the bizarre prototype was left to rust in a car park in Qinhuangdao. [6]

Catch it while you can?

Choked by cars and streets geared around them, stymied by solutions like electric vehicles that promise more than they can possibly deliver ('zero emissions'), it's no wonder the mayors and governments of polluted cities take desperate steps to clear the air. In London, during his tenure as Mayor, Boris Johnson gave the go-ahead to a fleet of trucks ('wonderful contraptions', as he called them) that sprayed congested roads with a kind of calcium-based glue designed to catch particles of air pollution and stick them harmlessly to the ground. The routes chosen for spraying just happened to include ones that were being monitored for compliance with European pollution laws – prompting harsh criticism from scientists and air-quality campaigners. Pollution expert Professor Frank Kelly of King's College, London told the BBC: 'I am just aghast that they are trying to hide the problem in this way from the European Commission ... This does not deal with the problem at source.' A later study by another team from King's College found the £1.4 million scheme ineffective at dealing with traffic emissions, but acknowledged that it might have a role in tackling other forms of dirty urban air. [7]

Although modern air pollution is often impossible to see (because it's made of things like carbon monoxide and micro-scopic particulates), there's an element of psychology in being *seen* to tackle it – to do *something* – and that explains why urban tree-planting schemes are so popular with elected politicians. In Tbilisi, Georgia, City Hall ordered 10,000 trees of various species to be planted in 2018 alone, claiming they were 'essential to pre-vent air pollution ... [in] an ecologically clean city with a healthy and attractive environment'. In Bogotá, Colombia, 100,000 trees have been poked into the ground in the last few years for the same reason. Some 5,000 trees were planted in Tirana, northern

Albania in 2019 as part of an initiative called 'create your oxygen, plant five trees', also partly conceived to reduce air pollution. All these efforts are overshadowed by the twice-yearly National Tree Planting Days in Mongolia, which have seen over 2 million more trees added to the country since 2010 alone. And they're utterly dwarfed by Ethiopia, which claims to hold the world record for planting the most trees in a day (an incredible – and some have said impossible – 350 million). [8]

Just as smiling local people always turn out in force to plant hopeful saplings, so they bitterly oppose anything that steals trees from urban spaces. In India, in 2018, thousands of angry protesters turned out to save 15,000 trees from being felled for a new housing and office development. One of them told the Chinese news agency Xinhua: 'Delhi is choking ... Our children and elderly are suffering from asthma and lung ailments. Isn't that enough to protect the trees?' Gandhi-style civil disobedience was similarly deployed in Mumbai in 2019 when dozens of eco-activists tried to stop the felling of 2,646 trees from Aarey, the bustling city's 'green lung'. While few would dispute that trees make cities better places, the assumption that they neutralise all passing pollution simply isn't valid. But that doesn't mean mature urban trees are fair game for the chainsaws, especially when feeble saplings are used to replace them. Swapping old trees for new is sometimes a kind of 'living greenwash' designed to make endless development seem more palatable. [9]

What if we could use plants as pollution traps in more effective ways? That's the thinking behind 'living walls', in which parts of the internal or external walls of a building are packed with plants specifically chosen to clean the air. Unlike those towering, air-cleaning chimneys in Beijing or the sticky pollution glue sprayed onto streets in London, this simple technology is cheap, natural, uses no energy and needs no expensive pipework or electronics. One example, a patented system called Aerogation, made by the AgroSci company in Colchester, Connecticut, claims to be 200 times more effective at cleaning air than ordinary plants, which might (or might not) absorb passing pollution through their leaves. In the Aerogation system, polluted air is mixed with water and pumped through a nozzle directly to the plants' roots and soil, where microbes remove VOCs, allergens and other toxic chemicals. One of Aerogation's first missions has been to clean the air in and around some of the buildings that belong to the 1 Hotel chain in the United States. At 1 Hotel Central Park, in New York City, the three-storey facade of the building is enlivened by 180,000 air-cleaning ivies and ferns; inside 1 Hotel South Beach in Miami, Florida, a 1,200-plant green wall can clean 20,000 cubic metres (700,000 cubic feet) of air per day. It sounds impressive, but we'd need to know how much air these hotels and their visitors are dirtying per day to know what difference they're making, if any. [10]

Smog-busters

How about some lateral thinking. Instead of 'how do we clean the air around buildings?', maybe we should be asking 'how can buildings clean the air around themselves?'. Instead of 'what plants can we grow up a wall to remove pollution?', we might try 'why not make office and hospital walls from materials that devour pollution from the minute they're built?'. Creative thinking like this points to one of the newest methods of fighting urban air pollution: smog-busting buildings made from photocatalytic concrete.

'Photo' comes from the Greek word for light, while a catalyst is something that helps to speed up a chemical reaction without fundamentally changing in the process. Photocatalysis is the power

Figure 46. This experimental 'City Tree' claims it can absorb as much pollution as 275 real trees using just 1 per cent of the space they'd need. Photo by Matt Brown published under a Creative Commons (CC BY 2.0) Licence. [11]

behind self-cleaning windows. They have a thin outer coating of titanium dioxide, which encourages chemical reactions that turn passing dirt (which is mostly carbon-based) into relatively harmless carbon dioxide and water. In photocatalytic concrete, the titanium dioxide coating attacks a wider range of pollutants, again producing relatively benign substances such as oxygen, nitrate and sulphate, plus water and carbon dioxide. Just as rain rinses self-cleaning windows, so it washes the dirt off photocatalytic concrete, which, by definition, is unchanged in the process – ready to start attacking more pollution in the air. [12]

Smog-eating, photocatalytic structures have already started popping up around the world. In Barcelona, the technology was used on the Sarajevo Bridge that crosses Avinguda Meridiana, a major approach to the city. In Mexico City, a mesmerising coral-like outer facade, made from a proprietary photocatalytic concrete called proSolve370e, sits on the front of the Manuel Gea González Hospital gobbling up smog. According to the manufacturers, it can neutralise pollution from about 1,000 cars a day and will keep on doing so for the lifetime of the material (approximately a decade). In Milan, the Palazzo Italia has a 'biodynamic skin', reminiscent of a kind of giant white cobweb, made from 900 photocatalytic concrete panels that cover a total surface area of about 9,000 square metres (11,000 square yards). The photocatalytic facades of these buildings are weirdly undulating in shape, not just for fun but because that maximises the active, air-purifying surface area.

Figure 47. The pollution-absorbing, photocatalytic 'skin' of the Palazzo Italia, Milan. Photo by Fred Romero published under a Creative Commons (CC BY 2.0) licence. [13]

Captivating, modern, 'green' architecture like this attracts huge interest – promotional photos go viral online as soon as they're released. But before we get too swept away, it's worth pondering just how effective this stuff is in reality. Manuel Gea González Hospital can clean up after 1,000 cars a day, but how many *visit* it over the same period? There are over 3 million vehicles in Mexico City, so we'd need 3,000 buildings like the Manuel Gea González Hospital to compensate. While it's not impossible that we could coat every single building with a pollution-absorbing facade, it's not especially realistic either. How much would it cost? How much difference could that money make if we invested it in other ways? [14]

What could we do instead? Since traffic pollution starts with cars, how about making highways out of photocatalytic concrete? That's what Professor Jos Brouwers and a team from Eindhoven University of Technology tried doing in Hengelo, in the Netherlands a few years ago, with apparently impressive results: nitrogen oxides were cut by a dramatic 25–45 per cent. That sounds great, but roads like this only clean the air at ground-level, not higher up where it matters. Also, the material is 10 per cent more expensive than a traditional concrete road. That might not sound too bad until you bear in mind that, in the United States, over 90 per cent of paved highways are surfaced with asphalt, despite its shorter lifespan, precisely because it's cheaper in the short-term; adding cost to concrete isn't going to change that for the better. [15]

What else, then? How about sticking smog-absorbing barriers alongside busy roads? Over in the UK, the government agency responsible for building and maintaining highways has tested just such a barrier, some 6 metres (20 feet) high, along a 100-metre (330-foot) length of the country's busy M62 highway, and even considered options like pollution-absorbing tents and tunnels. Given the vast length of the road network even in a small country like Britain (almost 400,000 kilometres or 250,000 miles), the cost of solving pollution that way would surely be astronomical. And we also have to consider the hidden environmental cost of manufacturing all that concrete – perhaps the most *destructive* construction material ever developed.[1] [16]

Still, the debate over whether smog-busting materials are worth a closer look continues. In 2004, European Research Commissioner, Philippe Busquin, told *Greener Building* that 'Smart coatings can cause a revolution, not only in the management of air pollution but also in how architects and town planners tackle the persistent problem of urban smog.' Fortunately, enthusiasm for these dubious ideas seems to have fizzled out since then. Back in the UK, Sheffield University chemistry professor Tony Ryan, interviewed in 2017 by *Wired* magazine, argued that plans to build pollution tents over highways are 'bonkers ... It's far better to get people to drive less'. The Air Quality Expert Group (AQEG), a panel of British academics and other professionals, has also panned photocatalytic paints, sprays and similar dirt-eating materials, which risk spawning other pollutants, including nitrous oxide and formaldehyde, and can't, in any case, purify pollution quickly enough. Tony Ryan, meanwhile, sees a place for photocatalytic textiles, such as banners, whose millions and billions of fibres have a bigger surface area and remove more pollution. A few years ago, his team printed a poem titled 'In Praise of Clean Air' on a giant

---

[1] One of concrete's main ingredients is cement, production of which causes an estimated 7–8 per cent of the world's total carbon dioxide emissions. If cement-making were a country, its CO_2 emissions would be the world's third largest, after China and the United States.

photocatalytic banner draped down the side of their huge university building to demonstrate the concept. [17]

Smokestack knockbacks

In a world of a billion cars, and millions of wood-burning stoves, factory and power plant smokestacks are no longer the villains they were a century ago. That's partly a victory for technology. Way back in 1906, American engineer Frederick G. Cottrell, sometime director of the US Bureau of Mines, figured out how to use high-voltage electricity to snag the tiny soot particles wafting up smokestacks – similar to rubbing a balloon on your sweater. Once the particles were charged, he used a metal cage with an opposite electric charge to attract and trap the soot, leaving the air escaping the factory relatively clean. In his honour, this magical process gained the name 'Cottrellizing'; the inventor himself thought his idea might be used for clearing fog from the land and mist from the sea. [18]

Modern smoke precipitators, as these bits of equipment eventually became known, use water sprays ('wet scrubbers'), chemical reactions ('neutralisers') and high-voltage electricity ('dry scrubbers') in a multi-stage air-cleaning process. Meanwhile, different technology has been fighting dirty air *inside* factories for almost as long. If you think vacuum cleaner pioneer James Dyson deserves the credit for inventing the dust-busting cyclone, you'd be mistaken. As his own patents make clear, cyclonic (air-spinning and sieving) technology developed by Bert M. Kent for sucking dust out of factories, way back in 1913, was a major inspiration for the modern-style cyclonic vacuums that Dyson popularised some 70 years later. [19]

Smokestack 'scrubbing' technology alone didn't clean the filth from our cities: it is complex and expensive, and cost-conscious factory owners and power plant operators had no incentive to use it. But once the technology existed, once there was community pressure to act on the problem of dirty urban air, laws and regulations could ensure that it was properly deployed and factories and power plants really did clean up their act. And, of course, if the technology exists and it's reasonably affordable, factory owners have no good excuse not to use it. Sooner or later, when all these things push in the same direction, we get a virtuous circle and (hopefully) ever-cleaner air.

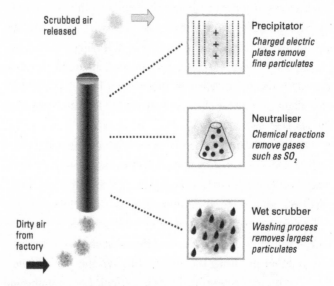

Figure 48. How smokestack scrubbers work. Polluted factory smoke enters at the bottom and passes through three separate cleaning stages, which remove particulates and gases such as sulphur dioxide.

Our polluted future?

Traffic that can't be tamed, urban trees that aren't as effective as we'd like and photocatalytic buildings that may, in the end, be little more than self-promotion for green architects – so-so solutions like these help to explain why the Chinese have been exploring such apparently improbable avenues as the pollution towers we saw at the beginning of this chapter.

Perhaps there is something in this idea, however, because they're not the only ones who've tried it. Dutch company Envinity has developed a giant, outdoor vacuum cleaner that can perch on the roof of a building to suck up particulates. According to their specifications, it cleans something like 25 football stadiums worth of dirty air per day, removing 100 per cent of PM2.5s and 95 per cent of super-dangerous PM1s (ultra-fine particulates). In Germany, a similar machine called Purevento, roughly the size of a shipping container, promises to catch 85 per cent of nitrogen oxides and particulates; impeccably eco-friendly, it's powered by solar cells, a hydrogen fuel cell or, if green power isn't available, conventional electricity. Meanwhile, back in Beijing, international architecture and engineering firm Arup has tested alternative air-cleaners hidden in roadside bus shelters. They use high-performance bag filters, somewhat like the ones in old-fashioned domestic vacuums, and promise a 40 per cent reduction in air pollutants. Over in Mexico, an enterprising new company called BioUrban has invented 4-metre (13-foot) high 'trees' made of steel, filled with algae that can clean as much air as 368 real trees. However sincere and well-meaning these sort of technologies are, they all suffer the same basic problem: they're much too close to the ground to affect the huge volume of polluted atmosphere that concerns us – and they simply can't process polluted air quickly enough to make any difference. [20]

Is this what our polluted future looks like? Cities filled with humming boxes and mechanical trees, sucking away day and night on all the microscopic bad breath our diesel engines, wood burners and other dirty things wheeze into the air? It just might be, although another possibility is also lurking on the horizon. The Dyson company, famous for the cyclonic vacuums I mentioned a moment ago, has recently filed a patent for a 'wearable air purifier', while a group of Taiwanese inventors filed a similarly named patent two years earlier. Curiously, no details of either invention seem to be available, but they suggest an alternative, somewhat dystopian future where grey-faced city-dwellers stalk the streets wearing goldfish-bowl helmets and air-cleaning backpacks. [21]

The inside story

You might think cleaning the air inside our buildings would be a shorter story than scrubbing up outside – and, in some ways, it is. We have complete control over our own indoor spaces, so we can clean them whenever and however we choose. They're usually pretty small, which means cleaning the air can be as simple as opening the window or turning on the extractor fan (assuming the air outside is clean enough for a simple swap). We have much more incentive not to make our personal air dirty to begin with, though we do still have to weigh trade-offs sometimes (if we're smoking inside, painting radiators, zapping bugs with fly spray or whatever it might be). Finally, it's usually pretty obvious where indoor air pollution is coming from, and relatively easy to tackle it at source. None of these things apply in quite the same way outdoors where the air is beyond our control, the sources of pollution are numerous and far from obvious and it often feels like, whatever we do, it's not going to make much difference. Of course, if everything were so straightforward indoors, the air in our homes would be mountain fresh all the time. In reality, as we saw in Chapter 7, half the world's air pollution deaths are caused indoors, while household air pollution is the world's eighth biggest killer overall. So what can we do about it?

Cleaner cooking

Since the vast majority of the world's indoor pollution deaths are caused by dirty fuels used for cooking and heating in developing countries, that's the best place to start. Broadly speaking, the solutions are to shift people from open (three-stone) fires to proper stoves and from hastily gathered fuels (wood, animal dung, waste crops and so on) to efficiently prepared ones (charcoal and pelleted wood). Better still, we can encourage them to upgrade to ventilated stoves (with chimneys and fans to improve the draught) and from inefficient solid fuels (coal) to cleaner gas and liquid fuels (perhaps ethanol, kerosene, biogas or liquid petroleum gas, LPG, similar to the stuff used in camping stoves). Ideally, they'd use cookstoves that don't involve combustion at all (electric induction stoves in countries where that type of power is available and affordable; solar cookers in hot rural countries where it isn't).

Simple technologies can make an amazing difference. Switching to a rocket stove (a super-efficient cookstove that uses pelleted wood) can reduce the fuel you need to burn by anything from a third (compared to a traditional stove) to a half (compared to a very basic three-stone fire). That brings major savings in time (if you have to gather your fuel yourself) or cost (if you have to pay for fuel). Although solar cookers take much more getting used to, they have the big advantage of needing no fuel. With their huge surfaces of reflective foil, they look like something from an episode of *Star Trek*, but the basic technology is older even than the traditional 'Franklin' stove (which dates from 1741). The first modern solar cooker was developed in the mid-18th century by a scientist and alpine explorer named Horace-Bénédict de Saussure (1740–1799). [22]

Given how many millions of people die early from using dirty stoves, it's astonishing how little media or public attention is paid to the problem, compared to other global public health issues such as malaria or HIV/Aids, which kill fewer. There have been some high-profile initiatives, sponsored by public figures such as Hillary Clinton and Bill Gates, though they've had mixed success. When Clinton launched the Global Alliance for Clean Cookstoves with a speech in 2010, she noted that: 'People have cooked over open fires and dirty stoves for all of human history, but ... they are slowly killing millions of people and polluting the environment ... By upgrading these stoves, millions of lives could be saved and improved. This could be as transformative as bed nets or even vaccines.' Five years on, as a critical report in the *Washington Post* noted, the Alliance had raised $400 million and put 28 million improved stoves into developing countries, but only 8 million of them met the WHO's definition of clean. The rest were relatively dirty biomass stoves supplied as replacements for open fires. [23]

Despite their health advantages, the uptake of clean cookstoves remains patchy and disappointing. Stoves have proved unreliable or unpopular, fuel isn't always affordable and people prefer to stick with cooking methods they know and trust, even if it means 'stove stacking' or 'fuel stacking' (running an old-style stove or fuel alongside your new one). Complications and quibbles aside, the bottom line remains the same: given that plenty of simple, technological solutions exist, and aren't that expensive, it's astonishing that the world doesn't do much more (as Hillary Clinton noted in her 2010 speech, cleaner stoves cost as little as $25). Air pollution scientists are fond of describing Western city smog as 'the invisible killer', which is one reason why it's so hard to tackle. But in developing countries, indoor air pollution is a very *visible* killer – and there's every reason for tackling it as a very high global health priority. The benefits of better cookers are simply too compelling to ignore. According to the Global Alliance for Clean Cookstoves, if people currently spend four hours a day cooking with traditional stoves, they can save an hour and ten minutes a day with a clean cookstove – time that can be invested in their families, social lives and children's education. So while change may happen very slowly, it will happen, sooner or later. And millions of lives will be saved as a result. [24]

Considering the mortal dangers of cooking and heating in the world's poorest countries (including the risk to personal safety of collecting wood fuel), it might seem overblown to suggest there are similar problems in richer places. Even so, it's well worth remembering what we discovered about ordinary (natural) gas cookers in Chapter 7, including the risks of creating smog-like amounts of nitrogen oxides and particulates. According to Brett Singer, a scientist at Berkeley Lab, everyday cooking exposes some 12 million Californians alone to unacceptable levels of nitrogen dioxide pollution: 'If these were conditions that were outdoors, the EPA [US Environmental Protection Agency] would be cracking down. But since it's in people's homes, there's no regulation requiring anyone to fix it. Reducing people's exposure to pollutants from gas stoves should be a public health priority.' Happily, that's relatively easy to do. Try to remember to switch on your cooker hood or kitchen extractor fan, if you have one, and make sure the filters are properly maintained so any compromised air is sucked from your building. Alternatively, open a window and a door to create a through-draught. [25]

Burning wood is no good

Back in 1952, the horrific Great Smog of London was caused largely by people burning dirty coal in their fireplaces – something not many of us do any more. What a lot of people have been doing instead, however, is switching to wood-burning stoves. These create a very different kind of winter air pollution, choked with fine (PM2.5) particulates, carcinogenic polycyclic aromatic hydrocarbons (PAHs) and numerous other toxic chemicals. When it comes to urban air pollution, diesel engines tend to dominate the headlines, but in Sydney, Australia, wood burners make 75 per cent of the city's particulate pollution. In the UK, they blow out 2.4 times more PM2.5 emissions than traffic (a real worry, since PM2.5s cause about 40,000 early deaths a year in Europe alone). These problems haven't suddenly leaped to light: way back in December 1984, *Popular Science* magazine warned of how 'popular airtight wood stoves belch huge amounts of smoke that can hang as a pall over whole communities'. [26]

Unlike traditional open coal fires, which can make a room very smoky if the wind is blowing the wrong way, wood burners are essentially sealed units, so any 'indoor pollution' they make is hurled outdoors instead, where it instantly becomes someone else's problem. According to Dr Dorothy Robinson of the Australian Air Quality Group, writing in the *British Medical Journal*: 'Few people who install wood stoves are likely to understand that a single log-burning stove permitted in smokeless zones emits more PM2.5 per year than 1,000 petrol cars and has estimated health costs in urban areas of thousands of pounds per year.' [27]

Although cosy ambience is certainly their main selling point, some people buy wood burners because of their apparent eco-friendliness. In theory, burning wood is carbon neutral, because trees absorb as much carbon dioxide when they're growing as they give out when they're burning. So you might think you're doing your bit for climate change by switching from natural gas or electric heating to a wood burner. In practice, that's unsound reasoning: you're burning a fuel *today*, unlocking what was safely trapped carbon *yesterday*, and you're releasing carbon dioxide emissions just at a time when the world needs no more. The saplings planted today to make firewood in the future won't absorb their fill of carbon dioxide for many decades or even centuries, while the need to cut carbon dioxide emissions is urgent. And, carbon dioxide emissions aside, you're pumping toxic levels of air pollution into the streets all around your home. Even the most modern, properly certified wood burners fall far short on air quality. Stoves made to standards such as 'Ecodesign' are a vast improvement on older ones, but they still blow out about eighteen times more particulates per hour than brand new diesel cars. While car emissions are tightly regulated, those from wood burners are not. [28]

Again, the solution is simple. If you like the ambience of a wood burner, and you care about climate change, get yourself a fake, electric log stove (many of them are superbly realistic, using water and steam to replicate the cosiness of a real fire). Then switch your electricity supplier to a company that makes all its energy renewably. If you're determined to keep your wood burner, do some research on the best fuel to use and learn how to kindle it the right way to minimise smoke.[2] If it's old, try to swap it for a new one – and maybe use it a bit less often, particularly on windless days where the smoke is likely to linger. If you're seriously concerned about climate change, forget wood burners

---

[2] In Australia, the New South Wales Environment Protection Authority has published ten tips to help homeowners reduce wood burner pollution: https://tinyurl.com/w3n3kpk

altogether. Look into better home insulation (which typically has a very short payback time), solar panels (for making electricity or hot water) and things like that.

TESTING TESTING

Hairspray

How do you avoid indoor air pollution? Stop making it in the first place.

Blast yourself with hairspray and this (according to my quick test with the Plume Flow air monitor) is what happens:

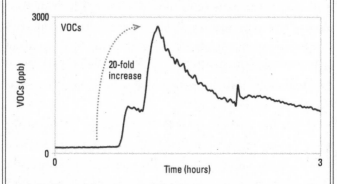

Figure 49. Chart shows: Y axis: Concentration of VOCs in parts per billion; X axis: time in hours.

A couple of determined sprays produce a rapid, 20-fold increase in volatile organic compounds (VOCs) that will stay with you – in your hair and in your room – for the next couple of hours. Now, as we've already seen, not all VOCs are toxic or harmful – but some of them are, and none of them are much good for you. Hairspray is a particular nuisance since it clings to you and, obviously, you take it wherever you go.

continued

> So what's the answer? Wear a mask? Open a window? Install
> some sort of photocatalytic gadget to break the chemicals down?
> Lobby the companies that make hair-care products? The simplest
> solution is obviously not to use the stuff to begin with. When it comes
> to your hair, avoid aerosols if you can; use waxes, gels or mister
> pumps instead. If you must use a spray, check the can carefully and
> choose one with a low-VOC content (reputable brands are often
> labelled).

A breath of fresh air?

If you're lucky enough not to live in a poor country and you don't
cook with gas or fry on a hob, if you avoid smelly household products and you don't have a wood burner, you probably don't worry
too much about indoor air pollution. But if you're unlucky enough
to have a medical condition like asthma, hay fever or some other
kind of respiratory illness, clean indoor air will be your highest
priority. What, then, can you do? You'll probably invest in an air-
cleaning machine and, like the outdoor air cleaners we explored
up above, they tend to work in one of two ways.

Some suck in air through a grille at the front, pass it through
what's called a High-Efficiency Particulate Air (HEPA) filter and
then blow it back into the room. HEPA filters were originally
developed for catching nuclear radiation as part of the Manhattan
Project (the massive scientific effort that built the atomic bomb
during World War II). Essentially, they're multiple layers of paper
folded tightly together so their dense, matted fibres mop up passing particulates, and they work on even the tiniest dust. A 'true'
HEPA filter is defined as one that traps 99.97 per cent of dust
particles 0.3 microns in diameter, which is 30 times smaller than
the coarse PM10 particulates and about eight times smaller than

the finer PM2.5 particulates we've encountered in this book. In theory, HEPA filters are effective even at catching airborne viruses, bacteria, spores and mould, but how well do they really work? In one recent study, experimenters gave out portable HEPA units to pregnant women in Ulaanbaatar (where, you'll remember from Chapter 2, super-high levels of winter air pollution have been linked with high rates of miscarriage). The results were encouraging: a 29 per cent reduction in indoor PM2.5s and a 14 per cent reduction in toxic cadmium in the women's blood suggests there is real scope for saving lives. [29]

As an alternative to HEPA, you can try what's called a photo-catalytic air purifier, and it uses similar technology to the concrete we explored up above. Inside one of these machines, there's a photocatalytic surface over which incoming air passes and an ultraviolet light to activate it. Unlike in a HEPA filtering machine, air pollution is chemically converted into more benign substances like water and carbon dioxide. Some air purifiers combine HEPA filters, photocatalysis and ionisation (charging up the air, like the electrostatic precipitator in a factory smokestack) to neuter an impressive range of airborne pollutants, from dust mites and pollen to bacteria and VOCs. But like other forms of photocatalytic cleaning, there's a drawback. Machines like this can make other kinds of pollution as a by-product, including formaldehyde and acetaldehyde. [30]

If techno-solutions don't appeal, there's a simple and very effective alternative: well-chosen houseplants. Twenty years ago, environmental scientist Dr Bill Wolverton carried out NASA's famous Clean Air Study, which demonstrated how common indoor plants (such as peace lilies and bamboo palms) can very effectively pull a range of toxic pollutants from the air. Though mainly geared to keeping air-tight space stations clean and healthy, the same research is broadly relevant in our own homes; Wolverton's book *Eco-Friendly Houseplants: 50 Indoor Plants That Purify the Air* is well worth a read. [31]

Cleaning up

Indoors or out, there's no shortage of pollution solutions; the real question is whether they're effective and, if so, how quickly we can put them in place. Some technologies demonstrably make a huge difference to outdoor air quality: power station smokestack scrubbers, for example, and car engines that run on unleaded petrol. Others are more dubious. While it's easy to show that photocatalytic, smog-busting buildings, bridges, highways and other structures can improve air quality in their immediate locality, do they really work at urban scale? How many would we need to make even a slight dent in today's pollution problems? It's one thing to delight in geeky gimmicks for their entertainment value; most people have a soft spot for daft inventions. But if these things lure us into a false sense of security that air pollution is under control, that we can safely leave everything to ingenious engineers while we carry on as we are, they could prove to be a fatal distraction. We have to be on guard for con artists and charlatans – always demand proof that technologies are effective, always ask who profits and always ask whether money could be better spent elsewhere.

Indoors, things are theoretically simpler. We know we could save millions of lives in developing nations by putting greater focus on cleaner, more efficient methods of home cooking. There are cultural and practical obstacles to the take-up of improved home stoves, especially if they mean a change to age-old, traditional methods of cooking that are deeply embedded in native cultures, but hopefully, approached with sensitivity and respect, these things are not impossible. What there shouldn't really be are financial obstacles. Simple, practical, clean, safe cookstoves are much cheaper than human lives. If they can really be made for $25 a piece, the $5 trillion we waste each year on the cost of air pollution would buy at least 25 of them for every woman, man and child on the planet.

Where outdoor air pollution is concerned, a very important complication is that different countries have different problems. According to the annual *State of Global Air* survey, the three biggest causes of fine (PM2.5) particulate pollution in China are industrial use of coal, transportation and home biomass burning, all of which cause very roughly the same number of deaths, and roughly 50 per cent more than power plant coal use. In India, by contrast, home biomass burning is far and away the most important factor, causing three times as many deaths as either power plant or industrial coal use. Elsewhere in the world, traffic is now a much bigger concern than industrial, power plant or home fuel use and home wood burners have also become an increasing concern. One pollution solution doesn't fit everyone, everywhere, all year round; beyond the universal importance of clean air, generalising about air pollution isn't always that helpful. [32]

The biggest stumbling block for some of these inventions is that there's simply too much dirty air for them to process. Do we seriously think, for example, that we could pave enough roads with photocatalytic concrete to make a difference to urban air pollution? Or build enough smog-busting towers in the world's most grossly polluted cities? We already know that electric cars won't eliminate traffic pollution; they're far from zero-emission vehicles. And however much we might like urban trees, it should be obvious that they can't transform our cities all by themselves.

Instead of trying to scrub the sky clean, what we need to do is stop making it dirty. Technology definitely has its place. But what we also need are lastingly effective legal and political solutions, brought about by a sea-change in public attitudes to the importance of clean air – and the need to keep it that way. This is what we'll explore in the final chapter.

REINVENTING CLEAN AIR

Set yourself one of those creativity challenges: sit down with a blank sheet of paper for five minutes and see how many different ways you can devise of tackling air pollution in a filthy city. Though you might list dozens, there are really only four: 1) collect the dirty air (essentially a physical method – trap or remove it); 2) avoid it somehow (another physical method – block it from reaching your lungs); 3) turn it into something else (a chemical method – convert pollutants into more benign things); 4) disperse and dilute it (the approach used by tall smokestacks, which simply pushes the dirt somewhere else).

It's amazing how many variations on those four methods inventors have come up with. Frederick G. Cottrell's smoke precipitator uses static electricity to scrub soot from waste plant gases (method 1) and tall smokestacks to disperse what remains (method 4). Catalytic converters use chemicals to bust pollution apart (method 3) and a traditional tailpipe to blow out the rest (method 4). Photocatalysis is a variation on method 3, while HEPA filters are an example of method 2. Orproject, an international architecture and design studio, has proposed a very different approach to method 2 for cities like Beijing. It suggests creating giant, clean-air-filled bubbles over botanical gardens and other public spaces to seal people off from the dirty air outside.

What if you have to get across a polluted city? What are your options, then? At one end of the spectrum, you could hop on the

continued

concept bicycle proposed by Bangkok's Lightfog design studio. It sucks in pollution at the front, passes it through a filter and replaces it with oxygen generated by what the inventors describe as a battery-powered 'photosynthesis' cleaner built into the frame. (Assuming it works – and that's a big question in itself – that would be an example of cleaning methods 1 and 3.) Or, if you're keen on cycling but prefer a more traditional bike, you could take inspiration from artist Matt Hope and a jokey video he posted on YouTube. Using a junk IKEA dustbin and a broken-down air cleaner, he built a pedal-powered, 5,000-volt elec-trostatic smoke precipitator into a bike helmet to deliver fresh air directly to a cyclist's face mask. (That's method 1 again.)

Inventors like inventing, but their elaborate workarounds are sometimes more trouble than they're worth: there are often simpler and much more effective solutions. Thanks to smartphones with built-in GPS, which always know where you are, air quality apps are an increasingly popular way of avoiding pollution. The best ones help you plan your route from A to B via any letters of the alphabet that don't involve dirty air. Sounds great, but it relies on there being lots of accurate, real-time pollution monitors and maps – and, at the moment, that's something most cities still don't have. [33]

CHAPTER 11

People power

Who will finally get a grip on pollution?

I took a ride on a restored steam train yesterday, packed full of children and their over-excited parents. The drifting smoke was so thick with soot that we could barely see the cows scattering as we rattled through the fields. Today, steam trains like this seem disarmingly charming and, where I live, their history and romance is a massive tourist attraction. Set that aside, however, and what we have, objectively, is horrific and unacceptable air pollution – far worse than you get from any modern power plant, diesel car or factory smokestack.

Here's the thing, though: I'm part of the problem. I've travelled on this train for 20 years and donated lots of money to keep it running. So even after all the time I've spent researching air pollution and the problems it brings, I knowingly make matters worse. I can reason that away quite easily – 'It's pathetic and churlish to complain about something so innocent that gives so many people such pleasure ... It's only a tiny little bit of smoke compared to all those power plants in China ... It really doesn't make any difference to anyone' – but, actually, we all say that, all the time, about all the little puffs of pollution we produce. And unfortunately, it all adds up. That's how air pollution is slowly becoming the world's biggest killer, one dirty little breath at a time.

As we saw in the last chapter, technology won't solve our pollution problems completely – for the simple reason that it doesn't really cause those problems in the first place. Steam engines like mine, wood burners like yours, the dirty diesel your neighbour drives because it's cheaper than her last car, the coal-fired power plants that fuel the presses on which many books are printed – these are all symptoms of a more fundamental issue: it's *people* who make pollution when they do things, not the machines they employ in the process. That means it's people, ultimately – you and me and the rest of humanity – who have the power to solve the problem, too.

How, though, will we go about it? If pollution kills millions and costs trillions, if it causes lung cancer and miscarriages, plants time bombs in our babies' brains, chokes our cities, and shrivels the crops that feed us, if it really is *that* serious, why do our governments do so little about it? Why does the political process let us down so badly? Is it simply the age-old conflict between powerful economic interests and (what are often perceived to be) feeble environmental concerns? Is it because politicians don't take the issue seriously – or is it because we don't take it seriously enough ourselves? Even in green-minded Germany, only a piffling 26 per cent of people think air pollution is one of the top three environmental issues, according to Ipsos. Perhaps because we often can't see modern air pollution, there's a huge disconnect between the objective importance of the issue (measured in death and suffering) and our subjective reaction to it (how much it actually bothers us and the changes we're prepared to make in our lives to stop it). [1]

TESTING TESTING

Steam trains

The old train I travelled on puffed out an awful lot of what you might charitably call 'good old-fashioned pollution': you can see it, smell it and – if you're lucky – take steps to avoid it. Most of a steam train's sooty smoke chuffs high above the locomotive and dissipates in the wind, but some does seep into the carriages behind; and you have to wonder what the engine driver and fireman are breathing in. I was carrying my Plume Flow air monitor throughout my trip and recorded the level of fine PM2.5 particulates. I've made this trip hundreds of times and this felt like a relatively clean journey to me. Even so, as you can see from this chart, tiny specks of engine soot can make the air in the very clean countryside where I live far dirtier than you'd find on an average day in Paris.

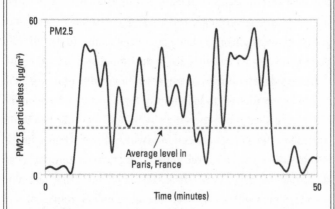

Figure 50. Chart shows: Y axis: Concentration of PM2.5 particulates in µg/m³; X axis: time in minutes.

The politics of pollution

A mixed record

If you're expecting politicians to clean the air for you, don't hold your breath. While I've been researching this book, I've witnessed four egregious examples, in four separate continents, that faith in politicians is fatally misplaced when it comes to pollution.

First there was India, where vomiting Sri Lankan cricketers were forced to halt play in New Delhi in smog levels twelve times higher than WHO guidelines. Only weeks before, flights to and from Delhi had been cancelled for days and thousands of schools closed as pollution hit record levels. Newspapers around the world ran headline after headline decrying India's foul air. Yet Prime Minister Narendra Modi – social-media savvy, with 50 million followers on Twitter – remained strangely silent. Meanwhile, in the UK, the government was squandering almost £400,000 of public money fighting a challenge in the courts to its 'illegally poor' plans for tackling dirty air. In the United States, Scott Pruitt, then President Trump's controversial environmental boss, had begun hiring advisers to help him systematically undermine the well-established link between air pollution and poor health. In Australia, after a national election in which climate change finally became a 'decisive issue', the government immediately approved the vast and hugely controversial AU$16.5 billion Carmichael mine project, which will see between 10 and 60 million tonnes of coal scraped from the ground and exported to dirty power plants in *India* each year. [2]

All four countries have a mixed record on tackling air pollution. In India, Modi's government has supplied LPG gas cylinders to some 50 million households so they can (in theory) stop burning dirty biomass and avoid its health risks. Modi also brought in tougher vehicle emissions standards and a long overdue National Clean Air Programme, with a five-year plan to tackle pollution. But critics say the proposal is weak (with modest reduction targets of just 20–30 per cent) and lacking specifics in how it will be implemented and enforced. Meanwhile, the Modi government has been charged both with failing to tackle pollution from coal-fired power plants and failing to invest in the renewables that would reduce its dependence on them. Half of all Indians consider air pollution one of the top three environmental issues, yet it barely figured in the country's 2019 election campaign beyond an absurdly ambitious pledge by government minister Nitin Gadkari that 'Delhi will be free of air and water pollution in the next three years'. That's just the kind of over-promise that undermines faith in politicians. [3]

In the UK, early deaths from air pollution halved between 1970 and 2010, but national government policies (promoting things like 'the biggest road-building programme since the Romans' and failing to tackle agricultural emissions) can't take the credit. One recent study found it was impossible to say exactly which policies – local, regional, national, European or (most likely) some combination – had made the difference. Over the last decade or so, according to Britain's leading air experts, progress has 'miserably stalled': they say there's been no change in air pollution levels either in Britain's capital or the UK as a whole. Those levels remain illegal in many urban areas, yet the British government repeatedly failed to come up with a credible plan to tackle the problem and, as a result, found itself losing three very embarrassing High Court legal challenges. [4]

In the United States, there were dramatic improvements in air quality during the second half of the 20th century, following President Richard Nixon's introduction of the Clean

Air Act in 1970 and its later extensions. Cuts in pollutants have made a very real difference: one recent study has calculated that improvements in ozone and fine particulate levels alone saved some 40,000 or so early deaths between 1990 and 2010. All very impressive, and yet, just as in the UK, US air quality falls far short of where it might be in such a wealthy country. University of North Carolina environmental scientists Jason West and Barbara Turpin made the point forcefully in a recent piece in *The Conversation*: dirty air still 'kills more Americans than all transportation accidents and gun shootings combined. More than diabetes or than breast cancer plus prostate cancer. More than Parkinson's disease plus leukaemia plus HIV/Aids. And unlike diabetes or Parkinson's, deaths from air pollution are entirely preventable.' It was frightening, then, to see numerous air-cleaning initiatives (including car-efficiency standards and a ban on dirty truck engines) rolled back by the Trump administration's EPA boss Scott Pruitt and his successor Andrew Wheeler, a former coal-industry lobbyist. [5]

In Australia, the 2019 national election brought real hope that the country was finally ready to shake off its reputation as an environmental laggard. In the 1990s, as a prominent member of an informal alliance known as JUSCANZ (Japan, the US, Canada, Australia and New Zealand), Australia helped to undermine climate science and opposed proactive measures to tackle global warming put forward by the low-lying Pacific nations who would be first to 'drown' in a world of rising seas. A decade later, former premier Tony Abbott made much of his personal climate denial, declaring himself 'unconvinced by the so-called settled science on climate change', which he referred to as 'absolute crap', and suggesting that global warming was 'probably doing good'. But strident voices backfire; since 2012, there has been a doubling in support for immediate action on climate change among Australians, with 84 per cent in a recent poll supporting a strong focus on renewables. On one hand, the government seems to play to that audience; in 2018, Australia claimed to have double the per-capita investment in clean energy of European countries. But the Australian coal industry has powerful political friends. Allowing the giant Adani company to mine millions of tonnes of Queensland coal for export to India, while supporting a shift to renewables at home, is one way politicians can square the circle. [6]

PRESIDENTS PONDER POLLUTION

Since the introduction of the Clean Air Act in 1970, US Republican presidents have repeatedly flip-flopped on the issue of air pollution...

Richard Nixon made the issue a centrepiece of his 1970 State of the Union address: 'Clean air, clean water, open spaces – these should once again be the birthright of every American. If we act now, they can be. We still think of air as free. But clean air is not free, and neither is clean water. The price tag on pollution control is high. Through our years of past carelessness we incurred a debt to nature, and now that debt is being called. The program I shall propose to Congress will be the most comprehensive and costly program in this field in America's history.' This speech paved the way for the 1970 Clean Air Act and the foundation of the Environmental Protection Agency, but the word 'costly' rang alarm bells with Republicans that continue sounding to this day.

In marked contrast, in the 1980s, **Ronald Reagan** was a notable air pollution denier: his speeches were littered with baseless claims suggesting trees and volcanoes are worse for the air than cars or

continued

trucks and, by implication, environmentalists are a serious threat to the economy. A role model for Donald Trump, he undermined the EPA by appointing as its head Anne Gorsuch, a fierce opponent of clean air legislation, who immediately attacked the agency with sweeping budget and staff cuts.

George H.W. Bush, by contrast, saw the need to work with Democrat opponents to strengthen the original Nixon Clean Air Act. Passed with overwhelming bipartisan support, the greatly extended 1990 Act has been widely credited with reducing acid rain and the ozone hole, and helping to improve air quality in a raft of other ways. It was for this achievement that Bush received an unprecedented standing ovation from the leaders of American green groups, even prompting Fred Krupp of the EDF (Environmental Defense Fund) to describe him as an 'environmental hero'.

His son, **George W. Bush**, launched a market-based initiative called Clear Skies that he claimed would balance society's competing demands: 'Our economy has grown 164 per cent in three decades. According to the EPA report released yesterday, air pollution from six major pollutants is down by 48 per cent during that time. It's possible to grow the economy and protect the air. We're proving it here in America.' At the same time, however, he was undermining the EPA's work in subtle ways, removing or delaying various existing protections, including rules on mercury emissions from power plants.

Donald Trump blended Reagan's polarising rhetoric with George W. Bush's subtle attack on science. Like Reagan, he promptly installed a hand-picked, hostile administrator at the EPA. Scott Pruitt immediately slashed the agency's workforce and budget, revoked carbon limits on vehicles following intense lobbying from the car industry, announced plans to repeal the Clean Power Plan (predicted to bring about up to $34 billion in health benefits by 2030), dismissed and repealed long-standing limits on 200 major pollutants (including arsenic and lead) as 'regulatory burdens' and, like George W. Bush, tried to neuter the evidence the EPA could use, in an attempt to undermine its effectiveness as a regulator. [7]

What should politicians do about air pollution?

On the face of it, a simple question with a simple answer. Tackling pollution politically ought to boil down to setting specific air quality targets (ideally, ambitious ones) and figuring out pragmatic, cost-effective ways to achieve them, making sure we monitor progress along the way and putting enforcement mechanisms in place to ensure there's a strong prospect of success. This is the approach that the International Energy Agency favours. Framing pollution as a problem of how we use (or abuse) energy, its process for achieving air quality goals is based on a three-pronged approach it calls A-I-R: Avoidance (preventing emissions through efficiency improvements and renewable energy), Innovation (in other words, new technology) and Reduction (setting strict limits on emissions that can't be avoided). [8]

That sounds easy enough if we're just talking about what drifts from smokestacks. But it's much harder when we start to tease out the details of how myriad individual pollutants drift into the sky – in other words, the wide range of problems that pollute the air around the world. In a country like India, political action plans need to be equally adept at reducing, for example, large emissions from a relatively small number of power plants and factories, and small emissions from a relatively large number of homes burning biomass. They need to tackle the chronic nuisance of traffic and industry as well as the acute, seasonal issue of agricultural stubble burning (one of the main causes of Delhi's annual winter 'airpocalypse'). It's also important to understand that pollution, as it impacts people, is a matter of *exposure* more than *emissions*; a problem of demographics (the ageing population suffering more), culture (it takes a lot to change how people cook, live or travel), natural causes (often beyond our control) and more. [9]

Targets and strategies are useless without the political determination to press them home, but in many countries, the messy, multi-level and not entirely hierarchical government system makes that frustratingly slow and complex. One reason Delhi has such persistent problems with pollution is an ongoing tussle between the national government and various state and municipal governments over who is responsible for what. In theory, the idea of cleaning the air is far more meaningful at a local level (people tend to live or work in one or two urban places and care most about the air quality there) than when it's averaged across an entire country (with a host of different problems that vary widely from one region to the next). But local governments trying to deliver clean cities and an improved environment sometimes find the public have different priorities. In the British city of Manchester, for example, ambitious attempts to set up a huge (210 square kilometre/80 square mile) clean-air zone were scrapped after almost *80 per cent* of the local people opposed the idea in a 2010 referendum. A decade later, a revised clean-air zone put forward by Manchester's local government failed to win the backing of Britain's national government. [10]

Clean-air zones are generally accepted to be the most effective way for cities to attack traffic pollution, but they're not always popular with elected politicians who inherit them from their predecessors. In Madrid when Isabel Díaz Ayuso, President of the Popular Party, swept to power in 2019, one of her very first acts was to target the city's congestion zone and a successful anti-pollution campaign called Madrid Central. Deriding these initiatives as a 'bungling ... fudge', she argued, instead, that traffic is integral to the city's culture and nightlife. 'Integral', perhaps, but not always in a good way. Madrid houses the Museo del Prado, home to some of the world's greatest art, which was once so filled with polluted air from the city that many famous canvases were damaged beyond repair. In an interview with the Spanish newspaper *El País*, she argued that 'congestion is a hallmark of Madrid' and that the city's 'always alive' nightlife 'goes hand in hand with traffic jams'. Plans to scrap the anti-pollution initiatives were immediately opposed by both the World Federation of Public Health Associations and the European Public Health Association, which argued that they were essential measures in a city criticised for its failure to meet air pollution targets for over a decade. The European Commission promptly warned Spain that it faced being taken to the EU Court of Justice if it failed to clean up its act. [11]

All this strongly suggests that we can't trust politicians to deliver us from the evils of pollution; and, of course, there are always conveniently competing priorities. When President Donald Trump tweeted that he was 'committed to keeping our air and water clean but always remember that economic growth enhances environmental protection. Jobs matter!', his left-leaning opponents were quick to scoff, yet most economists would certainly agree. Sometimes the falsely framed battle between economics and environmental priorities forces governments to ignore their very own conflicting research reports or kick difficult decisions further down the road, typically by launching lengthy public consultations that make tricky issues the next government's problem. Politicians necessarily have to keep happy the people who put them in place – sometimes the motoring lobby, the fossil fuel companies or other dirty industries who'd prefer us not to tackle pollution head-on. Even when they number millions and billions, the people who suffer most from dirty air – the poor, the sick, the elderly, the young and even the unborn – are no match for such politically adept and powerful vested interests. [12]

Sometimes, failure to act on pollution is much more serious than simple procrastination: we're now electing politicians who actively deny the health harms of air pollution and deliberately try to roll back proven, cost-effective measures like the US Clean Air Act. 'Air-pollution denial', as it's become known, is firmly on the rise among populist politicians the world over. In Spain, as we've just seen, Isabel Díaz Ayuso happily 'celebrated' the traffic in Madrid. In the United States, Donald Trump's EPA boss Scott Pruitt systematically weakened the agency's ability to tackle pollution. In India, Modi government environment minister (and doctor) Harsh Vardhan downplayed the link between air pollution and poor health; in 2017, he told New Delhi Television: 'To attribute any death to a cause like pollution, that may be too much', despite previously calling it 'a silent killer'. In Poland, meanwhile, energy minister Krzysztof Tchórzewski told all-too-receptive ears at a transport industry conference that 'pollution is ... definitely not the reason why someone will live shorter' (a glib assertion easily refuted by decades of peer-reviewed medical research). [13]

But isn't it too easy to blame politicians for failing to solve difficult problems? Who elected them in the first place? Perhaps, as philosopher Joseph de Maistre famously pointed out, we really do get the politicians and governments we deserve. Pollution is our problem, ours in the making and ours to solve; and if politicians can't deliver, we have to find other ways to tackle it instead.

See you in court

Maybe laws can help us out? Countries like Britain and the United States pioneered modern, industrial air pollution in the 18th and 19th centuries; they also introduced some of the first modern laws for tackling it, mostly in the 20th century. In both countries, major improvements in air quality came about through legislation passed in the wake of appalling urban pollution tragedies (the 1948 Donora disaster in the USA, and the 1952 Great London Smog in the UK), although it did take the rest of the century. On the other hand, most industrialised countries have now had air quality laws for decades, yet pollution remains rife – at life-threatening levels – almost everywhere in the world. Perhaps legal attempts to clean the air haven't been as successful as we might have hoped? Then again, if the laws were entirely ineffective, vested interests and their captive politicians wouldn't be quite so quick to unpick them. A recent review of international air pollution laws by Finnish researchers Yulia Yamineva and Seita Romppanen concluded that they 'do not provide a comprehensive response to air pollution', are 'ad hoc', have 'serious gaps' and fail to 'address the global impacts' of the problem. Like every other pollution solution, clean air laws have their place, but they're only one piece of the jigsaw. [14]

One of the drawbacks of anti-pollution laws is that they're invariably reactive: pollution has to become a major public nuisance before there's enough pressure to tackle it and, by that point, what causes it is already deeply ingrained. Returning to the example of the UK, although urban parts of the country such as London had experienced pollution problems for centuries, a raft of early clean-air legislation – from the Smoke Nuisance Abatement Act of 1821 to the Public Health Act for London of 1891 – proved unable to keep pace with the problem. That was how the Great London Smog came about and why a brand new law – Britain's 1956 Clean Air Act – had to be passed to stop it happening again. But the 1956 Act was a very specific response to the 1952 disaster, designed to control the mid-20th century nuisance of sooty smoke from home fires and power plant chimneys. This, and more recent legislation, has done little or nothing to rein in current pollution problems from such things as diesel engines and wood burners. [15]

In the United States, the Clean Air Act (originally passed in 1963, then extended in 1970, 1977 and 1990) is rightly regarded as one of the most effective pieces of environmental law ever created. A 1997 study found that, in 1990 alone, it prevented '205,000 early deaths, 10.4 million lost IQ points in children due to lead exposure and millions of other cases of health effects', and estimated that the total economic benefits between 1970 and 1990 amounted to $22.2 trillion. A follow-up study covering the period 1990–2020 suggested the Act would prevent 230,000 early deaths a year, 5.4 million lost school days, 17 million lost work days, 120,000 emergency room visits and many other public health benefits by 2020 – concluding that the economic value of all this would exceed the cost of bringing it about by around 30:1. It was therefore pretty baffling – to put it mildly – when the Trump administration set about dismantling measures like the Clean Power Plan (aimed at cleaning up pollution from the electricity industry), which helped to deliver some of the Clean Air Act's recent achievements. [16]

It's not just effective clean air laws that we need, but a willingness to enforce them; in that respect, official agencies that are subject to political pressure are sometimes found wanting. The task of prosecuting needless pollution – or failing to act on the wider problem – often falls on quick-witted campaigning lawyers who know the legislation inside out and figure out how to deploy it to maximum effect. In the United States, eco-law firm Earthjustice (a spin-off from the Sierra Club) has fought a decades-long battle against coal-plant pollution and campaigned effectively for tougher rules on mercury, helping to bring about an 80 per cent

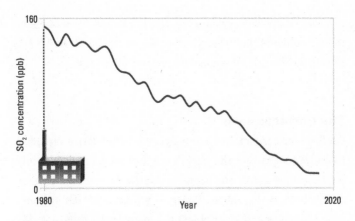

Figure 51. Smokestacks under control: the US Clean Air Act led to a dramatic reduction in sulphur dioxide emissions. Chart shows SO_2 concentration in parts per billion, drawn using data from the US Environmental Protection Agency (EPA). [17]

cut in emissions from power plants. In the UK, between 2010 and 2017, the international campaigning law firm ClientEarth scored three notable air pollution victories over the British government in the High Court over its failure to come up with a decent strategy for cleaning the air. In Australia, Environmental Justice has campaigned repeatedly against coal power plants and weak pollution limits. [18]

One problem with eco laws is that they have to be advanced by elected politicians; in other words, the legal process for protecting the environment rides on the back of an often-flawed political process. Another issue is that laws aren't immutable: the more effective they are, the more likely they are to come under attack from vested interests. A further difficulty, as I noted above, is that laws have to be specific to be effective, but the more specific they are the less likely they are to move with the times – and remain effective at tackling types of air pollution that have not yet been anticipated. But even if you doubt that environmental laws can ever completely regulate the people who put them in place, there's no doubt that when they work – as the US Clean Air Act undeniably has – they can make a massive difference.

The business case

Car firms, oil corporations, mining giants, factory farms – it's easy to find scapegoats for the world's eco problems. But does pointing the finger get us any nearer a solution? One of the themes of this book is that 'air pollution' is a misnomer: it's not one, neat and easy-to-tackle problem but many subtly different, difficult issues that don't always benefit by being lumped together. Since the problems vary from country to country, the solutions vary, too, and so do the people with the power to deliver them. Should we really be looking to businesses to tackle air pollution? Or should we be asking ourselves why we've created a culture of market- and customer-oriented businesses that don't respect environmental values like clean air? Are they to blame – or, in the end, are we?

It's complicated. In India and China, while home fuel burning is a big cause of pollution, factories and power plants are major polluters too, so industry certainly has a key part to play. Then again, as we saw in Chapter 6, a certain amount of air pollution snakes out of Chinese factories making unrealistically cheap goods for unquestioning, entitled Westerners. In the UK, the worst air pollution is now caused by urban traffic, yet drivers still strongly believe that the car industry should take the lead in cleaning up their mess. In South Africa, big businesses have often vigorously opposed efforts to cut spectacularly bad power plant and factory emissions. (The fact that a mere 15 per cent of South Africans view air pollution as an important problem – fewer than in almost any other major country in the world – really doesn't help.) In Australia, at a time when comparably wealthy nations are switching away from fossil fuels, choking coal power plants not only keep on burning, but keep on polluting thanks to much weaker emissions standards than in Europe, North America and even parts of Asia. According to campaigners like Environmental Justice, that's potentially putting thousands of lives at risk. The plant operators reject the claim and insist they operate within the law – but they could hardly be accused of being proactive. And in the end, is that a failure of business, law, politics or the people? [19]

It's easy enough to find examples of businesses doing commendably good things on air pollution. In Germany, bus companies such as Berliner Verkehrsbetriebe, Hamburger Hochbahn and Stadtwerke München have started the slow process of replacing their ageing diesels with fully electric vehicles. Meanwhile, the Climate Group (a non-profit that helps big businesses shift toward sustainability) has been working to electrify 2 million vehicles operated by 31 major businesses in the United States, the UK and India by the year 2030 (including IKEA, Bank of America, DHL and the Port Authority of New York and New Jersey). Not to be outdone, Amazon has recently announced that it will buy 100,000 electric delivery trucks for use across North America and Europe. In Britain's West Midlands, businesses are working with universities and local authorities on plans that include clean air zones, better air monitoring, better-planned use of vehicle fleets to reduce unnecessary travel and a new centre of excellence for developing state-of-the-art batteries for electric cars. Mahindra & Mahindra, one of India's biggest multinationals, has become an enthusiastic advocate of green technologies, from electric vehicles and LED lighting to renewable energy and tree planting. Search around online and you'll find many more examples like this. But here's the rub: you would have found plenty of similar examples 20–30 years ago. [20]

Back then, eco-minded members of the business community were saying exactly the same things as they are now. The prophets were self-proclaimed 'green capitalists' like John Elkington, telling us 'how industry can make money and protect the environment', and Paul Hawken, the 'natural capitalist' fond of platitudes like 'The bottom line is down where it belongs – at the bottom'. In those days, when 'corporate social responsibility' first became a thing, you might well have noticed Ben & Jerry's ice cream taking a stand on artificial growth hormones in cows (1989), the Patagonia clothing company announcing a switch to organic cotton (1994) or Britain's Cooperative Bank running TV advertisements about refusing to invest in 'companies who needlessly pollute the environment' (1994). But the rub of the rub is that you could have found similar examples way back in 1970. That year, Alvin Toffler published *Future Shock*, his astonishingly prescient bestseller about a looming future of too-much, too-now 'information overload'. In it, he cited AT&T 'worrying about air and water pollution', while 'the Vanderbilt Mutual Fund and the Provident Fund refuse to invest in liquor or tobacco shares' and 'the tiny Vantage 10/90 Fund invests part of its assets in industries working to alleviate food and production problems in developing nations'. [21]

Of course 'green' corporate initiatives to tackle problems like air pollution are very welcome, but we should greet them with a healthy pinch of salt. Business people would surely agree; how about this refreshingly honest quote from economist Frances Cairncross, written in 1995, which is just as true today: 'Companies are not individuals, with a moral obligation to be good environmental citizens, even in situations where that is not in their commercial interest. They are owned by their shareholders; and their overriding duty is to do what is in the long-term commercial interest of their owners.' Now you could reasonably argue, as 1990s green capitalists would have done, that environmental protection is a 'long-term commercial interest', but I wouldn't hold your breath waiting for that 'long-term' to arrive. It seems incredibly naive to me to think that any more than a tiny few businesses are genuinely interested in anything but the bottom line, while consumer pressure is more likely to deliver temporary 'greenwash' and distracting scandals like Dieselgate than any deeper and more authentic change. Paul Kingsnorth, an eloquent writer and disaffected campaigner who describes himself as a 'recovering environmentalist', reaches the same conclusion as Cairncross from the opposite direction. In his view, the 'terrible hollowness' of corporate exhortations to 'save the planet' is just another kind of business-as-usual; it's a superficial engagement with deep-seated issues – little more than 'a desperate attempt to prevent Gaia from hiccuping and wiping out our coffee shops and broadband connections'. [22]

The people versus... the people

Who benefits from air pollution? If we're talking about something like the Ontario Superstack, one of the world's tallest chimneys, which allegedly streamed its high emissions a distance of 240 kilometres (150 miles), the easy answer would be that one corporation and its shareholders benefited while millions of homes and their occupants downwind paid the price. The classic economic analysis of pollution describes it as an 'external cost' that businesses escape paying: it's free to blow your smoke into the air and expensive to clean it up so, rationally, unless something (like a law) stops you, polluting is your best course of action. The classic environmental solution is something called the 'polluter pays principle': it's the small number of offenders, not the large number of victims, who should pay the price of making or avoiding pollution.

The trouble with this analysis is that it's geared to them-and-us, polluters versus polluted, so it breaks down when we talk about messy real-world situations: the idea that we're all victims of someone else's pollution is far too simplistic in most everyday cases. Take, for example, indoor air pollution from cookstoves. The householders certainly benefit – but they also pay the price: the polluters *are* the polluted. Who should 'pay' in a world of crippling poverty where people can't even afford cleaner stoves and fuel? In most outdoor urban spaces, air is polluted by many different sources and, this time, many people suffer and simultaneously benefit. Again, the polluters and the polluted are generally the same people. We all benefit from road transportation even if we don't drive cars. We all use electricity from power plants. We all buy things made from metal that has to be mined and refined in highly polluting smelters. And even if you go out of your way to buy ethical things that aren't made by polluting the planet, you'll still have to engage with other people who do buy things from those places. So there's no avoiding being a polluter, once or twice or however many times removed, even if you can somehow live in a saintly bubble and pretend you're avoiding pollution yourself.

I feel that the only reasonable analysis of air pollution ('reasonable' in that it offers a realistic long-term prospect of tackling the problem) is to accept that we're all collectively responsible for making the mess – and we're all jointly responsible for cleaning it up. It's a kind of denial to expect politicians to sort out the problem, or the law, or business or just someone else, somehow forgetting that in democratic, capitalist societies all these things exist for the benefit or at the service of the rest of us.

Embarrassingly earnest though they can seem, there's something to be said for fluffy eco slogans like 'Think global, act local' and 'Be the change you want to see in the world'.

Unfortunately, many of us are too comfortable to change even slightly, never mind do anything as dramatic as 'be the change'. Even if we care about things like air pollution, we don't necessarily care for long. There are just too many competing demands on our time and attention: we have stressful jobs, ageing parents, stroppy teenagers, cancer scares and plenty of other daily headlines to fret about as well. Though we're sympathetic to the logic of green messages, and do what we can if it's quick and easy, most of us are not environmentalists and we never will be. Life revolves around our families, homes, friends, jobs and social lives – and if we can fit a bit of feel-good 'greenness' or social conscience into that somewhere, fine. But the fact that millions are dying every year from air pollution – and most of us are suffering from the problem in one way or another without even realising it – shows that we can't afford to take quite such a relaxed attitude.

Campaign games?

Of course, this is why we have campaign groups like Greenpeace, the Sierra Club, Amigos de la Tierra and all the rest: they're our green conscience, prodding us out of our apathy to shift our lazy behaviour, shout at politicians or fund legal challenges by eco lawyers. 'Top-down' campaigning can be spectacularly successful: the energetic efforts of just a handful of indefatigable individuals can tap into backing from thousands or millions of supporters, but its drawback is that it's manipulative (almost by definition) and often leaves the people at the bottom fundamentally unmoved and unchanged. Legal battles mounted by campaign groups are hugely and undeniably valuable, but they seem to me to suffer from that last problem even more seriously. Lawyers quibbling over the fine print of this or that Act are even further removed from you and me – the very people whose 'polluting behaviour' must be the heart of change.

'David and Goliath' legal fights mounted by individuals against their negligent governments might be more productive. Recently, a mother and her sixteen-year-old daughter won a landmark legal fight against the lax French government over the health impacts of living near a polluted ring-road in Paris. Shortly afterwards, three teenagers in Pakistan took their government to court to have its air pollution policy declared 'illegal and unreasonable' and force it to come up with something better. Perhaps this is the shape of legal things to come; perhaps we'll soon be seeing lawsuits against individual politicians or governments, like those that smokers brought against disingenuous tobacco companies who downplayed the links between cigarettes and cancer. Dr Maria Neira, WHO director for public health and the environment, hinted as much in a recent interview with *The Guardian* newspaper: 'Politicians cannot say in 10 years from now, when citizens will start to take them to court for the harm they have suffered, that they didn't know. We all know pollution is causing major damage and we all know it is something we can avoid.' [23]

All too often, however, single-issue campaigners play dubious games. When Greenpeace activists climbed seventeen statues in central London a few years ago, including Nelson's Column and Winston Churchill, and clamped papier-mâché gas masks to their faces to draw attention to chronic air pollution, there was plenty of news coverage – but how many ordinary people gave up their cars and wood-burning stoves as a result? [24]

For many people, 'preachy environmentalism' (as they see it) is either a direct turn-off or a dare to do the opposite. Just think how many people proudly refer to themselves as 'petrol heads' – a concept that would never have existed if environmentalists hadn't rubbed them up the wrong way. In the right-leaning *Daily Mail*, the world's most popular online newspaper, the London gas-mask action was reported with the sneering headline 'Greenpeace campaigners who scaled Nelson's Column for a publicity stunt and caused thousands of pounds worth of damage are spared jail', with a mere eight words noting that the objective was: 'to raise awareness over impact of air pollution'. It's important for environmentalists – and campaigners, who are trying to communicate and change things – to remember that they're radical outliers who can sometimes polarise opinion and make change harder to achieve. The mature starting point for politics isn't that everyone else is stupid and needs to be bullied into your superior way of thinking, but that people will always disagree about complex things; somehow, skilfully and cooperatively, we have to recognise this fact and get past our differences. The President who made arguably the greatest practical improvement in air pollution in the United States – George H.W. Bush – wasn't a polariser, like Reagan or Trump, but a respected, cooperative, bipartisan who knew how to bring people together. However inspiring they are, green activists won't 'save the planet' without a lot of help from people who, frankly, couldn't care less about it. One radical 1990s eco group, Earth First!, made their name locking themselves to bulldozers (and, occasionally, smashing them up or setting them on fire) with the motto 'No compromise in defence of mother Earth'. But I can think of plenty of sober-suited politicians who'd make a decent case for running that same sentiment in reverse: 'No defence of mother Earth without compromise.' [25]

Does gung-ho 'environmentalism' get in the way of air pollution campaigns? Maybe yes, maybe no; but it's far from clear to me

– a lifelong environmentalist – that it always helps. When it comes to campaigning, what I think *does* makes a difference is calls to action coming not from environmentalists, whose motives right-wingers tend to see as some sort of broader socialist plot, but from indisputably authentic people with a totally transparent agenda. In other words, doctors and medics, making a pure and simple public-health argument. Thus, we have compelling campaigns like Doctors and Scientists Against Wood Smoke Pollution advancing a tightly focused, evidence-based argument against wood burners. In India, a group called Doctors for Clean Air founded by Dr Arvind Kumar in New Delhi makes equally forceful arguments; noting, for example, that a child born in that city inhales pollution equivalent to smoking fifteen cigarettes in their very first day of life. That's a perfectly self-contained argument against air pollution; it needs no green packaging. [26]

By the same token, community campaigns – home-grown and locally motivated – seem to me to be a more promising proposi-tion than those imposed from outside by professional activists or ideologically tilted governments. Quite possibly, they're the key to the clean-air revolution. They might be clumsily organised (or dis-organised) in chilly church halls, with shambolic banners scrawled on torn bedsheets by badly face-painted children, but they have an undeniable integrity. To me, these sorts of authentic, local cam-paigns are infinitely more persuasive than slick but insincere PR stunts orchestrated from whiteboards by professional eco groups in distant cities. Local media love local champions of local causes; all it takes to kick-start a campaign like this is a couple of inspired, angry mums willing to knock on doors in their neighbourhood or ring around their friends. In the UK, parent-of-two David Smith started making national headlines when his well-argued website took aim at the London pollution he believed was threatening the health of his children. Sometimes small campaigns like that lead to much bigger things. In the United States, one of the most compelling voices against air pollution is the brilliantly named Moms Clean Air Force, a group of 1.3 million ordinary American citizens who combine the authenticity and integrity of deeply concerned parents with the slick savvy of a well-run campaign group. [27]

Shining light on the invisible

For campaigners, information is power, but how to find information about an invisible problem – air pollution – that can change from one day or hour to the next? That used to be a really big issue; in some parts of the world, it's still a stumbling block. For many of us, however, that's all changed thanks to digital technology and the Internet. Nip to your nearest web browser and it's possible to look up past or present air quality data for a big chunk of the planet. The World Health Organization's ambient air quality database keeps official tabs on 4,300 cities in 103 countries (with 1,000 more cities added since 2016 alone), while apps and websites give a reasonable live picture for some of the bigger urban areas. Search engines like Google and social media platforms, notably Facebook and Twitter, have an ever-increasing focus on delivering locally relevant results based on our physical location, and could prove to be invaluable allies in making people more aware of the air around them. Google's Street View tool, for example, can already help you plan your route through a city to avoid traffic congestion; what if it could help you avoid pollution, too? (Google is now equipping some of its Street View camera cars with mobile air sensors to help create better pollution maps.) [28]

If your local air quality isn't officially monitored, you can simply measure it yourself; the fashionable phenomenon called 'citizen science' (where ordinary people run inexpensive, DIY, community experiments and pool their data online) is playing a big part in helping bottom-up, grassroots campaigns to find greater credibility. Measuring air pollution can be technically difficult and very expensive, but there are plenty of community groups around the world who've figured out how to do it. There's also a raft of relatively affordable digital devices (like the Plume Flow I've been using throughout this book), linked to smartphone apps, that can collect data automatically and map the results in real time. Even the US EPA has been encouraging communities to have a go at air monitoring with something it calls the Air Sensor Toolbox for Citizen Science. The data from these sorts of efforts isn't going to be cutting-edge lab quality – it will never win a Nobel Prize in Chemistry – but that's not the point; it gets people talking, thinking and acting.

Armed with decent data, community campaigners have the power to make a difference. Properly organised and in sufficient numbers, they can also help to inform mainstream academic science. In Belgium, for example, University of Antwerp researchers enlisted the help of 20,000 community volunteers to take ground-level air samples that would otherwise have been prohibitively expensive. Carefully coordinated by the University of Leiden, Netherlands, people in eleven European countries made 5,386 air pollution measurements with simple sensors attached to their iPhones. In the age of 'big data', it won't be long before the ever-increasing mass of air pollution data is being analysed to name and shame the worst offenders in our local communities, whether they're roads, factories, waste incinerators or trash-burning neighbours; that could pay big dividends. Plume Labs, maker of the Flow device, has recently launched a phone app that combines a huge mass of pollution data from multiple sources to draw live street maps of the air quality in hundreds of US and European cities. [29]

Often, small community groups band together into bigger networks, making powerful local and regional forces. In the United States, there's the Clean Air Coalition of West New York, Clean Air Carolina and the Imperial County Community Air Monitoring Network in California – to name just three. In India, citizen scientists from Mumbai have joined forces with friends from the PakAirQuality project in Islamabad, Pakistan, to extend air quality testing in ten cities where official monitoring is poor or non-existent. [30]

What about the 99 per cent of the 'ordinary community' who don't want to get involved in activities like this? Fire up every politician, CEO, eco lawyer, environmental campaigner and local community group in the world and you'll reach only a fraction of the people you need to. Most of us will still be living our lives outside the fray, quietly polluting the planet in just the same way. I've come to believe that a key part of the solution is making invisible air pollution much more visible, much less ignorable, than it is at the moment. The routine monitoring of air quality needs to be much more prominent, so the numbers and the facts are constantly in our faces – in weather forecasts, in smartphone apps, on live street signs or wherever – in just the same way that pollution is getting up our noses. We're all attuned to the temperature in the daily weather report; some of us study the pollen forecast; a few of us might look at the UV index to see if it's safe to sunbathe. But almost none of us take any notice of the air pollution data, because it's generally too vague to be useful or not even reported. Knowing how dirty the air is from day to day and hour to hour, right where you're breathing it, is absolutely key to cleaning it up; without that information, we're all just guessing.

Does anyone care enough to care more? Where I live, a recent survey found that 58 per cent of people believe air pollution is harmful or very harmful to health. At first sight, that sounds encouraging, although, as we saw in Chapter 8, it's not a matter of 'belief' – it's a matter of absolute scientific fact – so the really important question is why that figure isn't 100 per cent. With better education and communication, science and public awareness, perhaps it would be. And perhaps there would then be a more receptive public environment for government 'nudges', like strong incentives for buying electric vehicles at the expense of diesel ones or deterrent taxes on wood burners. But measures like these will only succeed if they reward easy alternatives to polluting that ordinary people can quickly buy into and benefit from. And if, as with smoking, we truly understand the harms we and our children need to avoid. [31]

Meanwhile, thousands of scientists around the world will continue to probe the harm caused by air pollutants. So far, the emphasis has been on studying individual air pollutants in isolation; how these things affect us when they mix together to form toxic cocktails remains largely unknown. Future developments are likely to include much more work figuring out the exact biological mechanisms by which specific chemicals in the air damage our bodies in the short- and long-term. The complex interaction between climate change and air pollution is another major topic of concern (see box). While there's been a strong recent focus on fine PM2.5 particulates, tomorrow's research is also likely to probe the harm of even tinier ('ultra-fine') particulates (PM1 and smaller). That could yet lead to further upward revisions in the estimated air pollution death toll, making it ultimately the world's biggest killer.

Are we going to sit back and wait for that to happen? Or are we going to choose to clear the air – through the power of all these people combined?

THE CLIMATE CONNECTION

We tend to treat 'air pollution' and 'climate change' as two separate issues – and in lots of ways they are. Air pollution is the stuff that affects us at ground level in the short term, while climate change is more about a kind of long-term air pollution, higher up in the atmosphere, that radically affects the planet's climate. Because climate change is a whole huge topic of its own, and lots has been written about it already, I've deliberately kept mentions to a minimum in this book.

But the two issues interact. A warming world will make air pollution worse in all sorts of ways, from increased forest fires and longer pollen seasons, more soil erosion and wind-blown dust, to greater production of toxic ozone. Air pollution also affects climate change in ways that aren't fully understood, sometimes reducing its effects, sometimes making them worse.

When it comes to tackling these two issues, it makes perfect sense to couple them together. Both problems are essentially caused by how we use energy in archaic, inefficient ways. Solutions to air pollution, like switching from fossil fuels to renewable energy, better urban planning and cleaner cookstoves that reduce deforestation, are also solutions to climate change. Solve one problem and – with luck – we'll solve both.

We find it hard to motivate people to take action on climate change because it seems such a huge, far-off problem; coupling it with the more pressing problem of air pollution could make that easier. People in India, for example, might find it hard to buy into climate-change solutions that offer vague and distant promises of averting what could seem hypothetical problems far in the future, especially if they threaten the country's ability to expand energy use so people can escape poverty. But how would those people feel about *the same solutions* offered as a means of cleaning their city air in the short term and improving their children's health right now?

Coming clean

Towards a conclusion

I've trekked to the city of Birmingham in the English Midlands to conclude this book in a place that perfectly represents the past and present – perhaps also the future – of air pollution.

It's hard to believe now, but this part of England was once the dirty heart of the world: it's where the steam engine, the coal-powered Industrial Revolution and modern air pollution were born, just over three centuries ago. No one knows whether the Black Country, the area just west of here, got its name from the coal that people dug from the ground or the filth that hung in the air when they burned it, but the locals still, oddly and proudly, cling to the nickname to this day. It's hard to see why anyone would want to remember the polluted past, but they seem to cherish it. Picture postcards of the Black Country from the local archives romanticise the town of Dudley (where Thomas Newcomen built the first ever steam engine) exactly as a child would do, with happy horses hauling cheery piles of coal, toy trains tootling around vast slag heaps and thick smoke from the chimneys drifting thoughtfully high and considerately far away. It's so charming, it almost makes me want to go back 150 years and take a holiday there. [1]

When I was growing up near here, many of the streets were daubed in the very same black. The city's obsolete canals shone

Figure 52. Romanticising our polluted past. 'A Pair of the Earl of Dudley's Thick Coal Pits in the Black Country'. [2]

like toxic mercury and stank like sewers, cast aside in favour of tangled, concrete 'Spaghetti Junction' highways that tore through the sky, raining pollution down from above. Today, the Birmingham I stroll around couldn't be more different. The central streets are pedestrianised, for one thing, and there are plans to bring in a clean-air zone. No more blackened buildings; St Philip's Cathedral and The Grand Hotel behind it seem to gleam like new. Cars and diesel buses are banished from the immediate city centre and people get around on an eco-friendly, light-rail tram or simply walk instead. The coal-hauling canal barges, spruced up and painted, have become cosy house-boats; graphic designers and hipster-bearded illustrators slouch in the canal-basin coffee bars sipping lattes and tapping on their laptops. In the once famously filthy, subterranean New Street station (as I discovered in Chapter 5), restless diesel trains pour out thick clouds of NO_2 and particulates. But if you look very closely, you'll spot discreet scientific monitors inside protective cages, constantly sipping the air, noting its quality, on almost every platform. Everywhere you look, it seems someone is making an effort: there's optimism in the air, not filth. In that respect, Birmingham is representative of many cities – and the hopeful future of air pollution – right across the world. [3]

Yet, for all this welcome progress, there's much more to be done: flicking through the latest figures in the World Health Organization's global air quality database, I see that Birmingham only just squeaks inside the guidelines for PM10 pollution, while on dangerous PM2.5s (for which, remember, there is no safe level) it's about 50 per cent over the limit. Meanwhile, a recent news headline warns that, thanks to air pollution, children growing up in this city will die six months too soon on average (which means that while many will be unaffected, some will lose years off their life). And that's perhaps a signpost to the future: however much we might think we've scrubbed up our once-polluted cities, whatever we may think we're doing about air pollution, it still falls far short of what needs to be done if you make your measurement in human lives. [4]

From choking three-stone fires in Malawi to wood burners in Sydney, and from diesel SUVs in Texas to wildfires near Mexico City, air pollution is many tricky problems knotted up in one. There is no simple solution, no single string we can pull to make the whole thing vanish like magic. Maybe it's unhelpful to bundle so many different things together; or maybe the common thread – the critical importance of breathing clean air, whoever you are and wherever you live – is the simple thing we should stress. Air pollution is a global issue, an age-old issue (long pre-dating that first, pioneering, Black Country steam engine) and it's constantly mutating into new forms. The pea-soup fogs that killed people in Donora and London in the mid-20th century are a far cry from the silent, often invisible killer that plagues modern cities in the 21st. Today's air pollution is more insidious and, arguably, much more dangerous – simply because it's easier to ignore.

As we saw at length in Chapter 8, the health impacts of air pollution alone are very frightening. Something like 10 million premature deaths a year (about a million each in China and India), 90 per cent of all people on Earth breathing dirty air, and 98 per cent of under-fives exposed to toxic PM2.5s and finer particulates. It can affect you from birth till death – everything from miscarriages and low birth-weight to diabetes and dementia; a final, ironic indignity that wipes problems like pollution entirely from our minds. Places like Madrid, their politicians claim, are all the better for the dirty buzz of traffic. But that implies a city is no more than a snapshot of its nightlife, and the people who live there for years and decades – real people, real families, real children, some of whom are really suffering and dying with pollution-related illnesses ranging from asthma to lung cancer – might as well be brushed away with the broken bottles in the dawn.

Economists are fond of painting pollution as a problem that has to work its way through the system as an unfortunate by-product of development. The textbook theory says that all countries have to endure a rite-of-passage of intense economic growth and industrial development to generate the income that eradicates poverty and cleans up the problems it causes as an afterthought. Well, that's the theory – and, arguably, it's flawed in all kinds of ways. It discounts the present in favour of the future: it seems to be arguing that it doesn't matter if millions have to suffer and die from coal-powered air pollution today because (different) millions might not have to do so tomorrow. With its impressive, country-by-country charts of slowly vanishing pollution, it conveniently forgets the holistic, global picture – how Western nations have cleaned up at the expense of places like China, where many Western goods are now made and where, until recently, an awful lot of Western trash ended up. Or what will happen when we run out of poorer places happy to let us brush our pollution under their rug. It's great to celebrate the achievements of things like the Clean Air Act in the United States, but only if you factor in the export of manufacturing industry and pollution to other countries – a dirty air act, you might call that – in the process. Once China cleans up, India will be next, then African countries ... but then what? This development-beats-pollution theory, in short, appears to say that we don't have to worry about pollution today because we'll solve the problem tomorrow. And we don't have to worry about pollution in richer parts of the world because there will always be someone poorer willing to do our dirty work for less. All this is another way of saying that business as usual will always be fine. [5]

Except that it won't be. According to the International Energy Agency (IEA), the prognosis for air pollution is a steady global decline in emissions over the next few decades, to 2040, with continuing improvements in air quality in the West and even in China, powered by tighter pollution controls and a major shift to renewable energy. That's the good bit. The bad bit is that things will grow steadily worse in India, other parts of South Asia and sub-Saharan Africa, with outdoor pollution deaths increasing from 3 million a year today to more like 4.5 million a year by 2040. Improvements in home cooking (more clean stoves shipped to the developing world) and a determined shift away from dirty fuel burning will see a cut in indoor pollution deaths from 3.5 million to 3 million a year, giving a net *increase* of over a million air pollution deaths a year. If that's truly where we end up in 20 years, it's very hard to see it as progress. If at least 7 million people a year die early between now and then, that's 140 million premature deaths – about twice the total death toll of World War II. [6]

And there are some *huge* uncertainties in those numbers; there's an enormous amount we don't know about air pollution science that could radically change the estimates. We'll have new challenges like climate change to wrestle with, worsened by the very same coal-powered development that's supposedly such a vital part of solving the energy-security problems faced by countries like India (or so the coal-mining companies like to claim). Climate change will make air pollution worse in some ways (through more wildfires and increased ozone production, to name but two) and compound its effects (on things like fragile food production) in others. While we're querying the IEA's numbers, it's worth recalling that the World Health Organization's estimate of outdoor air pollution deaths increased five-fold from 0.8 million in 2000 to 4.2 million today. As scientific and medical knowledge continue to advance, there's no guarantee that toll won't climb again, making a mockery of our attempts to bring it back down, in theory or in practice. [7]

In Chapters 10 and 11, we saw no end of solutions to pollution, combining technology, politics, the law, business and community action. None of these approaches will work alone; even together, they might not be enough. Some might make things worse: it's hotly debated whether electric cars, for example, will end up spraying more particulates into the air than petrol and diesel ones. There's also a risk that ineffective, feel-good eco-solutions make us think we can take our eyes off the problem. A couple of smog-busting concrete buildings or a pollution-sucking tower here and there make no difference at all and don't mean we can carry on as we are.

We just don't take the problem seriously enough. It doesn't hit us hard enough. We hear the numbers but they rattle through our brains – like express trains – without stopping. Many of us don't care that we're still driving diesel cars that fire toxic particles, like deadly missiles, deep into the hearts and brains of *our very own* children. We don't care that, by buying cheap plastic junk from China, we're making Chinese children sick rather than our own. Many of us continue to smoke and would do so in crowded bars and restaurants if the law still allowed it. Lots of people – my neighbours included – still light up garden bonfires with not much care for where the wind blows. They cosy up around the wood burner in winter, oblivious to where its pollution is drifting when it seeps from their homes into other people's. So the problem really isn't a lack of solutions, it's an abject failure to properly grasp the problem and accept it as our own. Sometimes we care a little bit, but we don't really see an alternative. ('What about the diesel train I have to catch?'; 'Aren't all jeans made in China?'; 'I can't really help it if the trash I put out for recycling gets burned instead'.) In reality, those are often alternative ways of not caring much at all: no urban home in Sydney, Paris or London *needs* to use a wood burner; everyone has electricity.

Pollution is the status quo and polluting behaviour is the norm where, really, the opposite – the sanctity of clean, healthy air and a presumption against casually polluting it – should be the case. That might sound like a hopelessly idealistic, naive, extreme environmentalist argument; in reality, it's a hard-headed medical and economic one. I think the most persuasive case is the one advanced not by overly keen environmentalists but by increasingly alarmed, very sober, public-health doctors. In other words, people such as Dr Tedros Adhanom Ghebreyesus, the World Health Organization's Director-General, who describes air pollution as 'a silent public health emergency'. If that's true (and why should we doubt the world authority on the matter?), the medical argument becomes a moral imperative. And there's also a powerful economic argument. As we saw in previous chapters, the total economic advantages the Clean Air Act brought to the United States between 1970 and 1990 were valued at $22.2 trillion, while, between 1990 and 2020, the benefits it brought to society were estimated to outweigh its costs by some 30:1. In China, the recent £176 billion operation to clean the air brought benefits worth £202 billion, created 2 million jobs and saved 160,000 early deaths in 2017 alone. [8]

Why, then, don't we clean up the air right now? One explanation is the space-time chasm between cause and effect: you might die six years or two months earlier, but maybe not for 20, 40 or 60 years. It's hard to get too worked up about something so remotely theoretical, even when it's going to prove fatal. Another explanation is that it's a simple matter of ignorance and that there's an urgent need for better public education: six decades on from the groundbreaking epidemiological research of people like Sir Richard Doll, we all – even smokers – now make the connection between tobacco smoke and lung cancer; smoking is officially anti-social and tolerated very grudgingly. But it's also six decades on from the Great London Smog and Donora, yet we don't make exactly the same connection between air pollution and lung cancer, heart attacks, pneumonia or a dozen other diseases. Tobacco packs carry prominent pictures of blackened lungs; diesel cars and wood burners don't. Cigarettes can't be advertised on TV; polluting cars and noxious DIY products can. Yet another (classic) explanation is that the polluters and the polluted are different people: the powerless many who suffer the cost of pollution (or benefit from clean air), and the powerful few who benefit from polluting (and don't like the cost of cleaning it up). This is a false analysis because the polluters and the polluted are often the same people and, as Dr Tedros Adhanom Ghebreyesus readily points out: 'No one, rich or poor, can escape air pollution.'

Left to its own devices, the future arrives by itself – and it might not be the one we want or need. That best-guess at tomorrow's world, from the International Energy Agency, anticipates *a million* more deaths a year from air pollution than there are today by the year 2040. Cities like Birmingham might *look* cleaner, but they're not 'breathing' clean enough. So what would really make a difference? Not electric cars in Manhattan or smog-busting towers in Beijing, not cleaner cookstoves in Malawi or cleaner power plants in Johannesburg, but something much more fundamental: a huge shift in our collective attitude to air pollution.

Six big things, I believe, could make a real difference to every type of air pollution, everywhere in the world. First, we need to make the problem much more visible with better monitoring and widespread public awareness of just how dirty and dangerous the air is in some places. We also need to revisit some of the WHO guidelines to better reflect current understanding of the harm that modern pollution can do. Second, we need to see clean air as an absolute human right (something even the Romans accepted). Third, we need to link the problems of air pollution and climate change in people's minds; they have common solutions and tackling either one benefits the other. Fourth, just as there's now a presumption against public smoking, so there must be a presumption against casually polluting the air – it's fundamentally antisocial, sometimes fatally harmful and absolutely wrong. Fifth, we need to prompt our governments to start carrying out so-called 'cost-benefit analyses' of urban air clean-ups, just like they do for major road, rail and other public projects, because they show big returns on investments. From dams and tunnels to highways and rail, we hear plenty of arguments for investing ever more billions in dubious new infrastructure – but big investments in clean air and public health can pay off quicker, better, for everyone and forever. Finally, since there can be no rights without responsibilities, we must all accept responsibility for our own pollution, and not sit around waiting for someone else to clean it up. That doesn't just mean not smoking in public and thinking twice before lighting garden bonfires; it means thinking very hard about buying diesel cars and SUVs, scrutinising the hidden costs of electric vehicles before the carmakers fill the world with them, sparing a thought for who makes the things we buy and who suffers if we buy them too cheaply … and much more. Coming clean is hard work.

The real solution to air pollution is a personal one. It's like deciding to get fit or lose weight, but writ large across the globe. There's no shortage of ways to exercise or diet, but we have to click that hefty mental switch – make the big personal commitment – first. Coming clean really means being honest with ourselves and accepting our responsibility to one another. Crack that problem and I think the rest of it – the technological, political and legal solutions – will follow.

Then we really will clear the air.

And breathe a sigh of relief.

WHAT CAN YOU DO?

It's easy to feel overwhelmed by a complex global issue like air pollution. And while easy, feel-good eco-solutions don't always make as much difference as we think, that's no excuse for doing nothing. Much of the pollution you make will affect you, your family (your children in particular) and your neighbours most of all – so you have a real incentive to make some changes if you can. Tackling the air pollution that plagues somewhere like Delhi or Madrid means solving big problems that require big changes. Could you make a small difference? You could try. Here are six positive things you could do to help:

Commuting: Could you get around more efficiently? Walking and cycling is generally better for your health than sitting behind the wheel of a car. Taking the train might seem preferable, but beware if you'd commute some distance on a dirty old diesel. Maybe you could try to work from home a little more often? If you have to arrange work meetings with other people, how about doing it online instead of in-person?

School run: If you routinely drive your children to school, do at least consider the alternatives. Walking, cycling, taking the bus and car-sharing are all great options. Talk to other parents and your school and see what you can do together. Some schools have 'walking buses', where parents park a short distance from the gates and their children walk the rest of the way together in safe single-file. Apart from tackling pollution, initiatives like this help to cut road accidents – and they're good fun, too.

Heating and cooking: Watch that wood burner! If you have an old one, upgrade to a new, eco-certified model (they're not perfect, but they're much better) or switch to a fake electric version. Kindle it

continued

properly and use it more sparingly when pollution is hanging in the air. Invest in better home insulation so you're not setting fire to your money each winter just to keep warm. When it comes to cooking, remember that good ventilation is key, especially if you're using gas.

Cleaning up: Get into the habit of reading labels on cleaning and household/DIY products. Seek out things like low-emission paints and low-VOC hairsprays. Don't buy unnecessarily scented products and leave those air fresheners on the shelf. Fresh air is often the best air freshener – so (if the air is clean outdoors) open a window instead.

Green gardening: It's easy to make careless, long-lasting pollution with things like bonfires and weed killers. Compost your waste or send it to your local authority for proper disposal. Use techniques like mulching and ground-cover planting to keep weeds at bay: it takes very little effort and you'll do wonders for your soil. If you must use chemical pesticides, avoid spraying and breathing them in: 'paint' them on with a brush instead.

Donating: If you feel there's nothing else you can do, why not support one of the great charities and non-profits putting clean cookstoves into developing countries? Check out Practical Action, Clean Cooking Alliance, Solar Cookers International and many more.

Acknowledgements

This book draws on research by hundreds of scientists and other scholars, and I'm thankful to them all. It's impossible to name-check every researcher in the text of a non-academic book, but I've tried to acknowledge all my sources in the references.

I'm greatly indebted to Professor Peter Brimblecombe, who generously and very patiently read through the manuscript and made countless, excellent, thought-provoking suggestions. Thank you too to Dr Jon Woodcock for thoughts, insights and enthusiastic encouragement with this and many other projects over the years. It was a great privilege to have such wonderful help, but any lingering errors, omissions, over-simplifications or other problems are, of course, entirely my responsibility.

An enormous thank you to Duncan Heath, Philip Cotterell, Andrew Furlow, Hanna Milner and all at Icon Books, who keenly understood the importance of this issue, helped me shape the book and put it in your hands. Thank you to Marie Doherty, for typesetting everything beautifully.

Thank you to Andrew Lownie, my literary agent.

Thank you to Dr Chris Gillham and Andrew Wood.

References

This is not meant to be a scholarly book, but for readers who'd like to follow things up, I've listed my factual sources below. The URLs have been shortened with tinyurl.com both to save space and to help you type them into your computer or phone; for a longer version, with links to online documents, further notes and errata, please see my website: https://www.chriswoodford.com/breathless.html

Introduction
1. M. Safi, Guardian, 7 Nov 2017 [tinyurl.com/y7cytr7k]; E. Bannon, Transport and Environment, 9 Aug 2018 [tinyurl.com/r8rfvke].

2. M. Tainio et al, Prev Med, Jun 2016 [tinyurl.com/ub36h6d]; N. Van Mead, Guardian, 13 Feb 2017 [tinyurl.com/j4z8ukk].

3. World Health Organization (WHO), 2 May 2018 [tinyurl.com/yyjlue4o]; WHO 24 May 2018 [tinyurl.com/y7hccj5p]; D. Carrington, Guardian, 20 Oct 2017 [tinyurl.com/yaqov7nm]; D. Carrington, Guardian, 20 Nov 2018 [tinyurl.com/yddbk2yv]; J. Lelieveld, Cardiovasc Res, 3 Mar 2020 [tinyurl.com/rtqh8f4]; P. Walker et al, Imperial College, London, 26 Mar 2020 [tinyurl.com/qs4ru65]; D. Spiegelhalter, Medium, 21 Mar 2020 [tinyurl.com/t3gmttu].

4. M. Safi, Guardian, 5 December 2017 [tinyurl.com/yabhpkpr]; Y. Chen et al, Proc Natl Acad Sci, 6 Aug 2013 [tinyurl.com/uqt33n4]; S. Neuman, NPR, 29 Aug 2013 [tinyurl.com/uljxrh4]; AFP, Phys.org, 18 Mar 2015 [tinyurl.com/yx3npund]; A. Vaughan, Guardian, 8 Jan 2018 [tinyurl.com/hfpeo7l]; WHO, 2016 [tinyurl.com/tqnvg6j].

5. Univ of York, 2 Feb 2012 [tinyurl.com/vqm58su].

6. R. Pawankar et al, World Allergy Organization (WAO), 2013 [tinyurl. com/wps28da]; Wikipedia, Air travel disruption after the 2010 Eyjafjallajökull eruption [tinyurl.com/yc249zy9].

7. C. Rosen, Bus Hist Rev, Autumn 1995 [tinyurl.com/ucgxzxz]; F. Shapiro, The Yale Book of Quotations, Yale Univ Press, 2006; Institute for Health Metrics and Evaluation (IHME) News Release, 9 Sep 2016 [tinyurl.com/vylt3yx]; WHO Regional Office for Europe, 2015 [tinyurl. com/yceuhsqw]; World Bank Databank, Oct 2019.

8. H. Chen, Lancet, 18 Feb 2017 [tinyurl.com/srzhu9l].

9. US EPA, 2019 [tinyurl.com/zjycuzd].

10. K. Pohlman. Ecowatch, 12 Jul 2016 [tinyurl.com/rlf9m2m]; Friends of the Earth (FoE) UK [tinyurl.com/swrvaac]; Clean Air Day UK [tinyurl. com/yal5f7ar]; A. Kuhn, NPR, 4 Mar 2015 [tinyurl.com/yx2xdc2o]; M. Greenstone et al, North India AQLI, Univ of Chicago, 2018 [tinyurl. com/t66gacf].

11. WHO, 8 May 2018 [tinyurl.com/y5ounq23]; American Cancer Society (ACS), 16 Nov 2018 [tinyurl.com/y9o6zc2w].

Chapter 1

1. S. Cotton, Conversation, 12 Apr 2016 [tinyurl.com/gsz7p8n]; WHO, 2 May 2018 [tinyurl.com/yyjlue4o].

2. WHO, 2 May 2018 [tinyurl.com/yyjlue4o].

3. D. Fullerton et al, Trans R Soc Trop Med Hyg, Sep 2008 [tinyurl.com/ w3qvx3v].

4. UK National Health Service (NHS), 31 May 2018 [tinyurl.com/ rv5ebuw]; World Bank, 8 Sep 2016 [tinyurl.com/y5sg37fv]; WHO Air Quality Guidelines: Global Update, 2006, p.87.

5. K. Kuzek, Woods Hole Oceanographic Institution, 12 Jan 2007 [tinyurl.com/ud2kkfz]; J. Fox-Skelly, BBC Earth, 26 Jan 2017 [tinyurl. com/jcgssd3].

6. NASA, 16 Mar 2017 [tinyurl.com/yc2fdlos].

7. NASA, 27 Sep 2018 [tinyurl.com/y8pvlsac]; NASA, 18 Jul 2018 [tinyurl.com/y8bej5kq].

8. WHO Air Quality Guidelines: Global Update, 2006, p.1.

9. British Petroleum (BP), 2018, p.9 [tinyurl.com/yyf6js4x]; US Energy Information Administration (EIA), 25 Oct 2019 [tinyurl.com/le4vnc6]; J. Desjardins, World Economic Forum (WEF), 6 Sep 2017 [tinyurl.com/tqkcanu]; K. Arney, Chemistry World, 23 Nov 2018 [tinyurl.com/rwv9hke]; W. Calkins, Fuel, Apr 1994 [tinyurl.com/tzp5pxo].

10. V. Roshchina, Ozone and Plant Cell, Springer, 2013, p.9; Ozone, Pubchem [tinyurl.com/svx3xck]; ESVOC, Sep 2017 [tinyurl.com/qltv97r]; US Food and Drug Administration (FDA), Code of Federal Regulations Title 21, 1 Apr 2019 [tinyurl.com/w2mwtqf].

11. M. Dennekamp et al, Occup Environ Med, Aug 2001 [tinyurl.com/yxxc9vyw].

12. J. Emsley, Molecules of Murder, Royal Society of Chemistry, 2015.

13. L. Naranjo, NASA, 20 Nov 2011 [tinyurl.com/yx6ma3gs]; ESVOC, Sep 2017 [tinyurl.com/qltv97r].

14. C. Pope and D. Dockery, J Air Waste Manag Assoc, Vol 56, 2006 [tinyurl.com/rs426yz]; M. Loxham et al, BMJ 27 Nov 2019 [tinyurl.com/uupfaez]; C. Womack, Univ of Colorado Boulder, 11 Feb 2017 [tinyurl.com/ubg95wf]; State Of Global Air 2018. Health Effects Institute (HEI), p.1 [tinyurl.com/y2gcyncv].

15. Health Effects Notebook for Hazardous Air Pollutants, US EPA [tinyurl.com/vhmrrwq]; F. Harvey, Guardian, 13 Jun 2019 [tinyurl.com/y5wkradu]; D. Giannadaki et al, Sci Total Environ, 1 May 2018 [tinyurl.com/t4esd8m]; US CDC, 19 Jul 2018 [tinyurl.com/lm3zozl].

16. Trees and VOCs, Univ Boulder, Colorado [tinyurl.com/ry9gljy].

17. L. Wallace, Clin Exp Allergy, Vol 25, 1995 [tinyurl.com/utzt525].

18. M. Douglas, Purity and Danger, Routledge, 1966. WHO Air Quality Guidelines: Global Update, 2006, p.49; C. Pope and D. Dockery, J Air Waste Manag Assoc, Vol 56, 2006 [tinyurl.com/rs426yz].

19. WHO Air Quality Guidelines: Global Update, 2006.

20. WHO Air Quality Guidelines: Global Update, 2006, p.4, p.332; WHO, 2 May 2018 [tinyurl.com/yyjlue4o]; F. Kelly and J. Fussell, Environ Geochem Health, Aug 2015, p.644 [tinyurl.com/vzmnu2o].

21. J. Su, Light Sci Appl. Vol 7/3, 2018 [tinyurl.com/qn9hpnr]; WHO Ambient Air Pollution Database 2016 (retrieved Sep 2019) [tinyurl.com/wqucfjg]; B. Ferry et al, Air pollution and Lichens, Athlone Press, 1973, p.110; Univ of Antwerp, 2019 [tinyurl.com/tsb7osn]; A. Walston, Moms Clean Air Force, 4 May 2011 [tinyurl.com/rpfe8ja]; K. Klein and L. Tsutsui, Valley Public Radio, 23 January 2018 [tinyurl.com/ybknyuy5]; M. Natali, Environ Sci Pollut Res Int, Dec 2016 [tinyurl.com/qrrqk2m]; American Chemical Society, 17 October 2018 [tinyurl.com/tc5knvu]; R. Day and J. Ortmann, Popular Science, Oct 1970, p.97 [tinyurl.com/vmmztaa]; DEFRA, 2008 [tinyurl.com/upttwk9]; S. Larssen and L. Hagen, European Topic Centre on Air Quality, Nov 1996 [tinyurl.com/tn3dyzv].

22. M. Rigby et al, Atmos Chem Phys Vol 13, 2013 [tinyurl.com/v2b73u2]; US EPA Climate Change Indicators [tinyurl.com/y34z8jr2]; R. Baum, American Chemical Society, 2017 [tinyurl.com/ybl3j8ar]; Sulphur hexafluoride, Pubchem [tinyurl.com/tgnrxcj].

23. Pollution Probe, Feb 2003 [tinyurl.com/qrhwxyf].

24. S. Kim et al, J Toxicol Sci, Vol 40/5, 2015 [tinyurl.com/tcaojnp].

Chapter 2

1. J. Hincks, TIME, 23 Mar 2018 [tinyurl.com/sycg3m4]; E. Kwong, NPR, 30 Jul 2019 [tinyurl.com/y6a6msc5]; S. Guttikunda, Air Qual Atmos Hlth, Sep 2013 [tinyurl.com/uylhakj]; R. Allen et al, Air Qual Atmos Hlth, Mar 2013 [tinyurl.com/sgtp73a]; D. Enkhmaa et al, BMC Pregnancy Childb, 23 Apr 2014 [tinyurl.com/sarnlzn].

2. M. Kekana, Mail and Guardian (South Africa), 30 Oct 2018 [tinyurl.com/qsdwmuv]; O. Balch, Guardian, 6 Jul 2015 [tinyurl.com/ugukhdo]; R. Miles, Solenco, 4 Jan 2017 [tinyurl.com/qm5hjhc]; Business Tech, 19 Oct 2018 [tinyurl.com/ubm3wrp]; J. Stone, 2OceansVibe News, 17 Jan 2013 [tinyurl.com/tje7557]; K. Altieri et al, London School of Economics (LSE), 22 Nov 2016 [tinyurl.com/wmapomf]; African Regional

Implementation Review, UNEP, May 2006 [tinyurl.com/uglxtmx]; Government expenditure on education, World Bank, 2019 [tinyurl.com/v8y2kl3]; NASA Global OMI Catalogue, 2018 [tinyurl.com/vqljfy5]; S. Jain et al, Energy Procedia, Vol 143, 2017 [tinyurl.com/wneszvc].

3. M. Asgari. BBC News, 7 Jan 2013 [tinyurl.com/ao3bkgv]; Phys.org, 5 Feb 2018 [tinyurl.com/yc8hcpgt]; Financial Tribune, 5 Nov 2017 [tinyurl.com/qlya4pv]; A. Dehghan et al, BMC Pulm Med, Vol 18, 2018 [tinyurl.com/rmmnwpv].

4. R. Boland, Trip Savvy, 22 May 2017 [tinyurl.com/wevf97a]; B. Haas, Guardian, 16 Feb 2017 [tinyurl.com/zckq5qc]; S. Neuman, NPR, 29 Aug 2013 [tinyurl.com/uljxrh4].

5. Living Streets, 2016 [tinyurl.com/v5pp9k3]; Guardian, 4 Apr 2017 [tinyurl.com/kaaxfj5]; M. Taylor, Guardian, 26 Feb 2018 [tinyurl.com/y9t7ho6r]; F. Harvey and J. Otte, Guardian, 25 Mar 2019 [tinyurl.com/y55twd3q]; D. Carrington, Guardian, 6 Jan 2017 [tinyurl.com/zg3wbpu]; A. Vaughan, Guardian, 8 Jan 2018 [tinyurl.com/hfpeo7l]; D. Carrington, Guardian, 3 Oct 2020 [tinyurl.com/yx8mj84b]

6. M. Safi, Guardian, 6 Nov 2016 [tinyurl.com/j3tmzfh]; M. Safi, Guardian, 3 December 2017 [tinyurl.com/ycw5yqp2]; M. Safi, 7 Nov 2017 [tinyurl.com/y7cytr7k]; New Indian Express, 3 Nov 2016 [tinyurl.com/ur8xehm]; Guardian, 4 Nov 2019 [tinyurl.com/y6g69eyy]; BBC News, 1 Nov 2019 [tinyurl.com/y35s5ukq]; Greenpeace, 5 March 2019 [tinyurl.com/rno6gyl].

7. G. Guilford, Quartz, 3 Jan 2014 [tinyurl.com/rno6gyl]; B. Jiang et al, Lancet, 14 Oct 2017 [tinyurl.com/tf6b2j4]; O. Guonov, New York Times, 11 November 2015 [tinyurl.com/vmjpw8d]; China Daily/Xinhua, 12 Jul 2017 [tinyurl.com/yx4mxkep]; E. Pfeiffer, Yahoo News, 31 Jan 2013 [tinyurl.com/rxnto3c]; J. Garnaut, Brisbane Times, 29 Jan 2013 [tinyurl.com/w8wyq9a]; S. Neuman, NPR, 10 Apr 2014 [tinyurl.com/ur96ldc]; AirVisual, 2018 [tinyurl.com/y2h23up2]; G. Fuller, Guardian, 24 May 2018 [tinyurl.com/y8yvuwl8].

8. State of the Air Report, American Lung Association (ALA), 2019 [tinyurl.com/y32dc8gr]; R. Cisneros et al, J Environ Public Health, 2017 [tinyurl.com/vmrusyb].

9. Guardian, 18 March 2015 [tinyurl.com/r5jq4bq]; L. Malykhina, France24, 20 Mar 2015 [tinyurl.com/vhqyfgc]; The Local, 6 Dec 2016 [tinyurl.com/rqqkll9]; K. Willsher, Guardian, 3 Nov 2015 [tinyurl.com/qmnxt8a]; The Local, 16 Feb 2017 [tinyurl.com/shrofof].

10. D. Grosjean et al, Atmos Environ, Vol 24/1, 1990 [tinyurl.com/w8jhkou]; SugarCane.org, 2018 [tinyurl.com/v4uh9sv]; National Cancer Institute, 10 Jun 2011 [tinyurl.com/j8yhrzd]; S. Messenger, Treehugger, 24 Sep 2013 [tinyurl.com/ul7m9r2].

11. WHO Air Quality Guidelines: Global Update, 2006, pp.38, 222, 271; S. Emmanuel, Respirology, Vol 5, 2000 [tinyurl.com/ssz2qhv]; WHO Ambient Air Pollution Database 2016 (retrieved Sep 2019) [tinyurl.com/wqucfjg]; AP, Guardian, 21 Jun 2013 [tinyurl.com/s5me7nj].

12. J. McConnell, Conversation, 28 Jul 2014 [tinyurl.com/r2uuz65]; D. Zabarenko. Reuters, 10 May 2008 [tinyurl.com/yxyjsb7j].

13. US EIA, 25 March 2019 [tinyurl.com/y6nmqueo]; WHO Air Quality Guidelines: Global Update, 2006, p.396.

14. WHO Air Pollution, 2019 [tinyurl.com/yyz6ga42].

15. WHO, 2 May 2018 [tinyurl.com/yyjlue4o]; African Regional Implementation Review, UNEP, May 2006 [tinyurl.com/uglxtmx]; SO2 GDP and emissions data from Wikipedia [tinyurl.com/a4jgf5m and tinyurl.com/nluydn2]; WHO Air Quality Guidelines: Global Update, 2006, p.35; J. Vidal, Guardian, 20 Oct 2016 [tinyurl.com/j8cz6o4].

16. World Bank Databank, 2017 [tinyurl.com/y4ft7u4f]

17. WHO Health Effects of Particulate Matter, 2013 [tinyurl.com/kho9soq]; F. Kelly and J. Fussell, Environ Geochem Health, Aug 2015, p.644 [tinyurl.com/vzmnu2o]; World Nuclear Association, Nov 2018 [tinyurl.com/zke5la5].

18. WHO Air Quality Guidelines: Global Update, 2006, pp.31, 221; State of Global Air 2018, HEI, p.11 [tinyurl.com/y2gcyncv]; H. Ritchie, Our World in Data, 20 June 2017 [tinyurl.com/wnqzmaj]; India State-Level Disease Burden Initiative Air Pollution Collaborators, Lancet Planet Health, Jan 2019 [tinyurl.com/t7hq5r7]; C. Zhou et al. Int J Environ Res

Public Health, Aug 2018 [tinyurl.com/w6rstfd]; M. Greenstone et al, North India AQLI, Univ of Chicago, 2018 [tinyurl.com/t66gacf].

19. State of Global Air 2018, HEI, p.3 [tinyurl.com/y2gcyncv]; WHO Air Quality Guidelines: Global Update, 2006, pp.31, 32, 40, 45; H. Ritchie and M. Roser, Our World in Data, Apr/Oct 2017 [tinyurl.com/y9s4zm99]; Ipsos Global Advisor, May 2019 [tinyurl.com/qr6t2za]; H. Gilmore, Sydney Morning Herald, 28 Jun 2014 [tinyurl.com/v3w3q2l]; P. Hannam, Sydney Morning Herald, 13 May 2017 [tinyurl.com/shgzdqw]; Environmental Justice, 15 Aug 2017 [tinyurl.com/tjp4tgs]; R. Clun, Sydney Morning Herald, 14 Nov 2019 [tinyurl.com/wbydomf]; S. Sengupta et al, New York Times, 15 Aug 2019 [tinyurl.com/y6d8z92y]; BBC News, 13 Jun 2019 [tinyurl.com/y6djn6x6]; Canberra.com, 29 Mar 2017 [tinyurl.com/yj5roxbn]; BBC News, 6 Jan 2020 [tinyurl.com/yjkwo8rb]; J. Walls, New Zealand Herald, 26 Feb 2020 [tinyurl.com/ubxfwbr].

20. US EPA, 2019 [tinyurl.com/zjycuzd].

21. N. Popovich, New York Times, 19 Jun 2019 [tinyurl.com/y38fmpbl]; J. West and B. Turpin, Conversation, 2 May 2019 [tinyurl.com/r2wzjxk]; M. Solly, Smithsonian, 13 Mar 2019 [tinyurl.com/sgeohe5]; C. Tessum et al, PNAS, 26 Mar 26 2019 [tinyurl.com/w8stvpt]; P. McKenna, Inside Climate News, 2 Mar 2018 [tinyurl.com/y8tjlfah]; C. Katz, Sci Am, 1 Nov 2012 [tinyurl.com/y3pkqflb]; The Cost of Air Pollution, World Bank/ Institute for Health Metrics and Evaluation (IHME), 2016, p.24 [tinyurl. com/h4hbjta]; J. Davidson, Ecowatch, 20 Jun 2019 [tinyurl.com/ t7plbju].

22. WHO Air Quality Guidelines: Global Update, 2006, p.31, 53; BBC News, 15 May 2019 [tinyurl.com/y3e2anj2]; IHME, 9 Sep 9, 2016 [tinyurl.com/vylt3yx].

23. WHO Air Quality Guidelines: Global Update, 2006, p.160; J. Worland, TIME, 9 Sep 2016 [tinyurl.com/hxwjcbg]; IHME, 9 Sep 2016 [tinyurl.com/ vylt3yx]; The Cost of Air Pollution, World Bank/Institute for Health Metrics and Evaluation (IHME), 2016, p.24 [tinyurl.com/h4hbjta].

24. UK House of Commons: Environmental Audit Committee, Sixth Report of Session 2014–15 [tinyurl.com/qmhfrml]; Univ of Oxford, 6 June 2018 [tinyurl.com/v3wx4np]; UK National Audit Office

(NAO), 16 Nov 2017 [tinyurl.com/ycllnuhb]; M. Holder, Air Quality News, 28 Apr 2015 [tinyurl.com/qk57zrf]; Queen Elizabeth Hospital, Birmingham, 2017–18 [tinyurl.com/sfmally]; Y. Wei, BMJ, 27 Nov 2019 [tinyurl.com/r6g2q4t].

25. WHO Regional Office for Europe, 2015 [tinyurl.com/yceuhsqw]; Education and Military Expenditure data from World Bank Databank [tinyurl.com/v8y2kl3 and tinyurl.com/ux54dr7]; The Cost of Air Pollution, World Bank/IHME, 2016 [tinyurl.com/h4hbjta].

26. The Cost of Air Pollution, World Bank/IHME, 2016, p.6 [tinyurl.com/h4hbjta].

Chapter 3

Two wonderful references I've drawn on in multiple places in the early part of this chapter are S. Mosley, 'Chapter 5: Environmental History Of Air Pollution And Protection', In World Environmental History – Environmental History of Air Pollution and Protection by M. Agnoletti, S. Serneri (eds), Springer, 2014; and P. Brimblecombe, The Big Smoke: A History of Air Pollution in London Since Medieval Times, Methuen, 1987.

1. Calculation: tinyurl.com/r9m7aoj. See also S. Kean, The Epic Story of the Air Around Us, Doubleday, 2017.

2. P. Brimblecombe, Air Composition and Chemistry, Cambridge, 1986, p.5.

3. D. Chow, Space.com, 10 Nov 2011 [tinyurl.com/tjtkj4u].

4. E. Wayman, Smithsonian, 4 Apr 4, 2012 [tinyurl.com/smn4pnp].

5. F. Kelly and J. Fussell, Environ Geochem Health, Aug 2015, p.644 [tinyurl.com/vzmnu2o]; L. Capasso. Med Secoli, Vol 7/3, 1995 [tinyurl.com/rllzkbx]; S. Mosley, 2014; P. Brimblecombe, 1987.

6. J. Longman et al, Proc Natl Acad Sci, 19 Jun 2018 [tinyurl.com/sz78o2v]; S. Mosley, 2014 (Ibid.); J. Grout, retrieved 2019 [tinyurl.com/j9pxn]; K. Killgrove, Powered by Osteons, 20 Jan 2012 [tinyurl.com/87gnefy]; Mosley, 2014.

7. S. Mosley, 2014; P. Brimblecombe, 1987, pp.7, 35; Hippocrates, 'On Airs, Waters, and Places' [tinyurl.com/sazavab]; D. Gourevitch, Med Secoli, Vol 7/3, 1995 [tinyurl.com/wkv7n5x]; J. Jouanna, Brill, 2012, p.121 [tinyurl.com/vwrutcl]; R. Parker, Miasma, Oxford, 1996; C. Hannaway, 'Environment and Miasmata' in W. Bynum and R. Porter (eds), Companion Encyclopedia of the History of Medicine, Taylor & Francis, 1993. p.295.

8. S. Mosley, 2014; J. Lennon in Rome, Pollution and Propriety by M. Bradley and K. Stow (eds), Cambridge Univ Press, 2012, p.43; A. Wacke, Roman Legal Tradition, 2002, pp.1–24 [tinyurl.com/vddl6wq].

9. A. Ascenzi et al, in: K. Spindler et al (eds) Human Mummies, Springer, 1996 [tinyurl.com/swx7th5]; Seneca, Letters from a Stoic, R. Campbell (trans.), Penguin, 1985, p.185; J. Boyle (trans.), The Institutes of Justinian, Lawbook Exchange, 2002.

10. S. Connor, Independent, retrieved 2019 [tinyurl.com/sur3p32]; J. McConnell et al, Proc Natl Acad Sci, 29 May 2018 [tinyurl.com/v7blxwg]; L. Capasso, Lancet, 18 Nov 2000 [tinyurl.com/wgt9ch3]; F. De Vleeschouwer et al, Sci Total Environ, 15 May 2007 [tinyurl.com/qqnwxdu].

11. C. Loveluck et al, Antiquity, 31 Mar 2020 [tinyurl.com/s49en79].

12. J. Fearnley-Whittingstall, The Garden, Weidenfeld & Nicolson, 2002, p.15.

13. 'Scoland – Seacoal Lane' in A Dictionary of London, H. Jenkins, 1918; J. Morrison, Smithsonian, 11 Jan 2016 [tinyurl.com/yxu2o6qy]; M. Allaby, Fog, Smoke and Poisoned Rain, Facts on File, 2003, pp.64–65; P. Brimblecombe, 1987, pp.7, 30.

14. Science History [tinyurl.com/y6w8laf7]; Portrait of Boyle (1627–1691), Wellcome Collection [tinyurl.com/vh598qm].

15. J. Morrison, Smithsonian, 11 Jan 2016 [tinyurl.com/yxu2o6qy]; C. Uglietti et al, Proc Natl Acad Sci, 24 Feb 2015 112 [tinyurl.com/sxqojab]; Ohio State Univ, 9 Feb 2015 [tinyurl.com/qvkql8z].

16. J. Evelyn, Fumifugium, Godbid, 1661 [tinyurl.com/qvfywhs]; M. Willes, The Curious World of Samuel Pepys and John Evelyn, Yale Univ Press, 2017.

17. H. Ritchie, Our World in Data, 20 June 2017 [tinyurl.com/wnqzmaj]; C. Zerefos et al, Atmos Chem Phys, Vol 14, 2014 [tinyurl.com/shfun6v]; P. Brown, Guardian, 19 Feb 2017 [tinyurl.com/gkpboym]; M. Hudson, Telegraph, 15 Oct 2017 [tinyurl.com/udxdfad].

18. P. Thorsheim, Inventing Pollution: Coal, Smoke, and Culture in Britain since 1800, Ohio Univ Press, 2006, p.1, p.4; 'Coal Basins' in The Oxford Encyclopedia of Economic History, Vol 3, Oxford Univ Press, 2003, p.456.

19. S. Mosley, 2014.

20. H. Ritchie, Our World in Data, 20 June 2017 [tinyurl.com/wnqzmaj]; T. Hatton, Conversation, 14 Nov 2017 [tinyurl.com/yao9v7p9].

21. M. Akatsu, in: S. Sugiyama (ed), Economic History of Energy and Environment, Springer, 2015; 'Chapter 1: The History of Air Pollution' in R. Boubel et al (eds), Fundamentals of Air Pollution, Academic Press, 1994, p.7.

22. J. Goodell, Big Coal, Houghton Mifflin Harcourt, 2007, p.100; D. French, When They Hid the Fire, Univ of Pittsburgh Press, 2017; C. Beecher and H. Beecher Stowe, The American Woman's Home, J. B. Ford & Co., 1869, p.43, p.69; P. Thorsheim, Inventing Pollution: Coal, Smoke, and Culture in Britain since 1800, Ohio Univ Press, 2006, p.2.

23. Engineering and Technology History Wiki, 27 Jan 2016 [tinyurl.com/t2plugr].

24. A. Lockwood, The Silent Epidemic, MIT Press, 2012, p.67; T. McCarthy, Auto Mania, Yale Univ Press, 2007, p.110; The Henry Ford Museum [tinyurl.com/yxyzr5q8]; M. Brush, Michigan Radio, 15 Aug 2011 [tinyurl.com/yyskebqt].

25. R. Russell, London Fogs, Stanford, 1880 [tinyurl.com/qwy8rlb].

26. B. Nemery et al, Lancet, 3 March 2001 [tinyurl.com/vg76n3x]; J. Wagner, Univ of Guelph, 2017 [tinyurl.com/tknwq5f]; J. Firket, Trans Faraday Soc, Volume 32, 1936, pp.1192–96 [tinyurl.com/sb77kgt]; A. Zimmer and B. Nemery in Air Pollution Episodes by P. Brimblecombe (ed). World Scientific, 2018, pp.27–42.

27. P. Brimblecombe, in Air Pollution Episodes by P. Brimblecombe (ed). World Scientific, 2018, pp.57–72; E. Jacobs, Am J Public Health, Apr 2018 [tinyurl.com/vm5nz3g]; T. O'Neil, St. Louis Post Dispatch, 28 Nov 2016 [tinyurl.com/uxwt9b7]; D. French, When They Hid the Fire, Univ of Pittsburgh Press, 2017.

28. G. Fuller, The Invisible Killer, Melville House, 2018, p.39; M. Bell et al, Environ Health Perspect, Vol 112/1 2004 [tinyurl.com/yd5uag98]; P. Bharadwaj et al, Am J Respir Crit Care Med, 15 Dec 2016 [tinyurl. com/rc46fbb].

29. F. Kelly and J. Fussell, Environ Geochem Health, Aug 2015, p.644 [tinyurl.com/vzmnu2o]; A. Carlson and D. Burtraw (eds), Lessons from the Clean Air Act, Cambridge Univ Press, 2019; P. Brimblecombe, 1987, p.169; P. Brimblecombe, Weather, 2006, p.311 [tinyurl.com/v34ctkr].

30. M. Abella et al, Proc Natl Acad Sci, 30 Jul 2019 [tinyurl.com/ vokpr4j]; R. Rhodes, Dark Sun, Simon & Schuster, p.509.

31. R. Carson, Silent Spring, Houghton Mifflin, 2002, p.177; L. Cawley, BBC News, 16 May 2015 [tinyurl.com/vt3ejyl]; P. Grennfelt et al, Ambio 49, 21 Sep 2019 [tinyurl.com/r29oha5]; R. Turner Holmes and G. Likens, Hubbard Brook, Yale Univ Press, 2016, p.116ff.

32. I. Sinha, Guardian, 3 Dec 2009 [tinyurl.com/v5nwkgn]; I. Eckerman, The Bhopal Saga, Universities Press, 2005, p.96.

33. NASA, 19 Oct 2006 [tinyurl.com/tzcztxc]

34. UK Dept for Environment, Food & Rural Affairs (DEFRA), 14 Jan 2019 [tinyurl.com/ya6kflxb]; American Lung Association, 23 Apr 2019 [tinyurl.com/wv2guof].

35. C. Pope and D. Dockery, J Air Waste Manag Assoc, Vol 56, 2006 [tinyurl. com/rs426yz]; J. Kaiser, Science, 25 Jul 1997 [tinyurl.com/qtlgq2u].

36. World Bank, World Urbanization Prospects, 2018 [tinyurl.com/ yd5lp46y]; NASA, 19 Aug 2019 [tinyurl.com/ya8obxoe].

37. WHO Fact Sheet, 26 Jul 2019 [tinyurl.com/y66amzyz]; D. Carrington and M. Taylor, Guardian, 27 Oct 2018 [tinyurl.com/yarrqfd5].

38. D. Dockery et al, N Engl J Med, 9 Dec 1993 [tinyurl.com/v77qmwp];
J. Lepeule et al, Environ Health Perspect, Jul 2012 [tinyurl.com/
upvhrso]; WHO Ambient Air Pollution Database 2016 (retrieved Sep
2019) [tinyurl.com/wqucfjg]; C. Pope, Arch Environ Health, Mar–Apr
1991 [tinyurl.com/rs48d5y]; M. Smart, Brigham Young Univ Magazine,
Spring 2007 [tinyurl.com/qslkeva].

Chapter 4

1. S. Hare et al, Manchester Metropolitan University, 1999/2002
[tinyurl.com/uytxeft].

2. R. Pawankar et al, WAO, 2013 [tinyurl.com/wps28da]; Telegraph,
12 Jun 2009 [tinyurl.com/wzuz64a]; J. Emberlin, The Hay Fever Health
Report 2009, UK National Pollen and Aerobiology Research Unit, 2010;
M. Mahmood, Birmingham Univ, 18 Aug 2016 [tinyurl.com/qssphz8];
D. Mudarri, J Environ Public Health, 2016 [tinyurl.com/vocuvsq].

3. R. Pawankar et al, WAO, 2013 [tinyurl.com/wps28da]; UK Met
Office, Pollen Counts [tinyurl.com/vjeqjzn]; J. Derksen and E. Pierson,
Radboud Univ, 22 Aug 2012 [tinyurl.com/vqz3qmo]; K. Kornei, Science,
25 Jan 2018 [tinyurl.com/wc3kwjw].

4. R. Pawankar et al (eds), Allergy Frontiers, Springer, 2009, p.7;
M. Wyman, Autumunal Catarrh, Hurd and Houghton, 1876 [tinyurl.
com/rvx5dzo]; C. Blackley, Experimental Researches on the Causes and
Nature of Catarrhus Aestivus, Bailliere, Tindall, & Cox, 1873 [tinyurl.
com/uswfqlu]; M. Mahmood, Birmingham Univ, 18 Aug 2016 [tinyurl.
com/qssphz8];

5. R. Pawankar et al, WAO, 2013 [tinyurl.com/wps28da]; Asthma UK,
Apr 2019 [tinyurl.com/h65onpf]; K. Strick, Standard, 30 Apr 2018
[tinyurl.com/y9s8d6fk]; M. Mahmood, Birmingham Univ, 18 Aug 2016
[tinyurl.com/qssphz8]; K. Obtułowicz, Folia Med Cracov, Vol 34, 1993
[tinyurl.com/wk3ldfe]; G. D'Amato, Respir Med, Jul 2001 [tinyurl.com/
tjjb2qc]; J. Parker et al, Environ Health Perspect, Jan 2009 [tinyurl.com/
v9foosj].

6. D. Newton, Science and Political Controversy, ABC-CLIO, 2014, p.73;
O. Kardan et al, Scientific Reports, Vol 5, 2015.

7. L. Naranjo, NASA Earthdata, 20 Nov 2011 [tinyurl.com/v66lnr4]; W. Schlesinger, Nature, 6 Apr 2017 [tinyurl.com/wp6szav]; D. Nowak, US Dept of Agriculture (USDA) Forest Service, 2002 [tinyurl.com/wo2o2cm]; Wikipedia, Petrichor, retrieved 2019 [tinyurl.com/kcyga2n].

8. V. Yli-Pelkonen et al, Landscape Urban Plan, Feb 2017 [tinyurl.com/tmlwajh]; J. Vidal, Guardian, 1 Dec 2016 [tinyurl.com/jfdoxo8]; J. Jacobs, The Death and Life of Great American Cities, Vintage, 1961, p.91.

9. W. Wilson, Constructed Climates. Univ of Chicago Press, 2011; W. Date, Air Quality News, 30 Jul 2018 [tinyurl.com/tu33vwm]; Z. Chiam et al, Sci Total Environ, 19 Jun 2019 [tinyurl.com/rvrrnfx]; H. Wang, Environ Sci Technol, 18 Jun 2019 [tinyurl.com/vve2nmr]; Y. Xing and P. Brimblecombe, Atmos Environ, Vol 201, 15 Mar 2019 [tinyurl.com/yx7sv6yk]; X. Long et al, Atmos Chem Phys, Vol 18, 2018 [tinyurl.com/tjo9kj6].

10. Using data from World Cities Culture Forum [tinyurl.com/tjdwjw6]; PM10 data from WHO Ambient Air Pollution Database 2016 (retrieved Sep 2019) [tinyurl.com/wqucfjg].

11. European Environment Agency (EEA), EEA Technical report No 10/2012 [tinyurl.com/wlymy8y]; NASA Earth Observatory, 7 Mar 2017 [tinyurl.com/w83jwbd]; K. Granström, WIT Transactions on Ecology and the Environment, Vol 101, 2007 [tinyurl.com/qlwu5em]; BBC News, 2 Aug 2019 [tinyurl.com/y6g695vg]; N. Cushing, Conversation, 12 Jan 2020 [tinyurl.com/vmfvnb9]; N. Evershed et al, Guardian, 24 Jan 2020 [tinyurl.com/qlbjj4z].

12. G. Williamson et al, Environ Res Lett, Vol 11, 2016 [tinyurl.com/uxtbarb]; R. Peltier, Conversation, 16 Oct 2017 [tinyurl.com/voeseta]; X. Liu et al, JGR Atmospheres, 16 Jun 2017 [tinyurl.com/yx3v6wkp].

13. C. Miller and U. Irfan, Vox, 12 Oct 2017 [tinyurl.com/yd97jhb3]; J. Beitler, NASA, 17 Oct 2006 [tinyurl.com/u68kz6u]; C. Santiago and S. Scutti, CNN, 13 Oct 2017 [tinyurl.com/uqqq6v5].

14. WHO Air Quality Guidelines: Global Update, 2006, p.222; J. Simon, Quartz, 15 May 2019 [tinyurl.com/w66pgna].

15. M. Meyer, Conversation, 9 Jan 2013 [tinyurl.com/su7s2k3]; T. Glumac, ABC News, 4 Jan 2019 [tinyurl.com/wor9b3c]; K. Aubusson and N. Gladstone, Sydney Morning Herald, 14 Dec 2019 [tinyurl.com/qwn4y3l]; P. Gibbons, Conversation, 10 Jan 2013 [tinyurl.com/rdm6efl].

16. US National Interagency Fire Center, Total Wildland Fires and Acres (1926–2018), 2019 [tinyurl.com/h93hd55].

17. C. Santiago and S. Scutti, CNN, 13 Oct 2017 [tinyurl.com/uqqq6v5]; WHO Air Quality Guidelines: Global Update, 2006, pp.270–1; J. Liu et al, Environ Res, Jan 2015 [tinyurl.com/tljmxj8].

18. World Wildlife Fund (WWF), 19 May 2004 [tinyurl.com/w7mkjqo].

19. US EPA, Wildfire Smoke: A Guide for Public Health Officials, 2019 [tinyurl.com/r45cvhu]; A. Vu et al, Chem Res Toxicol, 17 Aug 2015 [tinyurl.com/wpxplbc]; C. McMahon et al, in: P. Jones et al (eds), Carcinogenesis, Vol. 3: Polynuclear Aromatic Hydrocarbons. Raven Press, 1978, pp. 61–73.

20. R. Pachauri et al, Climate Change 2014: Synthesis Report: Summary for Policymakers, Intergovernmental Panel on Climate Change (IPCC)/ World Meteorological Organization (WMO), 2014, p.4; AFP, Guardian, 29 Sep 2017 [tinyurl.com/ya75zgnx]; EPA, Overview of Greenhouse Gases: Methane, [tinyurl.com/mhkl3tv].

21. DEFRA, Air Pollution from Farms, 2013 [tinyurl.com/sqr8vmg]; Y. Wu et al, Environ Pollut, Vol 218, 2016 [tinyurl.com/wxlcpee]; B. Gu et al, Front Ecol Environ, Jun 2014 [tinyurl.com/yxxlkrn2].

22. EPA, Overview of Greenhouse Gases: Nitrous Oxide [tinyurl.com/h52dqox].

23. US Geological Survey (USGS), Pyroclastic flows, 25 Jun 1997 [tinyurl.com/unwwdlv]; USGS, 10 May 2017 [tinyurl.com/yxcgtogo]; S. George, International Pollution Issues, Dec 2014 [tinyurl.com/r9vjn63].

24. R. Russell, US Fish and Wildlife Service (USFWS) National Digital Library [tinyurl.com/qoz9d7l].

25. A. Schmidt and C. Witham, NERC Planet Earth, 29 Sep 2016 [tinyurl.com/rmspj6n]; Skeptical Science, 2 Jun 2017 [tinyurl.com/rlny7y6]; USGS, 18 Jan 2017 [tinyurl.com/ycb2e28m].

26. D. Newton, Science and Political Controversy, ABC-CLIO, 2014, p.73.

27. L. Martin, Guardian, 24 Dec 2018 [tinyurl.com/us2jbyr]; E. Venzke, Global Volcanism Program, 2013 [tinyurl.com/smrw5bp]; Wikipedia, 1815 Eruption of Mount Tambora, retrieved Dec 2019 [tinyurl.com/jjd4dna]; R. Stothers, Science, 15 Jun 1984 [tinyurl.com/te2yutd]; D. Cox, BBC News, 24 Jul 2017 [tinyurl.com/y7jd3p5r].

28. D. Cox, BBC News, 24 Jul 2017 [tinyurl.com/y7jd3p5r]; Der Spiegel, 26 Apr 2011 [tinyurl.com/w9ekyll]; H. Hlodversdottir et al, BMJ Open, Sep 2016 [tinyurl.com/r8jg592]; Ó. Gissurardóttir et al, Scand J Public Health, Mar 2019 [tinyurl.com/vufcde3]; Centre for Observation and Modelling of Earthquakes, Volcanoes and Tectonics (COMET), 2019 [tinyurl.com/r2kae3a]; M. Durand and J. Grattan, Lancet, 20 Jan 2001 [tinyurl.com/ucbgug3].

29. Volcano Discovery, 16 Feb 2015 [tinyurl.com/sf88apo]; A. Schmidt and C. Witham, NERC Planet Earth, 29 Sep 2016 [tinyurl.com/rmspj6n]; A. Schmidt et al, Proc Natl Acad Sci, 20 Sep 2011 [tinyurl.com/ru7lx5s]; A. Schmidt et al, JGR Atmospheres, 21 Aug 2015 [tinyurl.com/wyj8ox2].

30. USGS, 10 May 2017 [tinyurl.com/yxcgtogo]; W. Broad, New York Times, 9 Feb 1993 [tinyurl.com/slj4m3l].

31. WHO Air Quality Guidelines: Global Update, 2006, p.40; State of Global Air 2018. Health Effects Institute (HEI), p.3 [tinyurl.com/y2gcyncv]; The Cost of Air Pollution, World Bank/IHME, 2016, p.13 [tinyurl.com/h4hbjta].

32. UN Convention to Combat Desertification, 7 Jun 2001 [tinyurl.com/ryarymu].

33. US EPA, Health Risk of Radon, 2019 [tinyurl.com/j4fqgd6]; US CDC, United States Cancer Statistics, 22 Oct 2019 [tinyurl.com/tw5za4k].

34. NASA Goddard Space Flight Center, 19 Mar 2003 [tinyurl.com/rkxlfle].

35. K. Than, National Geographic, 10 Mar 2010 [tinyurl.com/qn5lwlm].

36. V. Gusiakov, in Extreme Natural Hazards, Disaster Risks and Societal Implications, A. Ismail-Zadeh et al (eds). Cambridge Univ Press, 2014, p.230.

37. G. Moran, Grist, 12 Sep 2018 [tinyurl.com/s6f47su]; WHO, Asthma:
Key Facts 31 Aug 2017 [tinyurl.com/ufwlgpb]; F. Johnston et al, Environ
Health Perspect, May 2012 [tinyurl.com/vgmvlef].

38. J. Upton, NRDC, 22 August 2016 [tinyurl.com/vroaq4s];
R. Pawankar, Asia Pac Allergy, Apr 2019 [tinyurl.com/slp2nf4]; J. Khan,
ABC News, 1 Oct 2019 [tinyurl.com/rjul2ro]; J. Corderoy, Sydney
Morning Herald, 18 Nov 2014 [tinyurl.com/scdghez]; E. Innes, Daily
Mail, 20 Mar 2014 [tinyurl.com/v6dl64t].

Chapter 5

1. H. Williams, Autogeddon, Jonathan Cape, 1990, p.28.

2. The websites quoted from are tinyurl.com/pq5hbq3 and tinyurl.
com/y8zsb2hv.

3. R. Wild, Times, 23 Jan 2018 [tinyurl.com/rbuhd6e]; G. Trachta, Crisis
of 1894, retrieved 2019 [tinyurl.com/qrsog8l]; S. Davies, Foundation for
Economic Education, 1 Sep 2004 [tinyurl.com/vrvz56w].

4. Times, 2 Aug 1827, p.2, 23 Jul 1875, p.9, 16 February 1909, p.4; D. Pool,
What Jane Austen Ate and Charles Dickens Knew, Simon and Schuster,
2012, p.30; C. McShane and J. Tarr, The Horse in the City, JHU Press,
2007, p.26.

5. New York Times, 19 Apr 1896 [tinyurl.com/wypjx36]; 12 Jan 1895
[tinyurl.com/woxylv9]; L. Brunt, Univ of Oxford, Discussion Papers
in Economic and Social History, Feb 2000 [tinyurl.com/uhfzbj8];
S. Rockman, Scraping By, JHU Press, 2010, p.1; Times, 18 Apr 1864, p.9;
J. Tarr, American Heritage, Oct 1971 [tinyurl.com/yxxfk4ug].

6. H. Ford, My Life and Work, Doubleday, 1922, p.26; S. Watts, The
People's Tycoon, Vintage, 2005.

7. A. Kander et al, Power to the People, Princeton Univ Press, 2014,
p.182; Cornish Mining World Heritage [tinyurl.com/t4qq36o];
P. Brimblecombe, The Big Smoke, Methuen, 1987, p.98.

8. C. McGowan, Rail, Steam, and Speed, Columbia Univ Press, 2004.
p.22.

9. UK Govt, Historical coal data 1853–2016 [tinyurl.com/cywdvuo];
P. Thorsheim, Inventing Pollution: Coal, Smoke, and Culture in Britain
since 1800, Ohio Univ Press, 2006, p.4.

10. Legislation.gov.uk, The Locomotive Act 1861 [tinyurl.com/qrpnldf].

11. C. McGowan, Rail, Steam, and Speed, Columbia Univ Press, 2004.
p.22.

12. Wikipedia, Energy Density [tinyurl.com/t83vmpx]; C. Woodford,
Bicycles, Explainthatstuff.com, 2007 [tinyurl.com/27nblfp].

13. S. Carnot, Reflections on the Motive Power of Fire, Dover, 1960
[tinyurl.com/wayfztd]; C. Gillispie and R. Pisano, Lazare and Sadi
Carnot, Springer, 2014, p.2; M. Grosser, Diesel: The Man and His Engine,
David & Charles, 1978, p.44.

14. M. Grosser, Diesel: The Man and His Engine, David & Charles, 1978,
pp.54–60.

15. G. Pahl, Biodiesel, Chelsea Green Publishing, 2008; N. Möllers and
K. Zachmann (eds), Past and Present Energy Societies, Transcript
Verlag, 2012, p.15; R. Diesel, Diesel's Rational Heat Motor: A Lecture,
Progressive Publishing, 1897, p.18 [tinyurl.com/u7r79qc].

16. S. Leitman and B. Brant, Build Your Own Electric Vehicle,
McGraw-Hill, 2008, p.34; EIA, Today in Energy, 10 Dec 2014 [tinyurl.
com/s3bc3o5]; P. Sisson, Curbed, 30 Jan 2018 [tinyurl.com/qmcsb4f];
Porsche, 20 Apr 2011 [tinyurl.com/u87n8nj]; D. Strohl, Wired, 18 Jun
2010 [tinyurl.com/vtjnpl2].

17. D. Hawranek, Der Spiegel, 21 Jul 2009 [tinyurl.com/sh994wj];
G. Gates et al, New York Times, 16 Apr 2017 [tinyurl.com/ydxfl5dk];
J. Ewing, New York Times, 13 Jan 2017 [tinyurl.com/snycf43]; BBC
News, 15 Apr 2019 [tinyurl.com/y485wgc4]; T. Leggett, BBC News,
5 May 2018 [tinyurl.com/ug5yw9p]; A. Neslen, Guardian, 28 May 2019
[tinyurl.com/yxtstx4f]; D. Carrington, Guardian, 30 Aug 2016 [tinyurl.
com/hz9g6re].

18. UK Govt, Cars registered for the first time by propulsion or fuel
type (Table VEH-0253), 2019 [tinyurl.com/aluqs2o].

19. P. Dauvergne, The Shadows of Consumption, MIT Press, 2010, p.62; J. Sousanis, Ward's Auto, 15 Aug 2011 [tinyurl.com/y8bp57kv]; S. Nathan, Engineer, 3 Jun 2019 [tinyurl.com/y3mbthpu]; M. Smith, WEF, 22 Apr 2016 [tinyurl.com/y74vgjhy].

20. UK Govt, National Travel Survey: England 2015, 8 Sep 2016 [tinyurl.com/zobdwqf]; C. Mims, Quartz, 15 Oct 2013 [tinyurl.com/yb7k6lnf]; E. Jaffe, City Lab, 7 Nov 2014 [tinyurl.com/sworrjp].

21. Statista, US Automotive Advertising, 18 Sep 2017 [tinyurl.com/rl86tde]; W. Duggan, Benzinga. 7 Jul 2016 [tinyurl.com/rupho4n]; D. Wood et al, Trunk Roads and the Generation of Traffic, HMSO, 1994; Royal Commission on Environmental Pollution, 18th Report: Transport and the Environment, HMSO, 1994; J. Adams, Transport Planning: Vision and Practice, Routledge, 1981.

22. Wisconsin Dept Health Services, Gasoline, 12 Mar 2018 [tinyurl.com/taxdb8f]; WHO, Lead Poisoning and Health: Fact Sheet 379, Aug 2017 [tinyurl.com/oppuccq]; L. Graber et al, Environ Health Perspect, June 2010 [tinyurl.com/vx7soaz]; UNEP Leaded Petrol Phase-out: Global Status, Mar 2017 [tinyurl.com/unyloa9].

23. P. Wolfe et al, Environ Sci Technol, Vol 50/17, 2016 [tinyurl.com/yx5chhvb].

24. S. Skerfving et al, Neurotoxicology, Jul 2015 [tinyurl.com/vv5xypp]; W. Stewart, Am J Ind Med, Oct 2007 [tinyurl.com/udlopw5]; W. Stewart et al, Neurology, May 2006 [tinyurl.com/vly79mr]; B. Schwarz et al, Neurology, Oct 2000 [tinyurl.com/v6dfmvx]; K. Drum, Mother Jones, 11 Feb 2016 [tinyurl.com/ybk52ryl]; R. Nevin, Figures [tinyurl.com/somdscn]; S. Mercurio, Understanding Toxicology, Jones & Bartlett, 2016, p.771; Reuters, New York Times, 7 May 2008 [tinyurl.com/tyukgsq]; J. Mouawad, New York Times, 8 May 2008 [tinyurl.com/wzoof4y]; D. Bellinger, PLoS Med, May 2008 [tinyurl.com/s6w843t]; S. Kumar, Indian J Occup Environ Med, Sep 2018 [tinyurl.com/y5bx3ood].

25. F. Kelly and J. Fussell, Environ Geochem Health, Aug 2015, p.644 [tinyurl.com/vzmnu2o].

26. EEA, 24 Nov 2015 [tinyurl.com/rp2oqyd]; K. Mathiesen, Guardian, 11 Mar 2015 [tinyurl.com/t3gcbey]; P. Nieuwenhuis, Conversation,

2 May 2017 [tinyurl.com/lct4lfp]; EEA, Air Quality in Europe, 2016, p.45 [tinyurl.com/tqzlos4]; F. Caiazzo et al, Atmos Environ, Nov 2013 [tinyurl.com/rq3e9of]; R. Cooper et al, Indian J Occup Environ Med, Apr 2009 [tinyurl.com/uugatwb].

27. UK House of Commons: Environmental Audit Committee, Sixth Report of Session 2014–15 [tinyurl.com/qmhfrml]; J. Chu, MIT News, 29 Aug 2013 [tinyurl.com/ps52l2u]; F. Caiazzo et al, Atmos Environ, Nov 2013 [tinyurl.com/rq3e9of]; Sierra Club, Driving Up the Heat: SUVs and Global Warming, retrieved 2019 [tinyurl.com/reyar52].

28. F. Caiazzo et al, Atmos Environ, Nov 2013 [tinyurl.com/rq3e9of]; S. Yim and S. Barrett, Environ Sci Technol, Vol 46/8, 2012 [tinyurl.com/vx3gej3]; J. Chu, MIT News, 29 Aug 2013 [tinyurl.com/ps52l2u].

29. İ. Reşitoğlu et al, Clean Technol Environ Policy, Jan 2015 [tinyurl.com/u7o3600].

30. N. Van Mead, Guardian, 13 Feb 2017 [tinyurl.com/j4z8ukk]; M. Tainio et al, Prev Med, Jun 2016 [tinyurl.com/vk3whno].

31. M. Holder, Air Quality News, 16 Feb 2016 [tinyurl.com/wcpfwmc]; Berkeley Wellness, 6 Dec 2016 [tinyurl.com/t5uv6rm]; R. Chaney et al, PLoS One, Vol 12/11, 2017 [tinyurl.com/rks8xmd].

32. R. Chaney et al, PLoS One, Vol 12/11, 2017 [tinyurl.com/rks8xmd].

33. A. Goela and P. Kumar, Atmos Environ, Apr 2015 [tinyurl.com/sbbm95w].

34. M. Lavery, Yorkshire Evening Post, 5 Dec 2017 [tinyurl.com/uozwror].

35. F. Gany et al, J Expo Sci Environ Epidemiol, Mar 2017 [tinyurl.com/s5j6z28]; China Dialogue, 3 Jan 2013 [tinyurl.com/t9dvhlu].

36. E. Zagury et al, Occup Environ Med, Jun 2000 [tinyurl.com/rhqvf9p]; S. Wu et al, Sci Total Environ, 1 Jun 2011 [tinyurl.com/sew3gdc]; F. Trevithick, Life of Richard Trevithick, Vol 1, E. & F.N. Spon, 1872, p.111.

37. EIA, 23 Mar 2018 [tinyurl.com/s6vo7ca]; J. Eckart, WEF, 28 Nov 2017 [tinyurl.com/yatetyw4].

38. F. Amato (ed), Non-Exhaust Emissions, Academic Press, 2018;
P. Kole et al, Int J Environ Res Public Health, 20 Oct 2017 [tinyurl.com/
yx769nqe]; J. Loeb, Engineering & Technology, 10 Mar 2017 [tinyurl.
com/wdgl8k8]

39. F. Cassee et al, Inhal Toxicol, Dec 2013 [tinyurl.com/ujkvafp];
F. Kelly, Guardian, 4 Aug 2017 [tinyurl.com/y9woeneb]; H. Williams,
Autogeddon, Jonathan Cape, 1990, p.41.

40. Berkeley Wellness, 6 Dec 2016 [tinyurl.com/t5uv6rm]; The Ecology
Center, Guide to New Vehicles, 2012 [tinyurl.com/txuuy2q]; K. Brodzik
et al, J Environ Sci (China), 1 May 2014 [tinyurl.com/r5mlo2h];
D. Gould, New Scientist, 29 May 1993 [tinyurl.com/th3obnb].

41. X. Wang et al, J Air Waste Manag Assoc, Apr 2015 [tinyurl.com/
ums8wp5].

42. A. Hickman et al, Proc IMechE Part F: J Rail and Rapid Transit,
Vol 232/6, 2018 [tinyurl.com/wmuxctp].

43. R. Reagan, Tear Down this Wall, The History Place [tinyurl.com/
y9v2jba]; R. Harrabin, BBC News, 8 Apr 2013 [tinyurl.com/cld6xel];
M. Hamer, Wheels Within Wheels, Routledge, 1987.

44. Eurostat, 2018 [tinyurl.com/uyqohos].

45. UK DVLA, 2015 [tinyurl.com/wk3d2a6]; UK Office for National
Statistics (ONS), 2017 [tinyurl.com/y3ly74to]; Transport for London,
2012 [tinyurl.com/owgy7pg]; Data.gov.uk, 2017 [tinyurl.com/y9hq5v2d];
UK Govt, National Travel Survey: England 2015, 8 Sep 2016 [tinyurl.com/
zobdwqf]; P. Gomm and I. Wengraf, RAC Foundation, London, 2013, p.11
[tinyurl.com/uhxdgkm]; Project WNYC [tinyurl.com/wus9f4w].

46. M. Sivak and B. Schoettle, Univ of Michigan, Report UMTRI-2016-4,
Jan 2016 [tinyurl.com/jc4vcm3]; J. Beck, Atlantic, 22 Jan 2016 [tinyurl.
com/ycrhzlpr]; M. Lavelle, National Geographic, 18 Dec 2013 [tinyurl.
com/u56fuma]; A. Rayner, Guardian, 25 Sep 2011 [tinyurl.com/
rc996rs]; International Organization of Motor Vehicle Manufacturers,
2017 [tinyurl.com/y97g3jjz]; H. Thompson, Fear and Loathing in Las
Vegas, Random House, 1971, p.18.

Chapter 6

1. J. Vidal, Guardian, 30 Oct 2006 [tinyurl.com/uy5lvq4]; W. Kremer, BBC World Service, 19 Feb 2013 [tinyurl.com/qwyohpp].

2. C. McNair, eMarketer, 29 Jan 2018 [tinyurl.com/y7rgygl3].

3. NYC.gov, 19 Apr 2018 [tinyurl.com/vwpehp6]; Joel Schwartz, American Enterprise Institute, 9 Aug 2005 [tinyurl.com/vw8qkje]; American Legislative Exchange Council, Environmental Stewardship [tinyurl.com/tknvwno].

4. F. Caiazzo et al, Atmos Environ, Nov 2013 [tinyurl.com/rq3e9of]; UK House of Commons: Environmental Audit Committee, Sixth Report of Session 2014–15, pp.8–9 [tinyurl.com/qmhfrml]; WHO Air Quality Guidelines: Global Update, 2006, p.20; US EIA, Electric power monthly, 2009–19 [tinyurl.com/s6vo7ca]; US EIA, FAQ, 22 October 2019 [tinyurl.com/vncfp84].

5. UK DEFRA, 15 Feb 2019 [tinyurl.com/tcn3jxx]; F. Caiazzo et al, Atmos Environ, Nov 2013 [tinyurl.com/rq3e9of].

6. H. Ritchie and M. Roser, Our World in Data, Apr/Oct 2017 [tinyurl.com/y9s4zm99].

7. The Henry Ford, Ford Company Chronology [tinyurl.com/v8h6fer]; Ford Operations Map 2019 [tinyurl.com/yx4btmqp]; History.com, 13 Nov 2009 [tinyurl.com/qquqmjy]; Economist Intelligence Unit, 22 Nov 2016 [tinyurl.com/rtdqhcq]; B. Vlasic, New York Times, 18 Oct 2016 [tinyurl.com/tmdpsgh]; K. Bradsher, New York Times, 21 Jun 2017 [tinyurl.com/ya8b5ygc].

8. P. Dauvergne, The Shadows of Consumption, MIT Press, 2010, p.62; J. Sousanis, Ward's Auto, 15 Aug 2011 [tinyurl.com/y8bp57kv]; R. Kuczynski, Foreign Affairs, Oct 1928 [tinyurl.com/us7heou]; NPR, 4 Jul 2006 [tinyurl.com/vsagg6b]; A. Kotlowitz in J. Schor and D. Holt (eds), The Consumer Society Reader, The New Press, 2000, p. 281; I. Morris, The Measure of Civilization, Princeton Univ Press, 2013; US EIA, Today in Energy, 18 Feb 2015 [tinyurl.com/ujddhk6].

9. H. Ritchie and M. Roser, Our World in Data, Apr/Oct 2017 [tinyurl.com/y9s4zm99], using original data from OECD, 2014 [tinyurl.com/

uz3z2gv], Z. Klimont et al, 2013 [tinyurl.com/vba9asj] and S. Smith et al, 2011 [tinyurl.com/t8skmlm].

10. A. Morton, Guardian, 12 May 2019 [tinyurl.com/sydgl9u]; NYC.gov, 19 Apr 2018 [tinyurl.com/vwpehp6]; ALA, 2019 [tinyurl.com/y32dc8gr].

11. C. Brahic, New Scientist, 28 Jul 2008 [tinyurl.com/wlhnxz7]; R. Harrabin, BBC News, 30 Sep 2009 [tinyurl.com/yandsd8]; R, Harrabin, BBC News, 5 Feb 2019 [tinyurl.com/ybvysvfc]; Z. Hausfather, Carbon Brief, 4 Feb 2019 [tinyurl.com/y9js43cm]; L. Hardt et al, Appl Energy, 1 August 2018 [tinyurl.com/udg84fw].

12. D. Helm and C. Hepburn (eds), The Economics and Politics of Climate Change, OUP, 2009.

13. Mongabay.com, 1 Dec 2005 [tinyurl.com/ut7jlvd].

14. S. Goldberg, Guardian, 19 Jan 2014 [tinyurl.com/vlw9tbh]; IPCC, AR5 Technical Summary, Feb 2018 [tinyurl.com/yx88zqcd]; Wikipedia, List of countries by carbon dioxide emissions, 2019 [tinyurl.com/a4jgf5m].

15. Environmental News Network, 21 Jul 2010 [tinyurl.com/w4lsy6q]; Reuters/South China Morning Post, 20 Jul 2017 [tinyurl.com/shf3bcw]; E. Wong, New York Times, 1 Apr 2013 [tinyurl.com/v7a25gf]; J. He et al, N Engl J Med, Vol 353, 2005 [tinyurl.com/vrw746b]; T. Wu et al, Environ Sci Pollut Res Int, May 2019 [tinyurl.com/v3qmdnx].

16. K. Than, National Geographic, 24 Jan 2014 [tinyurl.com/t2tsh2b]; J. Lin et al, Proc Natl Acad Sci, 4 Feb 2014 [tinyurl.com/y33h9fll].

17. Y. Zhou, Conversation, 22 May 2017 [tinyurl.com/sudw9v7]; X. Li and Y. Zhou, Strateg Manag J, 16 Mar 2017 [tinyurl.com/un4m8r4].

18. S. Bernard and A. Kazmin, Financial Times (FT), 11 Dec 2018 [tinyurl.com/ycwbp6oj]; K. Balakrishnan et al, Lancet, 1 Jan 2019 [tinyurl.com/y7kw6d6d]; S. Goldberg, Guardian, 19 Jan 2014 [tinyurl.com/vlw9tbh]; Phys.org, 10 Aug 2015 [tinyurl.com/ttx5878]; International Energy Agency (IEA), World Energy Outlook 2017 [tinyurl.com/y94q5eg9]; M. Greenstone et al, North India AQLI, Univ of Chicago, 2018 [tinyurl.com/t66gacf].

19. J. Knight and S. Ding, China's Remarkable Economic Growth, Oxford Univ Press, 2012, pp.4, 220. L. Brandt and T. Rawski (eds), China's Great Economic Transformation, Cambridge Univ Press, 2008; Cost of Pollution in China: Economic Estimates of Physical Damages, World Bank, 2007; C. Stockdale and D. McIntyre, NBC News, 30 Jan 2012 [tinyurl.com/u6w7nf5].

20. Cost of Pollution in China: Economic Estimates of Physical Damages, World Bank, 2007, p.xi; M. Wang et al, Public Health Rep, Mar–Apr 2011 [tinyurl.com/r8q26yg]; WHO Air Quality Guidelines: Global Update, 2006, pp.40, 49.

21. State of Global Air 2018, Health Effects Institute (HEI) [tinyurl.com/y2gcyncv]; P. Garzón and L. Salazar-López, New York Times, 21 Jul 2017 [tinyurl.com/y8m3es7d]; M. Forsythe, New York Times, 5 Jan 2017 [tinyurl.com/h68ys5m]; T. Donaldson. Sourcing Journal, 27 Oct 2017 [tinyurl.com/w6rpvgd]; Global Wind Energy Council, Global Statistics, 2019 [tinyurl.com/ryhtg2q]; T. Phillips, Guardian, 19 Jan 2017 [tinyurl.com/gvlnt6p].

22. Reuters, 21 Jan 2019 [tinyurl.com/w4ehsda]; Carbon Brief, 25 Mar 2019 [tinyurl.com/y5djatlg]; M. McGrath, BBC News, 20 Nov 2019 [tinyurl.com/v9jvfkp].

23. Cost of Pollution in China: Economic Estimates of Physical Damages, World Bank, 2007; N. Klein, This Changes Everything, Simon & Schuster, 2014, p.193 (ebook).

24. Q. Zhang et al, Nature, 30 Mar 2017 [tinyurl.com/svoj4vd].

25. BBC News, 5 Oct 2007 [tinyurl.com/txx4h9r]; A. Hasanbeigi et al, Lawrence Berkeley National Laboratory (LBNL), Dec 2015 [tinyurl.com/rrq9erk]; L. Tofani, Pulitzer Center, 16 Dec 2007 [tinyurl.com/se73atr]; C. Ivanovich et al, Atmos Chem Phys Discuss, 2019 [tinyurl.com/wljl64f].

26. C. Rose, The Dirty Man of Europe, Simon & Schuster, 1990; D. Pellow, Resisting Global Toxics, MIT Press, 2007.

27. Cost of Pollution in China: Economic Estimates of Physical Damages, World Bank, 2007; Greenpeace Press Release, 28 Oct 2009 [tinyurl.com/sywxtsw]; Greenpeace International, Dirty Laundry, 2011 [tinyurl.com/vdgof3g]; NASA, The World's Largest Urban Area, 15 Sep 2015 [tinyurl.com/ufoqqbq].

28. D. Steinbock, Foreign Policy Journal, 1 May 2019 [tinyurl.com/y4qcmssp]; J. Vidal, Guardian, 14 Dec 2013 [tinyurl.com/ybsfk8q3]; J. Vidal, Guardian, 30 Oct 2006 [tinyurl.com/uy5lvq4]; S. Needhidasan et al, J Environ Health Sci Eng, Vol 12/36, 2014 [tinyurl.com/jdk78zu].

29. S. Watson, NPR, 28 Jun 2018 [tinyurl.com/qkpk9zx]; World Trade Organization (WTO), Notification: China, 18 Jul 2017 [tinyurl.com/rl2lpxm]; M. Taylor, Guardian, 2 Jan 2018 [tinyurl.com/ybytq6ux]; Reuters, 22 May 2019 [tinyurl.com/y3rgkod2].

30. S. Edwards, Devex, 2017 [tinyurl.com/y3rgkod2]; R. de Jong, FIA Foundation, 15 Sep 2016 [tinyurl.com/whp9eky].

31. A. Leonard, Khian Sea, Free Press, 2010, p.224; D. Pellow, Resisting Global Toxics, MIT Press, 2007, p.108.

32. Basel Convention [tinyurl.com/ybz62z].

33. P. Pochanart et al in A. Stohl (ed), Intercontinental Transport of Air Pollution, Springer, 2004, pp.99–130; E. Wong, New York Times, 20 Jan 2014 [tinyurl.com/vocv857]; UCI Press Release, 20 Jan 2014 [tinyurl.com/sbsh3cj]; Phys.org, 10 Aug 2015 [tinyurl.com/ttx5878]; W. Verstraeten et al, Nat Geosci, Vol 8, 2015 [tinyurl.com/t77spwm].

34. NASA Earth Observatory: Image of the Day, 29 Oct 2004 [tinyurl.com/vs3yzra].

35. E. Hilaire and L. Guang, Guardian, 13 Jan 2015 [tinyurl.com/tcpmcc6]; D. Roberts, Bloomberg News, 27 Nov 2014 [tinyurl.com/wgl2czh].

36. P. Garzón and L. Salazar-López, New York Times, 21 Jul 2017 [tinyurl.com/y8m3es7d]; S. Sengupta, New York Times, 24 Nov 2018 [tinyurl.com/y8znpjcz].

37. World Energy Outlook 2017 [tinyurl.com/y94q5eg9]; J. Ambrose, Guardian, 11 Jun 2019 [tinyurl.com/yy44t7bh]; US EIA, Today in

Energy, 14 May 2014 [tinyurl.com/vscfggw]; US EIA, Today in Energy 27 Sep 2017 [tinyurl.com/ydhux6wd].

38. US EIA, Today in Energy, 27 Sep 2017 [tinyurl.com/ydhux6wd].

39. BBC News, 5 Oct 2007 [tinyurl.com/txx4h9r]; M. Albert, Stop the Killing Train, South End Press, 1994, p.41.

40. J. Kaiman, Guardian, 20 Dec 2013 [tinyurl.com/sdc3qu6]; T. Stoerk, EDF Market Forces, 17 May 2018 [tinyurl.com/t82cyhh]; J. Gan, GovInsider, 19 Jun 2019 [tinyurl.com/sgvjmq8]; BBC News, 20 Jan 2016 [tinyurl.com/yxqer5vq]; Greenpeace Asia, 11 Jan 2018 [tinyurl.com/skvb7sp]; Greenpeace Asia, 12 Jan 2018 [tinyurl.com/v39o5lp]; Reuters, 5 Mar 2017 [tinyurl.com/tod5gbk]; W. Wang et al, Environ Sci Technol, 15 Jul 2009 [tinyurl.com/wmju9dy]; A. Jamieson, Telegraph, 22 Jun 2009 [tinyurl.com/uouy9q6]; J. Huang et al, Lancet, 1 Jul 2018 [tinyurl.com/tlrw9tb].

Chapter 7

1. N. Klepeis et al, J Expo Anal Environ Epidemiol, May–June 2001 [tinyurl.com/upx577c]; C. Potera, Environ Health Perspect, Jan 2011 [tinyurl.com/s3rtkhq]; M. Dennekamp et al, Occup Environ Med, Aug 2001 [tinyurl.com/yxxc9vyw].

2. State of Global Air 2018, Health Effects Institute (HEI), p.1 [tinyurl.com/y2gcyncv]; Practical Action, Stop the Killer in the Kitchen [tinyurl.com/wclogrz]; WHO Air Quality Guidelines: Global Update, 2006, p.20; D. Carrington, Guardian, 22 Feb 2016 [tinyurl.com/se8dba2]; WHO, 8 May 2018 [tinyurl.com/y5ounq23].

3. Simon Nkoitoi, Opportunity Fund for Developing Countries, 2005 [tinyurl.com/ra7f3z6]; Global Alliance for Clean Cookstoves/Practical Action, Gender and Livelihoods: Impacts of Clean Cookstoves in South Asia, retrieved 2019 [tinyurl.com/sywk6vx]; E. Goulding, TIME, 5 Dec 2017 [tinyurl.com/u9ks9h5].

4. D. Fullerton et al, Occup Environ Med, Nov 2009 [tinyurl.com/un4sqkj]; WHO, 8 May 2018 [tinyurl.com/y5ounq23]; State of Global Air 2018, HEI, p.6.

5. H. Warwick and A. Doig, Smoke – the Killer in the Kitchen, ITDG Publishing, 2004; The Cost of Air Pollution, World Bank/Institute for Health Metrics and Evaluation (IHME), 2016, p.x [tinyurl.com/h4hbjta].

6. State of Global Air 2018, HEI, p.6; Women's Refugee Commission, 15 Mar 2006 [tinyurl.com/r5kp7gz].

7. WHO, 8 May 2018 [tinyurl.com/y5ounq23]; H. Warwick and A. Doig, Smoke – the Killer in the Kitchen, ITDG Publishing, 2004; E. Adaji et al, Environ Sci Pollut Res Int, Vol 26/4, 2019 [tinyurl.com/svsn5hz].

8. C. Buckley, New York Times, 28 Feb 2018 [tinyurl.com/yd6v5uv3]; US CDC, Carbon Monoxide, 2019 [tinyurl.com/gsfzhqf]; US EPA, Carbon Monoxide's Impact on Indoor Air Quality [tinyurl.com/hkqwww8]; E. Nagourney, New York Times, 26 Feb 2008 [tinyurl.com/s7q3976].

9. M. Dennekamp et al, Occup Environ Med, Aug 2001 [tinyurl.com/yxxc9vyw]; University Corporation for Atmospheric Research (UCAR) Center for Science Education, Nitrogen Oxides [tinyurl.com/sbyudt6]; I. Sample, Guardian, 17 Feb 2019 [tinyurl.com/yy8xpvq6]; J. Gillis and B. Nilles, New York Times, 1 May 2019 [tinyurl.com/y2ovjrhp]; ACS, 5 Jan 2016 [tinyurl.com/y3d3uw4s]; A. Kirby, BBC News, 29 Jan 2004 [tinyurl.com/3y7n2].

10. State of Global Air 2018, Health Effects Institute (HEI), p.8 [tinyurl.com/y2gcyncv].

11. World Bank, Sustainable Energy for All (SE4ALL) database/WHO Global Household Energy database, retrieved Jan 2020 [tinyurl.com/wxmz4v3].

12. T. Ng et al, Thorax, Aug 2001 [tinyurl.com/rm2q9pv].

13. US EPA, Volatile Organic Compounds' Impact on Indoor Air Quality [tinyurl.com/zdbrwth]; L. Hamers, Science News for Students 27 Feb 2018 [tinyurl.com/y7yumyh9].

14. E. Grossman, Science News for Students, 23 Sep 2016 [tinyurl.com/v55894o]; C. Potera, Environ Health Perspect, Jan 2011 [tinyurl.com/s3rtkhq]; US EPA, Volatile Organic Compounds' Impact on Indoor Air

Quality [tinyurl.com/zdbrwth]; S. Farmer et al, Am J Physiol Heart Circ Physiol, 15 Aug 2014 [tinyurl.com/snwajkz]; C. Callahan et al, Epidemiology, Mar 2019 [tinyurl.com/wax5eoy].

15. C. Woodford, Clothes dryers, Explainthatstuff.com, 2010 [tinyurl. com/tstende]; J. Konradsen et al, J Allergy Clin Immunol, Mar 2015 [tinyurl.com/trupp95]; M. Castro and M. Kraft, Clinical Asthma, Mosby/Elsevier, 2008, p.151; J. Hu et al, Int J Environ Res Public Health, Sep 2017 [tinyurl.com/sksud3s]; E. Bradford, BBC News, 2 Nov 2012 [tinyurl.com/tc65rkb].

16. J. Allen, Sunday Times, 11 May 2019 [tinyurl.com/wsvet79].

17. R. Maines, King Asoka: Asbestos and Fire, Rutgers University Press, 2005, p.26; UK NHS, Asbestosis, 7 Aug 2017 [tinyurl.com/sw3rl52]; F. Perraudin, Guardian, 7 Jul 2019 [tinyurl.com/y5cnjbjw].

18. US National Cancer Institute, Formaldehyde and Cancer Risk, 10 Jun 2011 [tinyurl.com/j8yhrzd]; M. Böhm et al, J Hazard Mater, 30 June 2012 [tinyurl.com/vbxrfke].

19. J. Vallette et al, Healthy Building Network, Oct 2017 [tinyurl. com/wbrmaqm]; Abrahm Lustgarten, CNBC, 9 Jul 2018 [tinyurl.com/ y9cz2nzy].

20. Center for Health, Environment and Justice, 12 Jun 2008 [tinyurl. com/rcpqcc4].

21. A. Pickett and M. Bell, Int J Environ Res Public Health, Dec 2011 [tinyurl.com/t5nj7ap].

22. WHO Air Quality Guidelines: Global Update, 2006, pp.65, 74, 269.

23. Ibid.; US EPA, Introduction to Indoor Air Quality [tinyurl.com/ yatpzfkc]; K. Sharma et al, Environ Sci Pollut Res Int, Jun 2019 [tinyurl. com/r8kakkd]; T. Jacobson et al, Nat Sustain, Aug 2019 [tinyurl.com/ wepro8k].

24. WHO Air Quality Guidelines: Global Update, 2006, p.65; G. Fuller, The Invisible Killer, Melville-House, 2018, pp.151–176; The Danish Ecological Council, Copenhagen, 2016 [tinyurl.com/t3q8b27].

25. V. Zagà et al, Pneumologia, Oct–Dec 2008 [tinyurl.com/u4zargd];
C. DiCarlo, Forensic, 1 Jun 2009 [tinyurl.com/rthp4a6]; H. Karagueuzian
et al, Nicotine Tob Res, Jan 2012 [tinyurl.com/rqny8yw].

26. R. Doll and A. Hill, BMJ, 30 Sep 1950 [tinyurl.com/t9owfqf]; BBC
News, 22 Jun 2004 [tinyurl.com/6f425t3]; T. Frank, The Conquest of
Cool, Univ of Chicago Press, 1997; P. Fischer et al, JAMA, Dec 1991
[tinyurl.com/v5bvcvt]; Louis V. Genco, Doctors Recommend Smoking
Camels, Old-Time Radio, retrieved 2019 [tinyurl.com/39ngcp].

27. G. Invernizzi et al, BMJ Tob Control, Vol 13, 2004 [tinyurl.com/
yx7stnl9].

28. WHO, Tobacco Fact Sheet, 26 Jul 2019 [tinyurl.com/y66amzyz],
Wikipedia, List of Smoking Bans, retrieved 2019 [tinyurl.com/
h894gsr].

29. US National Library of Medicine, The Smoke Nuisance [tinyurl.
com/t5l2jdt].

30. State of Global Air 2018, Health Effects Institute (HEI), p.6 [tinyurl.
com/y2gcyncv]; I. Sample, Guardian, 17 Feb 2019 [tinyurl.com/
yy8xpvq6]; J. Allen, Sunday Times, 11 May 2019 [tinyurl.com/wsvet79];
G. Invernizzi et al, BMJ Tob Control, Vol 13, 2004 [tinyurl.com/
yx7stnl9]; HO Ambient Air Pollution Database 2016 (retrieved Sep 2019)
[tinyurl.com/wqucfjg].

31. A. Gates, New York Times, 11 Sep 2006 [tinyurl.com/tkxg597];
E. Pilkington, Guardian, 11 Nov 2009 [tinyurl.com/td8m8jj]; C. Bankoff,
New York, 10 Sep 2016 [tinyurl.com/y3nbsxnp]; R. Shulman,
Washington Post, 23 April 2008 [tinyurl.com/nrbqzgt]; J. Walter,
Guardian, 10 Sep 2016 [tinyurl.com/j97llux]; L. Goodman, Newsweek,
7 Sep 2016 [tinyurl.com/yx5tmr8q]; J. Nadler, Press Release, 21 Apr
2008 [tinyurl.com/t9uqsq2]; N. Hopkins, Guardian, 12 Oct 2018 [tinyurl.
com/y9nu2onc]; S. Kennedy, Guardian, 29 Mar 2019 [tinyurl.com/
y3atqh8k]; K. Willsher, Guardian, 10 May 2019 [tinyurl.com/y54udokh];
A. Chrisafis, Guardian, 9 May 2019 [tinyurl.com/uhq6jb9]; E. Peltier
et al, New York Times, 16 Sep 2019 [tinyurl.com/yxfjwtas]; AFP,
Guardian, 4 Jun 2019 [tinyurl.com/yxbmqcao].

Chapter 8

1. D. Carrington, Guardian, 11 Jan 2019 [tinyurl.com/ydxrxn4u];
S. Roberts et al, Psychiatry Res, Feb 2019 [tinyurl.com/rxs6oyx];
R. Peters et al, J Alzheimers Dis, 11 Feb 2019 [tinyurl.com/trhkxur];
M. Taylor, Guardian, 25 Oct 2018 [tinyurl.com/y824l65d].

2. E. Kao, South China Morning Post, 2 Oct 2018 [tinyurl.com/
y8zcm89u]; S. Bernard and A. Kazmin, Financial Times (FT), 11 Dec
2018 [tinyurl.com/ycwbp6oj]; J. World, TIME, 9 Sep 2016 [tinyurl.com/
u7x6fee]; World Bank, Clean and Improved Cooking in Sub-Saharan
Africa, Nov 2014, p.20 [tinyurl.com/uoxlkym].

3. WHO Europe/OECD, Economic cost of the health impact of air
pollution in Europe, 2015, p.4 [tinyurl.com/yceuhsqw]; WHO, 2 May
2018 [tinyurl.com/yyjlue4o].

4. H. Devlin, Guardian, 29 Mar 2017 [tinyurl.com/m996cxl]; F. Kelly and
J. Fussell, Environ Geochem Health, Aug 2015 [tinyurl.com/vzmnu2o];
C. Pope and D. Dockery, J Air Waste Manag Assoc, Vol 56, 2006 [tinyurl.
com/rs426yz]; D. Brugge and K. Lane, Conversation, 15 Nov 2018
[tinyurl.com/u7xsbjn].

5. F. Kelly and J. Fussell, Environ Geochem Health, Aug 2015 [tinyurl.
com/vzmnu2o]; S. Farmer et al, Am J Physiol Heart Circ Physiol, 15 Aug
2014 [tinyurl.com/snwajkz]; C. Callahan et al, Epidemiology, Mar 2019
[tinyurl.com/wax5eoy]; D. Dockery et al, N Engl J Med, Dec 9 1993
[tinyurl.com/v77qmwp]; C. Pope et al, JAMA, Vol 287/11, 2002 [tinyurl.
com/uqg79n7]; M. Loxham et al, BMJ 27 Nov 2019 [tinyurl.com/
uupfaez]; Y. Wei, BMJ, 28 Nov 2019 [tinyurl.com/r6g2q4t].

6. J. Bosson et al, Am J Respir Crit Care Med, 6 May 2019 [tinyurl.com/
w2uuwny]; D. Wooding et al, Am J Respir Crit Care Med, 12 Apr 2019
[tinyurl.com/qrlxzpy].

7. D. Carrington, Guardian, 10 Apr 2019 [tinyurl.com/y295cpl7];
P. Achakulwisut et al, Lancet Planet Health, 10 Apr 2019 [tinyurl.com/
vttzaan]; N. Davis, Guardian, 8 Aug 2019 [tinyurl.com/y3srzpmu].

8. State of Global Air 2018. Health Effects Institute (HEI), p.1 [tinyurl.
com/y2gcyncv]; M. Bell et al, JAMA, 17 Nov 2004 [tinyurl.com/

vmfkvla]; WHO Air Quality Guidelines: Global Update, 2006, pp.316–17; C. Ogden, Air Quality News, 24 Jul 2019 [tinyurl.com/tqljkel].

9. E. Wilkins, Q J R Meteorol Soc, April 1954 [tinyurl.com/wlpohs3]; E. Wilkins, J R Sanitary Inst, Jan 1954, [tinyurl.com/wdj6xlr].

10. WHO Air Quality Guidelines: Global Update, 2006, pp.395–420; M. Amdur, Environ Health Perspect, May 1989 [tinyurl.com/se97clr].

11. WHO Air Quality Guidelines: Global Update, 2006, pp.21, 198; K. McClatchey (ed), Clinical Laboratory Medicine, Lippincott Williams & Wilkins, 2002, p.806.

12. P. Wolkoff et al, Toxicol Lett, 7 Mar 2012 [tinyurl.com/w3a369n]; US EPA, Limonene, 1 Sep 1994 [tinyurl.com/we4l3pj]; J. Wakefield, Napthalene: Toxicological Overview, Health Protection Agency, 2007 [tinyurl.com/ujnqby8]; US National Institute for Occupational Safety and Health (NIOSH), Benzene, 24 Jun 2019 [tinyurl.com/rp3eqbc]; EEA, 15 Apr 2013 [tinyurl.com/quueht4]; W. Ott and J. Roberts, Sci Am, Feb 1998, pp.86–91.

13. WHO, 2 May 2018 [tinyurl.com/yyjlue4o]; State of Global Air 2018, Health Effects Institute (HEI), p.1 [tinyurl.com/y2gcyncv].

14. J. Bosson et al, Am J Respir Crit Care Med, 6 May 2019 [tinyurl.com/w2uuwny]; World Bank, Clean and Improved Cooking in Sub-Saharan Africa, Nov 2014, p.20 [tinyurl.com/uoxlkym]; US CDC, 19 Jul 2018 [tinyurl.com/lm3zozl].

15. ALA, 20 Jul 2017 [tinyurl.com/s99dkcr]; 100 trillion trillion is a guesstimate based on the number of litres we breathe multiplied by the rough number of molecules in a litre.

16. S. Gordon et al, Lancet Respir Med, Oct 2014 [tinyurl.com/rg5atm9]; WHO, 8 May 2018 [tinyurl.com/y5ounq23]; WHO, Cancer, 12 Sep 2018 [tinyurl.com/vvhbsyv].

17. WHO, Pneumonia, 2 Aug 2019 [tinyurl.com/yx7g7l6s]; WHO, 8 May 2018 [tinyurl.com/y5ounq23]; A. Yura et al, Nihon Koshu Eisei Zasshi, Aug 2005 [tinyurl.com/wl7nbk4].

18. W. Gauderman et al, Am J Respir Crit Care Med, Oct 2000 [tinyurl.com/s982s29]; S. Farmer et al, Am J Physiol Heart Circ Physiol, 15 Aug 2014 [tinyurl.com/snwajkz]; BBC News, 2 May 2019 [tinyurl.com/y6hnpyva]; S. Laville, Guardian, 2 May 2019 [tinyurl.com/yxk36zs6]; P. Bharadwaj et al, Am J Respir Crit Care Med, 15 Dec 2016 [tinyurl.com/rc46fbb].

19. F. Kelly and J. Fussell, Environ Geochem Health, Aug 2015, p.644 [tinyurl.com/vzmnu2o]; WHO, 8 May 2018 [tinyurl.com/y5ounq23]; S. Farmer et al, Am J Physiol Heart Circ Physiol, 15 Aug 2014 [tinyurl.com/snwajkz]; F. Everson et al, Int J Environ Res Public Health, 28 Jun 2019 [tinyurl.com/veghs93]; M. Link et al, J Am Coll Cardiol, 27 Aug 2013 [tinyurl.com/wztsjbd].

20. D. Carrington, Guardian, 12 Jul 2019 [tinyurl.com/y2pledfv]; L. Calderón-Garcidueñas et al, Environ Res, Sep 2019 [tinyurl.com/sa3f9g5].

21. WHO, 8 May 2018 [tinyurl.com/y5ounq23]; World Stroke Campaign, Facts and Figures, 2019 [tinyurl.com/ua8vpug]; R. Maheswaran et al, Stroke, May 2010 [tinyurl.com/qlaogun].

22. C. Pope et al, JAMA, Vol 287/11, 2002 [tinyurl.com/uqg79n7].

23. WHO Air Quality Guidelines: Global Update, 2006, p.125; Cancer Research UK, Breast cancer risk, retrieved 2019 [tinyurl.com/y67p8o6p]; Z. Andersen et al, Environ Health Perspect, Vol 125/10, 2017 [tinyurl.com/w434bjd]; C. Yang et al, Asia Pac J Public Health, Jul 2016 [tinyurl.com/r5nbs4k].

24. D. Carrington and L. Kuo, Guardian, 27 Aug 2018 [tinyurl.com/y92t7yz9]; M. Ives, New York Times, 29 Aug 2018 [tinyurl.com/y92a3cv8]; Xin Zhang et al, Proc Natl Acad Sci, 11 Sep 2018 [tinyurl.com/yblouruc]; D. Carrington, Guardian, 5 Sep 2016 [tinyurl.com/zpt9ehr]; Barbara A. Maher et al, Proc Natl Acad Sci, 27 Sep 2016 [tinyurl.com/vcdbluw]; S. Weichenthal et al, Epidemiology. 6 Nov 2019 [tinyurl.com/veet4su].

25. J. Newbury et al, JAMA Psychiatry, 1 Jun 2019 [tinyurl.com/rw2gnc6]; S. Roberts et al, Psychiatry Res, Feb 2019 [tinyurl.com/rxs6oyx]; N. Davies, Guardian, 20 Aug 2019 [tinyurl.com/y538l5wf].

26. J. Lu et al, Psychol Sci, Mar 2018 [tinyurl.com/uztwwgp].

27. UNICEF, December 2017 [tinyurl.com/uyze9nn]; J. Burns et al, Cochrane Database, 2014 [tinyurl.com/vrk9kvc]; F. Kelly and J. Fussell, Environ Geochem Health, Aug 2015 [tinyurl.com/vzmnu2o]; E. Adaji et al, Environ Sci Pollut Res Int, Vol 26/4, 2019 [tinyurl.com/svsn5hz]; R. Walton et al, Environ Int, Nov 2016 [tinyurl.com/qmrl4ms]; R. Peters et al, J Alzheimers Dis, 11 Feb 2019 [tinyurl.com/trhkxur]; B. Zhao et al, Cardiovasc Diagn Ther, Aug 2018 [tinyurl.com/r8zbsyh].

28. D. Schraufnagel, CHEST, Feb 2019 [tinyurl.com/yj6b5lcb]; World Health Organization (WHO), 2 May 2018 [tinyurl.com/yyjlue4o].

29. S. Farmer et al, Am J Physiol Heart Circ Physiol, 15 Aug 2014 [tinyurl.com/snwajkz]; D. Carrington, Guardian, 11 Jan 2019 [tinyurl.com/ydxrxn4u]; R. Smith et al, BMJ, Vol 359, 2017 [tinyurl.com/tzzq78c]; D. Carrington, Guardian, 16 Sep 2018 [tinyurl.com/y9whjh49]; D. Carrington, Guardian, 17 Sep 2019 [tinyurl.com/y2q93ghs]; F. Kelly and J. Fussell, Environ Geochem Health, Aug 2015 [tinyurl.com/vzmnu2o]; A. Wdowiak et al, Int J Occup Med Environ Health, 14 Jun 2019 [tinyurl.com/qv464js].

30. S. Edwards et al, Environ Health Perspect, Sep 2010 [tinyurl.com/yx3shvt9]; F. Perera et al, Pediatrics, Aug 2009 [tinyurl.com/quho786]; UNICEF Press Release, 6 Dec 2017 [tinyurl.com/t25et52]; G. Solomon et al, NRDC/Coalition for Clean Air, 2001 [tinyurl.com/t6agggp]; NRDC, 15 Mar 2016 [tinyurl.com/qnub6vn].

31. UNICEF, December 2017 [tinyurl.com/uyze9nn]; M. Taylor, Guardian, 29 Oct 2018 [tinyurl.com/yczt6duf]; WHO Air Quality Guidelines: Global Update, 2006, pp.316–317; Sustrans, 25 Mar 2019 [tinyurl.com/ujz5eez].

32. State of Global Air 2018, Health Effects Institute (HEI), p.10 [tinyurl.com/y2gcyncv]; R. Peters et al, J Alzheimers Dis, 11 Feb 2019 [tinyurl.com/trhkxur]; BMJ, 2017 [tinyurl.com/yazkm97l]; King's College London News, 19 Sep 2018 [tinyurl.com/swvrkln].

33. WHO Air Quality Guidelines: Global Update, 2006, pp.121, 200, 373; WHO, Burning Opportunity, 2016.

34. J. Watts, Guardian, 23 Mar 2020 [tinyurl.com/yx4nv2wy]; G. da Silva, Univ of Melbourne [tinyurl.com/wjkcp6c]; J. Davidson, Ecowatch, 2 Apr 2020 [tinyurl.com/swks585]; D. Carrington, Guardian, 7 Jun 2020 [tinyurl.com/y9eqe25q]; D. Carrington, Guardian, 13 Jul 2020 [tinyurl.com/ycm942dz]; A. Mandavilli, New York Times, 11 Aug 2020 [tinyurl.com/y6o5btpc]; Plume Labs Blog, 13 May 2020 [tinyurl.com/yy78jbus].

35. World Bank, 21 Dec 2017 [tinyurl.com/vqnx9aj]; K. Altieri et al, Sci Total Environ, 20 Sep 2019 [tinyurl.com/vxvolbw]; F. Kelly and J. Fussell, Environ Geochem Health, Aug 2015 [tinyurl.com/vzmnu2o]; EEA, 15 Apr 2013 [tinyurl.com/quueht4]; H. Khreis et al, Eur Respir J, 8 July 2019 [tinyurl.com/t3czrr2]; Y. Zhang et al, Atmos Chem Phys, Vol 18, 2018 [tinyurl.com/v5x8z6z]; K. Abe et al, Int J Environ Res Public Health, 11 Jul 2016 [tinyurl.com/skanr55]; S. Jones et al, J Epidemiol Community Health, Jul 2017 [tinyurl.com/wfjk4p3].

Chapter 9

1. R. Ehrenberg, Nature, 2 Sep 2015 [tinyurl.com/y6onkrol].

2. N. Davis, Guardian, 5 Jul 2018 [tinyurl.com/yawtrglc]; D. Breitburg et al, Science, 5 Jan 2018 [tinyurl.com/rw7edz7]; US EPA, retrieved 2019 [tinyurl.com/jfgp6h5].

3. H. Thoreau, Walden or Life in the Woods, Heritage Press, 1939, pp.180, 311; W. Stevens, New York Times, 8 Oct 1991 [tinyurl.com/t5qr5ag]; J. Stager et al, PLoS One, 4 Apr 2018 [tinyurl.com/th8c7ve]; Y. Tayag, Inverse.com, 4 Apr 2018 [tinyurl.com/yd7azuqr].

4. US EPA, retrieved 2019 [tinyurl.com/z5f3t3z].

5. R. Smith, Air and Rain, Longmans, 1872, p.225 [tinyurl.com/skdcovm].

6. R. Turner Holmes and G. Likens, Hubbard Brook, Yale Univ Press, 2016, p.116ff.

7. B. Ottar, Water Air Soil Pollut, Jun 1976 [tinyurl.com/vseg8lw]; S. Sandøy and A. Romundstad, Water Air Soil Pollut, Dec 1995, pp.997–1002; Norwegian Environment Agency, 9 Apr 2018 [tinyurl.com/

tgvdwzb]; P. Brown, Guardian, 13 May 2019 [tinyurl.com/rrv66h4]; P. Wynn Davies, Independent, 18 Aug 1993 [tinyurl.com/tyfnned]; H. Klein et al, International Tech Meeting on Air Pollution Modelling and its Application, 2016 [tinyurl.com/sm79jyw]; H. Borchgrevink, Science Norway, 15 May 2014 [tinyurl.com/tyb9ry8].

8. The Cost of Air Pollution, World Bank/Institute for Health Metrics and Evaluation (IHME), 2016 [tinyurl.com/h4hbjta]; B. Webster, New York Times, 6 Nov 1979 [tinyurl.com/vwsclqw]; US EPA, 2019 [tinyurl.com/vcaljh8].

9. N. Bhatti et al, Environmental Management, July 1992 [tinyurl.com/u5287q8]; World Bank, Cost of Pollution in China, 2007; V. Bhaskar and P. Rao, J Atmos Chem, Vol 74/1 2017 [tinyurl.com/rp3woof]; NASA Earth Observatory retrieved 2019 [tinyurl.com/vutqs8u]; Greenpeace India, 19 Aug 2019 [tinyurl.com/rmc8b6w]; C. Li et al, Nature Scientific Reports, Vol 7, 2017 [tinyurl.com/ruy49ql]; H. Fountain and J. Schwartz, New York Times, 2 May 2018 [tinyurl.com/y5747lt8]; World Commission on Environment and Development, Our Common Future, Oxford, 1987, p.180.

10. Q. Zhen et al, JGR Atmospheres, 6 Jul 2019 [tinyurl.com/y3aafkc2].

11. T. Shibamoto et al, Rev Environ Contam Toxicol, Vol 190, 2007 [tinyurl.com/t6sup3t]; J. Dearden, UK Without Incineration Network [tinyurl.com/vtfuwa3]; R. Mason et al, Environ Res, Nov 2012 [tinyurl.com/w4qy7xg]; R.P. Mason et al, Geochim Cosmochim Acta, Volume 58/15, 1994 [tinyurl.com/vcl7gdz]; J. Doward, Observer, 14 May 2017 [tinyurl.com/mzn89fx].

12. US EPA Office of Water [tinyurl.com/vlwscrv]; R. Mason et al, Environ Sci Technol, 27 Feb 1997 [tinyurl.com/unaoqy4]; New Zealand Environment Ministry, Mercury in the Environment [tinyurl.com/rgpwvm5].

13. US National Centers for Coastal Ocean Science, 2016 [tinyurl.com/v5qqpgl]; J. Shannon and E. Voldner, Atmos Environ, Vol 29/14, 1995 [tinyurl.com/usfrvxj]; K. Vergel et al, Bull Environ Contam Toxicol, 2 Jul 2019 [tinyurl.com/wbkend5]; M. Onakpa et al, Ann Global Health, 31 Aug 2018 [tinyurl.com/wga5tbf]; K. Noh et al, Environ Sci Pollut Res

Int, 2 Jul 2019 [tinyurl.com/yx5awbfc]; P. Kapusta et al, Chemosphere, Sep 2019 [tinyurl.com/uon5qwa]; A. Mashau et al, Int J Environ Res Public Health, 13 Dec 2018 [tinyurl.com/w7gnscx]; Y. Hong et al, J Prev Med Public Health, Nov 2012 Nov [tinyurl.com/svkyn7g].

14. WHO Air Quality Guidelines: Global Update, 2006, p.92.

15. WHO Air Quality Guidelines for Europe, 2000; M. Klein et al, Sci Total Environ, 29 May 2019 [tinyurl.com/tqmo2no]; M. Singh, Guardian, 13 Aug 2019 [tinyurl.com/y2uyautj]; M. Bergmann et al, Science Advances, 14 Aug 2019 [tinyurl.com/y3lbyxsp]; D. Carrington, Guardian, 14 Aug 2019 [tinyurl.com/yyykmm5z]; D. Carrington, Guardian, 27 Dec 2019 [tinyurl.com/rfvtypm].

16. C. Woodford, Water Pollution, Explainthatstuff.com, 2006 [tinyurl.com/ybolhcwu]; EEA, 29 Nov 2018 [tinyurl.com/uxuhzh6]; NOAA News Release, 2 Aug 2017 [tinyurl.com/y2ldydad].

17. S. Fields, Environ Health Perspect, Jul 2004 [tinyurl.com/r2jyvrb].

18. H. van Grinsven et al, Environ Health, Vol 5/26, 2006 [tinyurl.com/wgmdf7d]; Science Daily, 16 May 2016 [tinyurl.com/zoyta2f]; R. Miller et al, Geophys Res Lett, May 2016 [tinyurl.com/rgsph5x]; G. Park et al, Sci Total Environ, 1 Sep 2019 [tinyurl.com/tyrhpg3].

19. Z. Shi, WEF, 4 Nov 2014 [tinyurl.com/uyccltd]; H. Griffiths, Ministry of Agriculture Ontario, June 2003 [tinyurl.com/pqu9rps].

20. H. Griffiths, Ministry of Agriculture Ontario, June 2003 [tinyurl.com/pqu9rps]; London Free Press, 13 Jun 2016 [tinyurl.com/vb5dnhq]; J. Gregg et al, Nature, 10 Jul 2003 [tinyurl.com/vhdhsso].

21. R. Allain, Wired, 24 Dec 2012 [tinyurl.com/rqk75yw]; USDA Science Perspectives, Winter 2010 [tinyurl.com/st72lfg].

22. R. Gast, Adirondack Almanack, 29 Aug 2017 [tinyurl.com/u25mnzz]; Adirondack Council Press Release, 2 Oct 2019 [tinyurl.com/w89y5s3].

23. Ibid.

24. H. Griffiths, Ministry of Agriculture Ontario, June 2003 [tinyurl.com/pqu9rps]; 'Chapter 8: Effects on Vegetation and Animals' in

R. Boubel et al (eds), Fundamentals of Air Pollution, Academic Press, 1994, p.116; J. Nigel et al, in R. Ambasht and N. Ambasht (eds), Modern Trends in Applied Terrestrial Ecology, Springer 2002.

25. J. Evelyn, Fumifugium, Godbid, 1661 [tinyurl.com/qvfywhs].

26. Z. Shi, WEF, 4 Nov 2014 [tinyurl.com/uyccltd]; S. Das, DownToEarth, 17 Sep 2015 [tinyurl.com/uwqjfvt]; Jennifer Burney and V. Ramanathan, Proc Natl Acad Sci, 3 Nov 2014 [tinyurl.com/rrn9wjd].

27. Z. Shi, WEF, 4 Nov 2014 [tinyurl.com/uyccltd]; World Bank, Cost of Pollution in China, 2007; China Power, 25 Jan 2017 [tinyurl.com/y9gdwht7]; Bloomberg News, 22 May 2017 [tinyurl.com/k7tspf3]; P. Bailey, Univ of California, Davis, 14 Mar 2017 [tinyurl.com/u9483u2].

28. 'Chapter 8: Effects on Vegetation and Animals' in R. Boubel et al (eds), Fundamentals of Air Pollution, Academic Press, 1994, p.116; R. Rowe et al, J Air Pollut Control Assoc, Vol 35/7, 1985 [tinyurl.com/tqlbjwc]; US EPA Publication: EPA-451/K-03-001 J, 2003/2014 [tinyurl.com/yb2h73vw]; J. Brown, Sustainable Food Trust, 3 May 2019 [tinyurl.com/vm837ey]; Center for Ecology and Hydrology, Air Pollution and Vegetation, 2011; UN Economic Commission for Europe, Air pollution and food production, retrieved 2019 [tinyurl.com/v7ugg7b]; A. Haagen-Smit, Engineering & Science, Dec 1950, p.7.

29. D. Velissariou in J. Fuhrer and B. Achennann (eds), Critical Levels for Ozone, Swiss Agency for Environment, Forest and Landscape, 1999, pp. 253–256; Univ of York News Release, 2 Feb 2012 [tinyurl.com/vqm58su]; J. Brown, Sustainable Food Trust, 3 May 2019 [tinyurl.com/vm837ey].

30. M. Rubin, Bull Hist Chem, Vol 27/2, 2002, p.81; Norwegian Environment Agency, 20 Sep 2010 [tinyurl.com/wgmnvvr]; W. Stockwell et al in Forest Decline and Ozone by Heinrich Sandermann (ed), Springer, 1997 [tinyurl.com/rqlcfhw].

31. G. Ferguson, Los Angeles Times, 19 Dec 2017 [tinyurl.com/v7byzsm]; Univ of Exeter News Release, 21 Dec 2018 [tinyurl.com/uuls89o].

32. P. Bailey, Univ of California, Davis, 14 Mar 2017 [tinyurl.com/u9483u2]; T. Wang et al, Sci Total Environ, 1 Jan 2017 [tinyurl.com/ulqdyt6].

33. S. Avnery et al, Atmos Environ, Vol 45, 2011 [tinyurl.com/w8swhhg]; UN press release, 15 Jul 2019 [tinyurl.com/y4pl496k].

Chapter 10

1. C. Jones, Phys.org, 30 Sep 30 [tinyurl.com/stz8dou]; M. Cerini, CNN, 30 Sep 2016 [tinyurl.com/ufjbe4p]; S. Chen, South China Morning Post, 16 Jan 2018 [tinyurl.com/y6ftpaby].

2. D. Carrington, Guardian, 30 Aug 2016 [tinyurl.com/hz9g6re]; EEA, Air Quality in Europe, 2016, p.45 [tinyurl.com/tqzlos4].

3. C. Woodford, Catalytic converters, Explainthatstuff.com, 2007/2018 [tinyurl.com/sj6zjhb].

4. V. Sumantran et al, Guardian, 16 Oct 2017 [tinyurl.com/y7klgtd5].

5. M. Taylor, Guardian, 27 Sep 2018 [tinyurl.com/y7m7b8yj]; Stagecoach UK Bus Industry FAQ [tinyurl.com/yx43nd82]; G. Paton, Times, 18 Apr 2019 [tinyurl.com/tlgr2xn]; Statista, 2019 [tinyurl.com/tsdvxwh]; P. Crerar, Standard, 24 Jul 2015 [tinyurl.com/wveybxt]; UK House of Commons: Environmental Audit Committee, Sixth Report of Session 2014–15, p.18 [tinyurl.com/qmhfrml].

6. T. Phillips, Guardian, 26 May 2016 [tinyurl.com/z47hfqc]; J. Fullerton, Guardian, 7 Jul 2017 [tinyurl.com/yacc743f]; BBC News, 4 Jul 2017 [tinyurl.com/rskwmxt]; G. Huang, Global Times, 7 Aug 2016 [tinyurl.com/sbl9klg].

7. R. Chrystal, BBC News, 18 Nov 2011 [tinyurl.com/weefc9m]; A. Vaughan, Guardian, 13 Feb 2013 [tinyurl.com/wjhxkwu].

8. Agenda.ge, 18 Oct 2018 [tinyurl.com/uwdzgds]; Tirana Times, 12 Mar 2019 [tinyurl.com/u3wefyn]; Mongolian News Agency, 12 Oct 2018 [tinyurl.com/socz6q4]; BBC News, 29 Jul 2019 [tinyurl.com/yyj6op59]; BBC News, 11 Aug 2019 [tinyurl.com/y24fpk3k]; Daily Sabah, 30 Jul 2019 [tinyurl.com/ume2wc6].

9. Xinhua, 25 Jun 2018 [tinyurl.com/w8u7xnz]; The Wire, 5 Oct 2019 [tinyurl.com/vyvx66b]; O. Wainwright, Guardian, 16 Apr 2015 [tinyurl.com/wajy28e].

10. AgroSci News Release, 3 Nov 2016 [tinyurl.com/wkj93r8]; AgroSci Green Walls Portfolio, retrieved 2019 [tinyurl.com/rb576uw].

11. CityTree by Matt Brown, published on Flickr in 2018 under a Creative Commons BY 2.0 licence [tinyurl.com/vgy9u7o].

12. C. Woodford, Self-cleaning windows, Explainthatstuff.com, 2010/17 [tinyurl.com/y9fcgpqq].

13. Milano – Palazzo Italia / Italian Pavilion by Fred Romero, published on Flickr in 2015 under a Creative Commons BY 2.0 licence [tinyurl.com/y2yufvoy]

14. J. Temperton, Wired, 24 Mar 2015 [tinyurl.com/rxwx6un]; Centre for Public Impact, 3 Mar 2016 [tinyurl.com/qksl2ot]; M. Novozhilova, Inhabit.com, 16 Jun 2015 [tinyurl.com/sol2ygq]; Birmingham Mail, 16 May 2015 [tinyurl.com/tr5g9ww]; World Bank, 1 Jan 2010 [tinyurl.com/y75hn6sd].

15. Eindhoven Univ of Technology, ScienceDaily, 8 Jul 2010 [tinyurl.com/vswqrw6]; Ayres Associates, 25 May 2016 [tinyurl.com/tvvakxt].

16. S. Sheehan, Autocar, 3 Aug 2017 [tinyurl.com/ql8f5gr]; M. Burgess, Wired UK, 3 Aug 2017 [tinyurl.com/w4928vx]; UK Dept for Transport Statistical Release, 5 Jul 2018 [tinyurl.com/uzxtrgu]; J. Watts, Guardian, 25 Feb 2019 [tinyurl.com/y5kz9g8l].

17. M. Burgess, Wired UK, 3 Aug 2017 [tinyurl.com/w4928vx]; M. Holder, Air Quality News, 15 Apr 2016 [tinyurl.com/wmr8mdq]; GreenerBuilding, 11 Mar 2004 [tinyurl.com/voc7gl7].

18. Chemical Heritage Foundation, Frederick Gardner Cottrell, archived 4 June 2016 [tinyurl.com/vhorgbo]; F. Cottrell, US Patent 895,729, 11 Aug 1908 [tinyurl.com/sb3uz3p].

19. C. Woodford, Vacuum Cleaners, Explainthatstuff.com, 2007/2017 [tinyurl.com/uboxg23]; J. Dyson, US Patent 4,373,228A, 15 Feb 1983 [tinyurl.com/wasfkkp]; B. Kent, US Patent 1,220,641A, 3 Feb 1917 [tinyurl.com/ulrblnh].

20. AFP, Guardian, 26 Oct 2016 [tinyurl.com/h9f6wqz]; Purevento, 2019 [tinyurl.com/udq8mb8]; J. Cheung, Arup, 2 Jul 2015 [tinyurl.com/tmknvru]; AFP, Yahoo News, 15 Aug 2019 [tinyurl.com/waw5qmn]; A. Lewis, Conversation, 25 Jan 2018 [tinyurl.com/so3y8e8].

21. Dyson Technology Ltd, GB Patent GB201811994D0, 23 Jul 2018 [tinyurl.com/tn2owqe]; C. Hsu and C. Lin, Taiwan Patent TWI589331B, 25 Aug 2016 [tinyurl.com/s6maekz].

22. WHO, Guidelines for Indoor Air Quality: Household Fuel Combustion, 2014; World Bank, Clean and Improved Cooking in Sub-Saharan Africa, Nov 2014 [tinyurl.com/uoxlkym].

23. US Dept of State, Remarks by Secretary Clinton, 21 Sep 2010 [tinyurl.com/rsuaddt]; Washington Post, 29 Oct 2015 [tinyurl.com/qdd22po].

24. E. Hoffner, Guardian, 30 Oct 2015 [tinyurl.com/wyjuogs]; M. De Fazio, Humanosphere, 30 Dec 2016 [tinyurl.com/w72a2wy]; A. Revkin, New York Times, 23 Sep 2010 [tinyurl.com/w72a2wy]; Global Alliance for Clean Cookstoves/Practical Action, Gender and Livelihoods: Impacts of Clean Cookstoves in South Asia, 2015 [tinyurl.com/sywk6vx]; J. Rosenthal et al, Environ Health Perspect, Jan 2017 [tinyurl.com/w69luf5].

25. M. Dennekamp et al, Occup Environ Med, Aug 2001 [tinyurl.com/yxxc9vyw]; S. Marsden, Telegraph, 6 Jun 2012 [tinyurl.com/th2fqxt]; J. Chao, Berkeley Lab News Release, 23 Jul 2013 [tinyurl.com/y3687rug].

26. D. Robinson, BMJ, 22 May 2015 [tinyurl.com/yblvv4dk]; H. Gilmore, Sydney Morning Herald, 28 Jun 2014 [tinyurl.com/v3w3q2l]; G. Turbak, Popular Science, December 1984, p.90.

27. D. Robinson, BMJ, 22 May 2015 [tinyurl.com/yblvv4dk]; DEFRA, Air Quality Expert Group, 2017, pp.16–17; H. Gilmore, Sydney Morning Herald, 28 Jun 2014 [tinyurl.com/v3w3q2l].

28. Doctors and Scientists Against Wood Smoke Pollution [tinyurl. com/te82rsa].

29. C. Woodford, HEPA filters, Explainthatstuff.com, 2008/2018 [tinyurl.com/sqnqcx3]; Telegraph, 3 Nov 2013 [tinyurl.com/r5qqty4]; P. Barn et al, Sci Total Environ, Feb 2018 [tinyurl.com/unwqke5].

30. C. Woodford, Photocatalytic air purifiers, Explainthatstuff.com, 2010/2018 [tinyurl.com/w86pgwv].

31. B. Wolverton, Eco-friendly Houseplants, Weidenfeld & Nicolson, 1996; B. Wolverton et al, NASA John C. Stennis Space Center, 15 Sep 1989 [tinyurl.com/gu7g8a4].

32. State of Global Air 2018, Health Effects Institute (HEI), pp.16–17 [tinyurl.com/y2gcyncv].

33. New Atlas, 26 Feb 2014 [tinyurl.com/vqkz9nn]; S. Brownstone, Fast Company, 10 Dec 2013 [tinyurl.com/wjl39u4]; Cool Sparks, YouTube, 27 Jan 2013 [tinyurl.com/rlkn9pp].

Chapter 11

1. Ipsos Global Advisor, May 2019 [tinyurl.com/qr6t2za].

2. M. Safi, Guardian, 5 December 2017 [tinyurl.com/yabhpkpr]; AFP, Phys.org, 8 Nov 2017 [tinyurl.com/ycf6q3fq; Financial Express, New Delhi, 8 Nov 2017 [tinyurl.com/tskmb9v]; J. Gettleman et al, Sydney Morning Herald, 9 Dec 2017 [tinyurl.com/qlfhdtt]; S. Sengupta, New York Times, 13 Jun 2019 [tinyurl.com/yy7kr5dw]; M. Walden, Al Jazeera, 17 May 2019 [tinyurl.com/yxg8ouqy].

3. S. Bernard and A. Kazmin, Financial Times (FT), 11 Dec 2018 [tinyurl. com/ycwbp6oj]; J. Basu, Telegraph India, 11 Apr 2019 [tinyurl.com/ t5g8nv6]; M. Abi-Habib and H. Kumar, New York Times, 11 Jan 2019 [tinyurl.com/yb597r33]; D. Spears, Foreign Policy, 9 Jul 2019 [tinyurl. com/smwweou].

4. E. Carnell et al, Environ Res Lett, Vol 14/7, 2019 [tinyurl.com/uvvyq9m]; M. Taylor, Guardian, 28 Aug 2018 [tinyurl.com/y7ftmu4w]; D. Carrington and M. Taylor, Guardian, 27 Oct 2018 [tinyurl.com/yarrqfd5]; UK House of Commons: Environmental Audit Committee, Sixth Report of Session 2014–15, p.6 [tinyurl.com/qmhfrml]; F. Kelly and J. Fussell, Environ Geochem Health, Aug 2015, p.644 [tinyurl.com/vzmnu2o].

5. J. Lloret, Biogeochemistry, Aug 2016 [tinyurl.com/vs9zrlg]; T. Sullivan et al, Environ Sci Policy, June 2018 [tinyurl.com/ydy8gajk]; Y. Zhang et al, Atmos Chem Phys, Vol 18, 2018 [tinyurl.com/v5x8z6z]; N. Popovich. New York Times, 19 Jun 2019 [tinyurl.com/y38fmpbl]; J. West and B. Turpin, Conversation, 2 May 2019 [tinyurl.com/r2wzjxk]; US EPA, 2019 [tinyurl.com/vxe7rfo]; E. Kaufman, CNN, 28 Feb 2019 [tinyurl.com/wte843s]; J. Turrentine, NRDC onEarth, 3 Aug 2018 [tinyurl.com/t7m7399].

6. M. Brown, Conversation, 12 Jun 2019 [tinyurl.com/vafw3tu]; K. Matthiesen, Guardian, 9 Oct 2017 [https://tinyurl.com/ycmvqlxv]; G. Foyster, Eureka Street, 24 Apr 2019 [tinyurl.com/t3rv3xp]; M. McDonald, Conversation, 21 Jun 2018 [tinyurl.com/y82nocyr]; N. Toscano and D. Gray, Sydney Morning Herald, 3 Sep 2019 [tinyurl.com/y6mgjld4]; G. Readfearn, Guardian, 11 Nov 2019 [tinyurl.com/rr2fc5m].

7. R. Nixon, American Presidency Project, 22 Jan 1970 [tinyurl.com/ttvj79q]; J. Goffman, Clean Law Podcast, Harvard Law School, 6 Dec 2018 [tinyurl.com/qp3fkzb]; G. Bush, Remarks on Clear Skies Legislation, 16 Sep 2003 [tinyurl.com/ua7y4yy]; US EPA, Nov 2015 [tinyurl.com/ycuqo59h]; F. Krupp, EDF, 4 Dec 2018 [tinyurl.com/uhdtym6]; L. Fredrickson et al, Am J Public Health, Apr 2018 [tinyurl.com/yx2vupja]; E. Howard and L. Carter, Greenpeace Unearthed, 12 Apr 2018 [tinyurl.com/smd4p4m]; J. Walk, NRDC, 10 Oct 2017 [tinyurl.com/yd78k8k7]; US EPA News Release, 10 Oct 2017 [tinyurl.com/ybd7kvwl]; M. Talbot, New Yorker, 2 Apr 2018 [tinyurl.com/y7gm6etp]; US EPA News Release, 25 Jan 2018 [tinyurl.com/qs29f42]; A. Thomson and R. Lebe, Mother Jones, Mar/Apr 2018 [tinyurl.com/yde5uqha]; S. Slesinger, NRDC, 14 Jun 2017 [tinyurl.com/w7q3972].

8. IEA, World Energy Outlook: Energy and Air Pollution, 2016, p.3 [tinyurl.com/uo54nze].

9. IEA, World Energy Outlook: Energy and Air Pollution, 2016, p.3 [tinyurl.com/uo54nze]; State of Global Air 2018, Health Effects Institute (HEI), pp.16–17 [tinyurl.com/y2gcyncv].

10. A. Chandrasekhar, 8 Nov 2019 [tinyurl.com/urhasmg]; D. Ottewell, Manchester Evening News, 19 Apr 2010 [tinyurl.com/wr2ymek]; News for Trafford, 16 Jul 2019 [tinyurl.com/v28sbu8].

11. D. Carrington, Guardian, 26 Jun 2019 [tinyurl.com/y6ey422s]; A. Intxausti, El País, 24 Apr 2019 [tinyurl.com/uq7os9q]; Por Europa Press, Moncloa, 12 Jul 2019 [tinyurl.com/yx2q5a28]; Catalan News, 6 Jul 2019 [tinyurl.com/rpd8wgt]; M. Planelles, El País, 11 Jul 2019 [tinyurl.com/y2c99txs]; C. Swan, Christian Science Monitor, 10 Jul 1984 [tinyurl.com/sp7zqzk]; G. Glueck, New York Times, 3 Apr 1972 [tinyurl.com/u2vb9ha].

12. D. Trump, Twitter, 2:49pm, 22 Apr 2017 [tinyurl.com/veqh9f6]; F. Cairncross, Green Inc., Earthscan, 1996; H. Ritchie and M. Roser, Our World in Data, Apr/Oct 2017 [tinyurl.com/y9s4zm99]; H. Ritchie, Our World in Data, 20 June 2017 [tinyurl.com/wnqzmaj].

13. P. Bagla, NDTV, 11 Nov 2017 [tinyurl.com/yc9gbcya]; S. Bernard and A. Kazmin, Financial Times (FT), 11 Dec 2018 [tinyurl.com/ycwbp6oj]; E. Howard and L. Carter, Greenpeace Unearthed, 12 Apr 2018 [tinyurl.com/smd4p4m]; C. Davenport and L. Friedman, New York Times, 7 Apr 2018 [tinyurl.com/y9fl5xb6]; A. Barteczko, Reuters, 17 Feb 2017 [tinyurl.com/u7c5pkj]; E. Howard, Guardian, 16 Nov 2017 [tinyurl.com/y7r5fyfy].

14. Y. Yamineva and S. Romppanen, Rev Eur Comp Int Environ Law, Nov 2017 [tinyurl.com/v58l6uh].

15. UK National Archives, Clean Air Act 1993 [tinyurl.com/y4r6m88q]; Friends of the Earth UK, 26 Apr 2017 [tinyurl.com/qtcjce6]; ClientEarth Press Release, 17 Feb 2017 [tinyurl.com/vpd3kxq]; P. Brimblecombe, The Big Smoke, Methuen, 1987, p.108.

16. 'Chapter 23: The US Clean Air Act Amendments of 1990' in R. Boubel et al (eds), Fundamentals of Air Pollution, Academic Press, 1994, p.395; US EPA, 2019 [tinyurl.com/zjycuzd]; US EPA, June 2015 [tinyurl.com/shpulm7]; US EPA, 2019 [tinyurl.com/yxgerese]; J. West and B. Turpin, Conversation, 2 May 2019 [tinyurl.com/r2wzjxk].

17. US EPA, 2019 [tinyurl.com/ychj35y8].

18. R. McKie, Observer, 7 May 2017 [tinyurl.com/lgz8fvz]; Earth Justice, Victories, 2019 [tinyurl.com/vdb88xf].

19. S. Kings, Mail and Guardian (South Africa), 4 Jan 2019 [tinyurl.com/wn9bojw]; Ipsos Global Advisor, May 2019 [tinyurl.com/qr6t2za]; State of Global Air 2018, Health Effects Institute (HEI), pp.16–17 [tinyurl.com/y2gcyncv]; N. Davis, Guardian, 14 Feb 2017 [tinyurl.com/zeo3grh]; P. Hannam, Sydney Morning Herald, 21 Nov 2018 [tinyurl.com/ydxwm36f].

20. Sustainable Bus, 5 Nov 2018 [tinyurl.com/yacd5vtt]; M. Coren. Quartz, 19 Sep 2019 [tinyurl.com/wyq3oma]; Climate Group, 4 Feb 2019 [tinyurl.com/sn7hxzp]; I. Courts, Air Quality News, 28 Jun 2019 [tinyurl.com/vxqh7pc]; R. Bundhun, The National, 12 Nov 2016 [tinyurl.com/we2gvxn]; Mahindra Group, 2019 [tinyurl.com/w54hc97]; A. Singh Nagpure, WRI India, 3 Jun 2019 [tinyurl.com/wfpz3h8].

21. J. Elkington and T. Burke, The Green Capitalists, Gollancz, 1989; P. Hawken, The Ecology of Commerce, HarperCollins, 1994; F. Cairncross, Green Inc., Earthscan, 1996; Patagonia, 2019 [tinyurl.com/y63kuvml]; A. Toffler, Future Shock, Bodley Head, 1970.

22. F. Cairncross, Green Inc., Earthscan, 1996; P. Kingsnorth, Confessions of a Recovering Environmentalist, Faber, 2017.

23. A. Chrisafis, Guardian, 25 Jun 2019 [tinyurl.com/yxhpgglq]; D. Carrington and M. Taylor, Guardian, 27 Oct 2018 [tinyurl.com/yarrqfd5]; A. Hussain, BBC News, 10 Nov 2019 [tinyurl.com/y2nrbmwx].

24. D. Boyle, Telegraph, 18 Apr 2016 [tinyurl.com/rgrsop3].

25. J. Curtis, Daily Mail, 16 Nov 2016 [tinyurl.com/t9so8os].

26. R. Mason, Guardian, 7 Nov 2019 [tinyurl.com/y39pkbtk]; Doctors and Scientists Against Wood Smoke Pollution [tinyurl.com/te82rsa]; UN BreatheLife2030, 4 Dec 2018 [tinyurl.com/ubclg2q].

27. M. Taylor, Guardian, 30 Sep 2018 [tinyurl.com/vnpttol]; D. Smith, Little Ninja, 2019 [tinyurl.com/rwzhfw9]; Moms Clean Air Force, 2019 [tinyurl.com/u5dubbz].

28. A. Larkin and P. Hystad, Curr Environ Health Rep, Dec 2017 [tinyurl.com/u7afn2v]; Mayor of London Press Release, 15 Jan 2019 [tinyurl.com/vynwwxv].

29. WHO, 2 May 2018 [tinyurl.com/yyjlue4o]; A. Irwin, Nature, 23 Oct 2018 [tinyurl.com/y7xvw4b6]; N. Davis, Guardian, 30 Aug 2015 [tinyurl.com/yx43x2jp]; R. Day and J. Ortmann, Popular Science, Oct 1970, p.97; Plume Labs, 10 Dec 2019 [tinyurl.com/rvgxr8y].

30. B. Chatterjee, Hindustan Times, 7 Aug 2019 [tinyurl.com/y585px68].

31. D. Carrington, Guardian, 12 Aug 2019 [tinyurl.com/y29teeun]; Edie, 14 Feb 2017 [tinyurl.com/uuhvheb].

Coming clean

1. S. Laville, Guardian, 8 Jul 2019 [tinyurl.com/yy4rl8k8].

2. S. Griffiths, Iron Trade of Great Britain, Griffiths, 1873, p.112 [tinyurl.com/uhpgb9a].

3. BBC News, 13 Jan 2020 [tinyurl.com/rj8zoht].

4. J. Halifax, Birmingham Mail, 5 May 2015 [tinyurl.com/ukd4qg9]; WHO Ambient Air Pollution Database 2016 (retrieved Sep 2019).

5. H. Ritchie, Our World in Data, 20 June 2017 [tinyurl.com/wnqzmaj].

6. International Energy Agency (IEA), World Energy Outlook 2017 [tinyurl.com/y94q5eg9].

7. S. Sengupta et al, New York Times, 15 Aug 2019 [tinyurl.com/y6d8z92y].

8. D. Carrington and M. Taylor, Guardian, 27 Oct 2018 [tinyurl.com/yarrqfd5].